G000167896

RUBICON

Professor Anthony K. Campbell

Anthony Campbell was born in Bangor, North Wales in 1945, but grew up in London. He was educated at The City of London School and at Pembroke College, Cambridge, where he obtained a first-class degree in Natural Sciences and a PhD in Biochemistry. He moved to Cardiff in 1970, where he still lives and works as Professor in Medical Biochemistry at the University of Wales College of Medicine, though he also regularly frequents his beloved Anglesey, in the North.

Anthony Campbell is a true natural scientist. His researches have taken him from the biochemistry of deep-sea bioluminescence to the molecular basis of rheumatoid arthritis. He has pioneered an experimental strategy to study the chemistry of living cells based on the genetic engineering of bioluminescent proteins. He has also developed chemical reactions that generate light to replace radio-isotopes in immunoassay and DNA technology, a technique used to detect and measure blood proteins, drugs and infections, including bacteria and viruses. These probes are in use worldwide.

Anthony Campbell is an international authority on intracellular signalling, particularly calcium, and on chemi- and bio-luminescence. He has written two books, *Intracellular Calcium: Its Universal Role as Regulator* and *Chemiluminescence: Principles and Applications in Biology and Medicine*, and is co-author of two other books, *Detection and Measurement of Free Ca²⁺ in Cells* and *Light and Life in the Sea*. He has published more than 200 individual scientific articles, and registered several patents which are being exploited worldwide. His research is generously funded by the Arthritis and Rheumatism Council, and the Medical, Agriculture and Food, and Natural Environment Research Councils.

He has recently established an educational initiative, The Darwin Centre for Biology and Medicine (Canolfan Bywydeg a Meddygaeth Darwin), which aims to catalyse fresh inspiration in the teaching of science.

Anthony Campbell is a keen musician, both as a tenor and conductor, and is also an enthusiastic naturalist, often to be found burning the midnight oil on the beaches or in the vales looking for glow-worms and other examples of living light. He has a wife, who is a consultant clinical biochemist, and four children.

RUBICON

The Fifth Dimension of Biology

Anthony K. Campbell

Duckworth

First published in 1994 by
Gerald Duckworth & Co. Ltd.
The Old Piano Factory
48 Hoxton Square, London N1 6PB
Tel: 071 729 5986
Fax: 071 729 0015

A catalogue record for this book is available
from the British Library

ISBN 0 7156 2499 7

Picture acknowledgments

The author and publishers are grateful to the following for supplying and
giving permission to reproduce illustrations: Plate 1(a) Lotte Meitner-Graf;
Plates 1(b), 4(a), 7(a), 8(b) and 8(c) The President and Council of the Royal
Society; Plate 1(c) Godfrey Argent; Plates 2(a) and 2(b) Academic Press; Plate
3(a) Dr Peter Herring; Plate 4(b) University College Medical School; Plate
5(a) University of Pennsylvania, Philadelphia; Plate 7(b) Professor George
Reynolds; Plate 8(a) (Darwin) by courtesy of the National Portrait Gallery,
London; Plates 8(a) (Emma Wedgwood) and 9(a) The Darwin Museum; Plate
9(b) The Council of the Vale of Glamorgan; Plate 12(b) Cold Spring Harbor
Symposia; Plate 13(a) Lakärtidningen, Swedish Medical Journal, 8/91; Plate
13(b) reprinted by permission of the publishers from *Explorations into the
Nature of the Living Cell* by Robert Chambers and Edward L. Chambers,
Cambridge, Mass.: Harvard University Press, Copyright © 1961 by the
Commonwealth Fund.

Typeset by Ray Davies
Printed in Great Britain by
Redwood Books, Trowbridge

Contents

Plates

Preface

Welcome and congratulations, you have just crossed the Rubicon for the first time! A few seconds ago this book was closed, but now your eyes have gone through a visual threshold, able to see the words on this page which are visible now that the book is open. Many of our everyday experiences involve events, discontinuities and inhomogeneities. So *with* life as *in* life. A movement, a birth, death, these are events which involve the whole human body. Examples can be found in other animals, plants and microbes. But what of the cells, and the structures within the cells, that make up the whole? When you switch on the light to increase the illumination on this page more of the light-sensitive cells in your retina are responding than respond in dim light. More cells have crossed the Rubicon. But what about other cells in the body: the muscles, the cells in your gut which release enzymes to digest your food, the white blood cells capable of defending your body against attack but which can turn against their host in diseases such as multiple sclerosis or rheumatoid arthritis?

Rubicon takes as its central theme the fact that all real biological phenomena occur through leaps and jumps, by crossing thresholds, rather than by developing in a smooth, graded manner. These quantal events involve molecules, cells and the tiny structures within them, organs, whole organisms and even ecosystems crossing a series of thresholds, or rubicons. Unless these rubicons occur at the right time and in the right place, the biological event does not take place. Standard textbooks, and previous attempts to provide a unitary hypothesis covering the whole of biology, have failed to address this fundamental feature of *all* natural phenomena. This is why biologists cannot really explain how an orgasm occurs, why a leaf falls in autumn, or what is the difference between a headache and an inspired idea. Nor are we able to explain why some people can carry the AIDS or hepatitis virus without being ill, while to others either would be lethal. Throughout nearly 4,000 million years of evolution rubicons abound; yet they have been either ignored or unexplained. The mysterious disappearance of the dinosaurs 65 million years ago is but one of many examples throughout evolution. In living things, extant or extinct, small groups of molecules right up to complete ecosystems behave in a quantal manner. What animals, plants and microbes do, and how they react to stress and illness, is dependent on the crossing of thresholds, quantal leaps, rubicons. Life does not behave in a graded manner as a car does when its speed is controlled by one's foot on the accelerator. Only when we understand the rubicons upon which the survival of life depends will we truly determine where physiology ends and pathology begins.

The book consists of ten chapters. In most sections I have tried to begin from a simple starting point, a question about a phenomenon known to most people, and then to lead the reader into the jungle of scientific jargon and technicality and through to the other side. The book is thus aimed at a wide, non-specialist audience, but I hope will also be thought-provoking and provocative to my fellow professionals. It is negative by being positive. It knocks several icons on the head: Gaia, the misconception of homeostasis, and contemporary evolutionary theory, to name but three. I introduce the reader to many famous and infamous scientists. Some are familiar names. Others will be new. Yet all have played a vital part in the development of biological thought and deserve to be remembered. Some are re-established as philosophical giants whose real contribution has been lost over the centuries because of malicious misunderstanding or sheer ignorance. Jean-Baptiste de Lamarck is such a one. Best known to the scientific community for a famous mistake in evolutionary theory, yet he was one of the earliest users of the word 'biology', and an inspiration to the young Darwin. We have much to learn from the wisdom of past generations.

Chapter One introduces the reader to a number of *crises* in contemporary biology and medicine. In spite of more than a century of intense effort in physiology, medicine and environmental studies, and many obvious and exciting successes, the central problems of biology remain unsolved. What is more, the general public has been conned into thinking that this century has been a great success medically. Of course there have been important advances and discoveries. Yet in spite of dozens of Nobel prizes, and billions of dollars spent on the development and application of pharmaceutical 'poisons', the main afflictions of man in the West and the Third World remain: heart disease, cancer, arthritis and infections such as the common cold, for example. If this is not a crisis, I don't know what is. To resolve these crises a new framework is required, together with an experimental strategy to test it. I aim to convince you that *Rubicon* is such a framework. The resolution of crises in science has always required a lateral jump, to a new concept. *Rubicon* takes the reader on such a leap.

Chapters Two, Three, Four and Five illustrate the principle embodied within Rubicon by describing thresholds and quantal leaps in health and disease, and in death. Examples are to be found in living organisms and ecosystems as well as in those long extinct. Without death there can be no life! Without extinction there can be no evolution! We find that the rubicons of familiar biological events such as movement, reproduction, defence and death, are themselves dependent on mini-rubicons in individual tissues and cells, and even in single molecules within them.

Chapter Six asks you to imagine a biochemist trying to decide whether a bag of chips or a sack of potatoes is alive. Is it really possible to answer this question by making them both into a soup? If a scientific hypothesis is to have any credibility it must be possible to test it experimentally. Chapter Seven therefore shows the reader that, by using the exciting new technology of the chemical microscope and genetic engineering, it is now possible to light up the chemistry of individual human living cells, in health and disease. It is also possible to manipulate the living cell, not only to discover how it works, but also to correct its malfunction in disease, thereby heralding a new era in natural therapy, taking us away from the 'chemical poisons'.

Chapter Eight takes us back into antiquity for a conversation about an issue which has run through biology since the time of Aristotle: 'Is there a vital force inherent in living things which distinguishes not only animate from inanimate, but also living from dead?' In Chapter Nine the possibility of defining scientific laws of biology, analogous to those found in physics and chemistry, is discussed. Anti-Popperians will find solace here. In the final chapter the author introduces himself personally to the reader, elaborating on the similarities in creativity between musicians, artists and scientists.

Throughout the book there are implied criticisms of current approaches in science. Science has become soulless, mechanistic, fragmented and over-competitive. To the enthusiast science itself used to be more important than the career of the scientist himself. No longer. As in academic medicine for decades, so in science, personal ambition and self-glorification have clouded and even distorted the path of true knowledge and understanding in science. By opening the door to so many questions *Rubicon* seeks to re-establish and catalyse the inspiration that can be found in the true natural scientist. There is but one science, Natural Science. *Rubicon* seeks to stimulate positive thoughts, and to show that it is possible to be both a holist and a reductionist, to appreciate the originality and elegance of both philosophies, without being schizophrenic. This is no wishy-washy compromise, but rather an appreciation of the true strength and appropriate place of these apparently opposing standpoints. Biological molecules are fascinating and beautiful, as are the whole animals and plants from which they came. But as Wordsworth once wrote, 'We murder to dissect.' As we dissect, what we learn should enhance, rather than diminish, our appreciation of natural beauty.

But I have further hopes for my scribblings.

There is a general lack of awareness in the public at large about the inspiration and creativity inherent in the study of Natural Science. Few understand the distinction between science and technology. Nor do many appreciate the importance of fundamental questions about natural phenomena in the making of discoveries and inventions which they see as the reason for funding science through the public purse. Medical problems often highlight and open up major areas of fundamental biology. The barriers between the Arts and Science remain as solid as they were when C.P. Snow exposed the cold war between the 'two cultures' several decades ago. Reading lists in schools are virtually devoid of scientific literature. Surely no child should leave school without at least opening *The Origin of Species*. In a recent series in a Sunday newspaper of '1,000 makers of the twentieth century' a scientist, discoverer or inventor appeared on virtually every page. Yet the ordinary reader will not have heard of many, if any, of them, let alone of what they discovered or invented. No wonder that few appreciate the importance of scientific thought in the development of the Western democracies. This lack of appreciation is exacerbated by the paucity of scientific thought and debate in English (and Welsh) literature.

Much has been achieved in primary schools. But the teaching of science, particularly the curriculum, in schools and universities still lacks the inspiration of discovery and experiment, is poor on scholarship, does not explain clearly enough the differences between science and technology and how each feeds off the other, fails to explain how the scientific method works in practice, and is often presented in a sterile manner though addressed to talented A level and University students. The essential problem is that science teaching is too descriptive and lacks the excitement of the pathway of discovery and invention. No wonder so many become disillusioned with science. Even on TV, in spite of beautiful photography and cleverly presented programmes, the real essence of science is often missing or lost.

And what of the practical application of scientific discoveries in biology and medicine? There has been much hype about biotechnology, but its impact on the real problems of pain and suffering, on starvation in the Third World and protection of the environment has so far been disappointing. Industry and the bankers still lack the wisdom and vision to back and invest in the real inventors and creative thinkers. The major causes of morbidity and mortality in both the West and the Third World remain unconquered. The horror of a major viral calamity looms large.

If this book can contribute something towards a resolution of some of these problems, and can inspire some of its readers, as I have been inspired in writing it, I am content.

I have many people to thank. First, the many members of my research group over the last twenty years, who have made day-to-day experiments so enjoyable and rewarding: my present group especially, Mike Badminton, Bob Kendall, Stephanie Matthews, Graciela Sala-Newby, Kathryn Taylor, Catherine Thomson, Andrew Trimby, John Watkins and John Waud, and the others in the ARC molecular signalling group, Maurice Hallett, Paul Morgan, Bryan Williams, David Llewellyn, Eryl Davies, Jane Jones and Iraj Laffafian. Thanks to all in the Department of Medical Biochemistry, especially Bob Dormer, Chris, Dot, Jeannie, Dilys, Becky, Dawn and Phylis, Dave MacKay, George Elder, the Department of Medical Illustration, particularly Janice Sharp for the jacket illustration, and many others in the University of Wales College of Medicine who have given me support and comradeship since I first came to Cardiff in 1970.

Special appreciation for particular friends with whom I have had so many rewarding conversations and experiments over the years: Paul Luzio, Ken Siddle, Nick Hales FRS, Rod Thompson and the Isle of Wight,

Gerry Brenchley and the Tea House in the Prescellys, John Maddocks, Jean-Marie Bassot and the inspiration of Le Marteau, Peter Herring and all on RRS *Discovery*, Professor Freddie Gutfreund FRS, Sir Eric Denton FRS and the Marine Biological Association Laboratory, Plymouth, and more recent kindred spirits, Marc Knight and Tony Trewavas in Edinburgh. I also thank Granville Davies and Professor Sir John Meurig Thomas FRS for their enthusiastic response to my ideas for a new science initiative in Wales – The Darwin Centre for Biology and Medicine, or Canolfan Bywydeg A Meddygaeth Darwin. I thank in particular John Green and Philip Morris, who have given me invaluable advice and encouragement about this book. I am grateful to Lawrence Rivington for his initial interest in *Rubicon* and for introducing me to Colin Haycraft of Duckworth, whom I thank for his enthusiasm and guidance.

Though the term 'rubicon' itself only appeared in print in an article I published in 1991, my research over the past twenty years has been dominated by experiments and the development of new technology to establish the validity of the essential principle, thresholds. I have tried to use this to get closer to the origin and prevention of a crippling and painful disease, rheumatoid arthritis, which afflicts several million people in the UK alone. For me there is another exciting possibility: to use *Rubicon* to resolve what is perhaps the central problem in contemporary biology, the apparent conflict between molecular evolutionary information and Darwinian natural selection. My research has been generously funded by the four research councils of the United Kingdom – MRC, SERC, AFRC, NERC – and also in a major way by the Arthritis and Rheumatism Council who had the vision to back my research at a particularly difficult time for funding research. I also thank the Welsh Office, the DHSS, the HEFCW and the Browne and Maurice Hill Fund of the Royal Society for supporting my visits to Plymouth and on RRS Discovery. There I found it was possible to marry the aesthetic appeal of a truly remarkable phenomenon, the emission of light by coastal and deep-sea animals, with a fascination for the molecular detail responsible for taking these animals across the Rubicon, so that they could flash.

Finally, I thank my family for their love and understanding, particularly through difficult times: my wife, Stephanie, and my children, David, Neil, Georgina and Emma, with whom I have had so many happy times and in anticipation of times to come, my mother and late father who encouraged me to follow science and music together at an early age, and my sister Caroline Sewry and her family for so many happy family occasions. I also thank my godfather, Anthony Mallinson, for his encouragement and for the respect for books which he taught me from an early age. I am particularly indebted to the late Leslie Cooper FRS for his interest in me over many years.

The families of scientists have a lot to put up with. Mine have chased me across beaches and up mountains at night, as I excitedly looked for new animals which glow and flash in the dark. They have had to put up with singing practice early in the morning and late at night when I was rehearsing for a concert or show. They have been generous enough to gain solace by pushing me off to Anglesey, where I find inspiration and joy endless. Thanks.

This book is a musician's celebration of science. The professional scientist will no doubt think some of the explanations trite, oversimplified and even overstated, while the non-scientist may still find them incomprehensible, in spite of my struggles to discover ways of putting across difficult concepts and technology devoid of jargon. I hope that everyone, scientist or not, expert or novice, student or teacher, will find inspiration and enthusiasm in every page of this book. Remember, once you have crossed the Rubicon and read the first page, life can never be the same again!

As in all science, the key to enjoying *Rubicon* is discovery. Frederick Gowland Hopkins, Nobel Laureate of 1929 and a pioneer of biochemistry, towards the end of his Presidential address to the London Natural History Society in 1936, sums up the philosophy of the entire book in my epigraph: 'All true biologists deserve the coveted name of naturalist. The touchstone of the naturalist is his abiding interest in *living* Nature in all its aspects.'

This book was written in a part of the United Kingdom tucked away on the left-hand side. Wales has a scholarly history, a sensitive culture, and an inspiring natural environment. Many distinguished men and women over the past three centuries have found inspiration here and have written thus in their Tours of Wales: Darwin, Wallace, Faraday, to name but three. I have been lucky enough to have a cottage on Anglesey (Ynys Môn) where Stone Age burial chambers feel the salt spray, and to look over bays and estuaries where some of the finest and rarest flora and fauna can be found growing on the oldest sedimentary rocks on Earth.

I await the reader's judgment – rather as the great British naturalist Gilbert White awaited in trepidation the reaction to *his* life's work, *The Natural History of Selborne*, when he wrote in 1789:

> Go, view that house, amid the garden's bound,
> Where tattered volumes strew the learned ground,
> Where Novels, Sermons in confusion lie,
> Law, ethics, physics, school-divinity;
> Yet did each author, with a parent's joy,
> Survey the growing beauties of his boy,
> Upon his new-born babe did fondly look,
> And deem Eternity should claim his book.
> Taste ever shifts: in half a score of years
> A changeful public may alarm thy fears;
> Who now reads Cowley? – Thy sad doom await,
> Since such as these are now may be thy fate.

I know how he felt!

Ynys Môn, October 1993   A.K.C.

This book is dedicated to two very special women in my life:

First, my mother,

JENNET CAMPBELL

You enabled me to cross my first Rubicon. Without your wonderful encouragement and love over all these years I wouldn't have had the confidence to try crossing any more!

And second, one of the nicest people I have ever met,

STEPHANIE

You helped me reach and cross many Rubicons
Without you I would never have got back!

With all my love to you both
Thanks for everything

All true biologists deserve the coveted name of naturalist. The touchstone of the naturalist is his abiding interest in *living* Nature in all its aspects.

Frederick Gowland Hopkins (1936)

1

The Banks of the Rubicon

QUESTION, PROBLEM AND ANSWER?

What do an orgasm and a falling leaf in autumn have in common? Come to that, compare the smell of honeysuckle from a summer hedgerow with the sight of a rainbow, or an Olympic runner leaving his starting blocks with the opening chord from a symphony orchestra. Does the inspiration of Archimedes in his bath two thousand years ago have anything in common with a headache? Should we consider the flash of a firefly separately from the disappearance of dinosaurs 65 million years ago simply because a firefly's flash may last only a few hundredths of a second while the demise of those 'terrible lizards' may have taken several thousand, or even a million, years? Which did come first – the chicken or the egg?

These are events which we have all felt, smelt, seen, heard, or heard about. But what do we know about the mechanisms within ourselves or other organisms that generate these events? Why does a particular nerve within our brain decide to fire when we have an inspired idea, and how does it do it? What determines when a muscle moves and how strong the contraction will be? What really happens when a sperm fertilises an egg, or when blood clots? What causes a cell to die at a particular point in time, or a whole organism for that matter? How is it that two people living together can have the same virus or bacterium growing within them, and yet only one of them is ill? The answers to these questions can be found in any good encyclopaedia, or failing that in a standard textbook of physiology, biochemistry or pathology. Or can they?

All the phenomena I have just listed have one crucial thing in common. They involve a threshold. In each case a molecule, a cell, an organ, an organism or an ecosystem has 'crossed the Rubicon'. Before the threshold was crossed there was no event. Yet the mechanisms responsible for this central feature of *all* biological phenomena throughout nearly 4,000 million years of evolution are not addressed in any textbooks of biology, even in those whose main emphasis is molecular. These phenomena have a second vital feature in common. In order to feel, smell, see, hear or think about them the organism generating them must remain whole, intact. The problem is that, in spite of an intensity of effort into biological research equivalent to the building of a thousand pyramids, something is still missing.

Compare what we know today about living things, from whole ecosystems down to the molecules from which organisms are made, with what was known a century or so ago. Discoveries and inventions abound. Science has provided a detailed description of the structure of ecosystems down to the minutest resolution of an individual protein molecule. In 1868 Johann Friedrich Miescher (1844-1895) extracted a substance from the nuclei of white blood cells isolated from pus, containing both phosphorus and nitrogen. At first it was called nuclein. But once he had separated it into protein and an acidic molecule in 1874, it became known as nucleic acid. Miescher had discovered DNA. Yet a hundred years ago we knew nothing of the real significance of DNA, or how its information is decoded into proteins. Its discoverer had a wild notion that it might have something to do with heredity but decided that this was too crazy an idea! So instead he spent the next thirty years studying a family of basic proteins found in sperm known as protamines. It was not until the experiments of Avery in the 1940s that it was shown that, if DNA could be transferred from one organism or cell to another, hereditary factors were indeed transferred with it. Today DNA research and genetic engineering are perhaps the most exciting areas of research in biology and medicine. So what is missing?

At the turn of the century the very substances and molecular structures of which life is made were only beginning to be isolated and identified: proteins, membranes, fats, sugars, vitamins and nucleic acids. We now know how the manufacture and handling of these substances is carried out by cells. The precise functions of structures within each cell of our body have been identified. The nucleus houses most of the genetic material, the DNA. A simple list of letters, following a strict code formed from only four letters, is how the DNA stores within its template the information for all the proteins of the body. The endoplasmic reticulum and the Golgi apparatus are minute protein and membrane factories within cells, decoding the nucleic acid messages and then processing and packaging them in the right form for them to be directed to their site of action within the cell. The chemical pathways that link absorption of sunlight by green plants to sugar manufacture have been fully characterised. The power-stations within each cell, known as mitochondria, have been identified. They provide the energy our cells need to make the substances upon which the structure, function and reproduction of our body depends. These have all been dissected in minute detail and full descriptions can be found in any standard biochemistry textbook. We even know how many of the enzyme proteins, the catalysts without which none of the chemical reactions of life would take place, are folded and where they bind the reactants. Yet something is missing! What?

To help you discover what I am getting at let me fire off a few more questions.

How would you define the difference between a sack of potatoes and a bag of chips? Ask a biochemist this question and he will tell you that both contain starch, protein, fat, salts, DNA and, of course, water. Not much help really. But any gardener knows the answer. Plant them in the ground, of course! I doubt whether even the most optimistic biochemist would expect to see a potato plant appearing from the plot containing the bag of chips.

Here is another conundrum. You are sight-seeing in a foreign city. You pass a concert hall and hear a choir and orchestra rehearsing for tonight's concert. What's on the programme, you wonder? How many are there in the choir? What sort of orchestra – chamber or full symphony? Who is conducting and when does the concert start? What are the acoustics like? The problem is that the doors are locked and all the posters are out of sight in the foyer! Well, being a resourceful person, though somewhat over-enthusiastic, you see a bulldozer parked nearby with the keys still in. What luck! By the time you have driven it through the closed doors it is too late. The building collapses into a heap of rubble. Fortunately the performers have escaped through the stage door on the other side, though their instruments have been crushed beyond recognition and there are sheets of music strewn everywhere. Try as you will you can't put the pieces together again.

The point I am getting at is that the real *problem* in contemporary biology and medicine is that we don't have explanations of how living things actually work. We know a lot about their components. We use the terms 'alive' and 'dead' daily in the lab to describe individual cells, tissues and even organisms. Yet we cannot define in molecular terms what these holistic concepts mean. The biochemist grinds up living cells and tissues to find what's inside. As with our mythical bulldozer, life cannot be regenerated from this homogenate. Many of the key molecular events responsible for controlling the behaviour of a cell have been destroyed for ever, or irrevocably disrupted and disorganised.

Some may say that it is meaningless to try to answer, in molecular terms, the question 'What is life?' Yet the problem of defining criteria, enabling us to discover whether life exists, or ever existed, on other planets, was taken seriously enough by NASA when designing the Viking space-craft. Vast sums of money went into the project.

The *answer* therefore is that we need both a new conceptual framework and a new technology to follow the physics and chemistry of cells, organ-isms and even ecosystems without having to snuff out the very essence of their existence.

Rubicon: the fifth dimension

Rubicon is the fifth dimension of biology. Dimensions are the fundamental units by which science measures things. Length, breadth and height are the first three, and time the fourth. These four dimensions are valid wherever we care to look. We can use them to describe what we are seeing at present, how we think of the past, and how to predict the future. We can even use them to define a point millions of light years away from the Earth.

Yet out in space or in a vacuum nothing is happening. What really matters are events, *rubicons*. Thus the fifth dimension must be considered first. For only when the sequence of events upon which a phenomenon depends has been defined can we begin to unravel how and why they occur, and by how much (dimension = mass), in relation to the four dimensions of space and time.

Between events physical and chemical changes are also occurring. In contrast to the quantal nature of the principal events, intermediary changes are smooth and gradual. The accumulation or loss of components at a critical point in space and time then provokes the event. *Rubicon* therefore classifies biological phenomena into threshold and non-threshold events, from the molecules upon whose reactions life depends, up to whole ecosystems and Mother Earth, Gaia herself. *Rubicon* not only provides a new way of viewing the phenomena themselves but also identifies the correct pathway required to discover the mechanisms which cause them. It is a conceptual and experimental framework for examining the life and death of both contemporary organisms and those which have been extinct for millions of years. It gives a new insight into why particular organisms, cell types and molecular events appeared and then sometimes disappeared during some 4,000 million years of evolution. *Rubicon* also provides a new perspective on the health of our bodies. It forces us to re-examine the conflicts and symbioses which determine the stability of Gaia, or undermine it as the case may be. *Rubicon* highlights the need for new technology to measure and manipulate chemical and physical processes in living systems, thereby providing the new experimental methods needed to view the molecular details of events or thresholds.

Rubicon is about presenting natural phenomena in a form in which their causes, functions and origins can be truly investigated and really explained.

Finally, *Rubicon* provides a route to answering a question which has dominated the thinking of many great minds since the scientific revolution began in earnest some four or five centuries ago: Is there a missing law which provides a simple quantitative description of the fundamental difference between life and death?

Rubicon refutes the ancient maxim upon which classical mechanics is based, *Natura non facit saltus*, 'Nature makes no leaps'. This dogma could not be further from the truth, for in biology, as in physics and chemistry, our true understanding of natural phenomena is critically dependent on the identification and characterisation of quantal leaps.

But why do we need *Rubicon*? The aim of this chapter is to answer this question.

Let me first illustrate the thrust of my argument by examining a few examples in physics, chemistry, physiology, pathology and ecology; where rubicons in the mind of a few creative scientists thinking laterally resolved what were real conflicts between experimental data and the theories of the time, and others where lateral thinking is needed to solve problems as yet unsolved.

A CRISIS?

A crisis about light

At the end of the nineteenth century human understanding of the physical nature of the universe was revolutionised by two German physicists. The key concept was introduced by Max Planck (1858-1947) and developed by Albert Einstein (1879-1955) (Plate 1). They argued that the energy of any body cannot be regarded as continuous. Rather, energy should be considered as discrete packets, or quanta as Planck named them. The speedometer on a car increases smoothly, and apparently continuously, as the car gathers speed. Its velocity and acceleration obey Newton's laws of motion. The kinetic energy of the car can be calculated from half its mass multiplied by the square of its velocity. What we now know to be an approximation works for large bodies like cars, but the approximation breaks down catastrophically when we consider the energy of an atom or an electron. When an electron increases its energy it has to do it in jumps. Its energy is discontinuous.

The origin of this revolutionary idea can be traced back to a 'crisis' point in nineteenth-century physics, the so-called 'violet or ultraviolet catastrophe'. We are all familiar with the fact that very hot bodies emit light. At about 525°C, some five times the temperature of boiling water, liquid and solid objects start to glow faint red. As the temperature rises, the colour emitted changes to yellow, then to white and finally to blue-white. The catastrophe arose because there was a clear conflict between this experimentally observed colour, or in scientific terms the spectrum of light emitted from a hot body, and that predicted by the existing theory. Another German physicist, Gustav Kirchoff (1824-1887), established laws governing this type of radiation, known as 'incandescence'. In particular he established the dependence of the intensity and colour of the light on the temperature of the emitting body. The Stefan-Boltzmann Law further established a precise mathematical relationship between the amount of radiant energy and the absolute temperature (i.e. a fourth-power relationship to temperature measured relative to absolute zero). Yet no one was able to explain why, as the temperature increased, the *peak* in the emission spectrum shifted to shorter wavelengths – that is, towards the blue-violet. The accepted theorem to use to work out the colour of the light emitted had been derived by two physicists: at first in 1859 for gases by a Scot, James Clerk Maxwell (1831-1879), and then more generally in 1871 by an Austrian, Ludwig Eduard Boltzmann (1844-1906). The theorem is now known as the Maxwell-Boltzmann Law of Equipartition of Energy. The random, equal energy distribution of their theory works for many phenomena but breaks down catastrophically when we try to predict what happens in incandescence. The 'violet catastrophe' predicted by this theory was that the radiation of a hot body should consist almost entirely of violet, or invisible ultraviolet, light. The observations showed quite the opposite! All sorts of ingenious twisting and turning of energy theory was carried out by distinguished physicists. But the only way to explain it properly was to consider energy not as a continuum but in packets, or quanta.

The coupling of quantum theory with the discovery of the electron, ascribed in 1897 to J.J. Thompson (1856-1940), led to a mathematical explanation of another puzzle about light. How could light be emitted from solids, liquids or gases without requiring heat – the yellow flash of a firefly or the green glow of a glow-worm, the blue flash from the cracking of a crystal of raw sugar or a peppermint, the blue glow visible to the naked eye from the mineral fluospar exposed to UV light, which cannot be visualised by the human eye, or the multicoloured phosphorescence of certain chemicals and paints seen when the electric light is turned off? Phenomena of this sort were classified by the term *luminescence* by Eilhardt Wiedemann in 1888. This distinguished them clearly from incandescence. Luminescence occurs when an electron within an atom or molecule decays from a raised energy level to ground state. Only when the 'energy' crisis of nineteenth-century physics was resolved was it understood how these luminescent phenomena could occur, and how the energy of the electron could be converted into light.

Not even modern physics and chemistry are free from such crises. The latest 'crisis' has arisen recently in astronomy and physics because one of the key predictions of the big-bang theory of the origin of the universe is not apparently holding up. In contrast there has been a recent discovery about carbon, an element whose chemistry was thought to have run out of steam. The 'fullerenes', named after the architect Buckminster Fuller (1895-1983) who knew how to use the design of a football to construct a metal dome, are hexagons and pentagons of pure carbon atoms linked together to form spherical shapes. These dissolve in certain organic solvents, are coloured red and can trap metals, becoming superconductors. The key to their discovery was that a 'spectrum' from a small portion of the carbon isolated from soot or a benzene flame showed a molecular complex of carbon with exactly 60 atoms, or sometimes 70 atoms. The only forms of carbon previously known were graphite, in which the carbon atoms are arranged in hexagonal arrays, and diamond, where the carbons are in a 3D rhomboid matrix. It was thought that all the carbon in soot was amorphous, having no regular arrangement of the atoms. It was impossible to fit C60 or C70 into any of these previously known shapes. But Buckminster Fuller was ahead of the chemists. He had already constructed domes of aluminium and other materials, made up of hexagons. In order to produce a curved shape without excess strain, however, and thus prevent breakage of the dome, a few pentagons had to be inserted into the lattice. *Tout à fait remarquable.* An element whose chemistry was apparently exhausted has been revived as a result of the resolution of a crisis where experimental data were in conflict with current dogma.

Crisis points in science stimulate creative minds to think laterally. They can open the way to a new vision of natural and man-made phenomena.

Physicists seem to regard them as way of life. Yet they have also been known to have a constructive impact on biology.

A crisis in biochemistry

Let us now examine a famous crisis in biochemistry – a crisis resolved by Peter Mitchell (1920-1991), the British Nobel Laureate for Chemistry of 1978 (Plate 1). He proposed 'chemiosmosis' as a radical solution to a crisis in biochemistry which had arisen during the late 1950s and early 1960s. It was a cause of great excitement when I was a student.

Energy is something we all know we need. But what exactly is energy? A car needs petrol. An electric train needs electricity. A torch needs a battery. A mill needs a flow of water to keep the water-wheel turning. But we need sugar and fat. This is the form in which we eat energy, but just as a car cannot move on crude oil, so our food has to be refined. The liver is a major processing factory, but in fact all our cells have the capacity to refine fat and sugar into the principal fuel of all cells. It has the mnemonic ATP.

Energy is the capacity for doing work. Mechanical, electrical, thermal, nuclear or chemical energy are all forms of energy involved in living systems. But the most vital form of energy is chemical, for we are essentially chemical not electrical or thermal machines. The energy laws of physics and chemistry – that is, thermodynamics – are among the most fundamental in Nature. Mitchell used these laws to revolutionise our understanding of the 'generators' within all our cells, the mitochondria.

Mitochondria make ATP, which stands for 'adenosine triphosphate'. It is a chemical found in every live cell. Indeed without it the cell would be dead, for it is the internal fuel which provides the energy for the cell to survive and carry out its specialised functions. It is centre-stage in our story about the crisis that Mitchell resolved.

Our body 'burns' sugars, fat and protein from our diet, or between meals mobilises internal reserves, to provide the energy needed to maintain itself. In chemical terms 'burning' is called 'oxidation'. Every cell in the body has the ability to behave like a miniature power-station, oxidising the fuel it takes in. The touchstone of a power station is of course its ability to convert one form of energy into another. So with the cell.

When a cell metabolises its food, it converts the energy available from this process into a chemical fuel, ATP, which only works within the cell. ATP was discovered by Lohmann in 1929, and its structure confirmed by chemical synthesis in 1948. Between 1937 and 1941 Belitzer, Tsibakova and Kalckar established that the oxidation of foods lead to the formation of ATP. The energy requirements of virtually every chemical or physical process in our bodies are dependent ultimately on a supply of ATP inside each cell. Without an inner supply of ATP a cell will die, and quite rapidly.

This dogma is valid for all cells on the Earth, be they of bacteria, plants or animals.

So the energy turnover in the cell involves the manufacture of ATP, and then its breakdown:

Synthesis
'burning' of nutrient + ADP + phosphate → ATP
Utilisation
ATP + consumer → ADP + phosphate + event (product or work)

All the energy that a muscle cell needs to contract when you run is provided directly by ATP. When used to fuel a reaction or process inside a cell, the ATP is converted to ADP and phosphate. But unlike the petrol engine in your car, which burns its fuel directly to form carbon dioxide and steam, the living cell can control its energy requirements by remaking the ATP again from ADP and phosphate, using the energy from the metabolism of its food supply to do this. The problem was to discover the precise link between the oxidation of foods and ATP, the key energy converter inside the cell.

Chlorophyll is the substance which makes plants green. A further problem in plants was how they could convert light energy, absorbed from sunlight by the chlorophyll, into sugar via the same energy intermediate as in animal cells, i.e. ATP.

The key to understanding the energetics of cells, and the organisms themselves, is therefore the manufacture of ATP. But first we have to identify where ATP is manufactured in the cell.

Some ATP is made in the so-called 'cytosol', the gel in which all the other sub-cellular structures reside. But most animal cells use oxygen, and most of this oxygen is consumed by a sub-cellular particle called the mitochondrion, which is the main ATP factory for the cell. Many nineteenth-century microscopists had seen various particles inside cells, and given them names, though they were not sure exactly what they did. Benda was one of the first to use the vital dye crystal violet to stain live cells. He called the tiny particles which were stained violet by this dye 'mitochondria' (from the Greek *mitos*, 'thread' and *chondrion*, 'grain' or 'granule'). Some twenty other names have been used to describe these particles, including the even more indigestible terms 'blepharoblasts', 'fuchsinophilic granules' and 'vermicules'. But it is the name 'mitochondrion' that has survived.

A school of cytologists at the beginning of the century led by Meves thought that these sub-cellular particles had something to do with development and heredity. But it was the pioneering work of Albert Claude (1898-1983) at the Rockefeller Institute in New York in the 1940s, that separated out the sub-structures of the cell that lead to the identification of their true function. The chemical power they generated was ATP. By 1948 Claude had a preparation of pure mitochondria in a test-tube and could say for sure that they were the power-houses of the cell. His experiments were followed by the laboratories of many distinguished biochemists including Ochoa, Cori, Lardy, Green, Lipmann and Lehninger. By the early 1950s it was accepted that the ability to make ATP from the energy released by 'burning' food was the exclusive property of the mitochondria.

A single mitochondrion is a cylinder a millionth of a metre long and half as wide. Over 200,000 will fit onto the head of a pin. The number varies with cell type. Some cells may have only 20, whereas some giant cells may have several hundred thousand. A liver cell, for example, has 1,000-2,000. But a red blood cell has none. It keeps all its oxygen intact. It can then give all of it to the mitochondria-containing cells, which cannot survive without it. Every mitochondrion can make ATP. As a result of the experiments of Chance, Lehninger, Slater, Lardy and others, it was argued, quite reasonably, that in the mitochondria there must be a sequence of chemicals linking food oxidation and ATP formation.

Put hydrogen and oxygen gas together and light a match and there will be an explosion. But where do the two gases go? Of course they form water. But what the mitochondria are able to do is to use the energy in burning hydrogen to form water without causing an explosion. The energy goes instead into forming ATP. First, the mitochondrion generates an active form of hydrogen, which has the mnemonic NADH. This is achieved by a chemical cycle which was discovered by another Nobel Laureate, Hans Krebs (1900-1981), and published in 1937. It is the oxidation of the H on the NADH which then generates the ATP. In fact three ATPs are formed for every molecule of NADH oxidised by oxygen to NAD and water. So the 'burning' of one molecule of glucose to carbon dioxide and sugar can generate as many as 38 molecules of ATP. But how was the energy in the 'burning' of the active hydrogen actually converted into ATP?

It was here that the trouble arose. Search as they might, nobody could find any chemical intermediates linking the two processes together. A biochemical crisis-point had been reached!

There are no such chemical intermediates, said Mitchell. All you need is a mitochondrion impermeable to the charged form of hydrogen, i.e. hydrogen ions. He then proposed that the chemical pathway leading to a chemical bonfire burning the active hydrogen in NADH to form water was actually a hydrogen ion pump, pushing hydrogen ions (H^+) out of the mitochondrion. Since H^+ is responsible for acidity, the outside of the mitochondrion became more acid and the inside more alkaline, and at the same time a voltage was generated across the membrane of the mitochondrion because of the charge on each H^+.

The mitochondrion really is like the turbine in a power-station. Except that the voltage each generates is some one-thousandth of the voltage in the mains electrical supply of your house, and fifty times less than the voltage generated by the batteries in a torch. Yet it is enough, Mitchell calculated, to make ATP. That was what mattered. Just as a hydro-electric dam allows water to flow downwards through the turbines, generating usable energy in the form of electricity, so the tiny power-houses in each of our cells use the electrical potential and the hydrogen ion gradient they generate to make ATP.

In plants it is the chloroplast which contains the green chlorophyll converting light energy into ATP. Like mitochondria, in chloroplasts the energy in chlorophyll following absorption of light is converted into a hydrogen ion gradient across the membrane enclosing the chloroplast, only this time the outside becomes alkaline and the inside acid. Nevertheless, as for mitochondria, a combination of an electrical and chemical gradient is used to generate ATP, which can then fuel the synthesis of sugar from carbon dioxide when darkness comes.

Precisely how ATP synthesis is achieved is still controversial. But the principle remains; a crisis was resolved by a radical new hypothesis, which held up to experimental testing. Mitchell called it the 'chemiosmotic hypothesis'.

Traffic-lights in cells

A universal property of cells, whether animal, plant or microbe, is their ability to do things in response to an external agent or as a result of internal programming. Cells can move, secrete digestive juices, transform into a new cell type or a cancer cell, or divide. Some can be excited electrically. Some can even be instructed to die. The external agents which provoke these responses in cells, and sometimes in complete organs, are hormones, neurotransmitters, certain physical stimuli such as touch or light, pathogens including bacteria, viruses and toxins, and drugs. But, so that the cell does what these agents want, the traffic-lights of each cell have to be switched from red to green. Otherwise the cell will not budge from its resting state.

In real traffic-lights an electrical signal lights the red or green light. But in cells the signals are chemical. This remarkable chemical-switching device has played a central role in the evolution of life. Without it multicellular organisms would not have been able to evolve from simple, single primaeval cells. It will play a key role in the argument for Rubicon throughout this book.

The cornerstone of the traffic-lights inside cells, the intracellular signalling system, is the generation of a chemical signal within the cell as a result of provocation by an external agent interacting with the outer membrane of the cell. It is this signal within cells that tells them to move, secrete, divide and so on. A crucial question for the molecular scientist is therefore 'How does the signal cause the cell to respond?' In spite of more than a century of work on these signals, we still don't know how they cause the ultimate cellular or tissue event to occur.

Rubicon tells us that we must identify and define the timing of the individual rubicons in each cell which determine if and when a particular cell undergoes an event. Only then will we know what molecular mechanisms to look for. Only then will we know what we are trying to explain in molecular terms, and how it contributes to the survival and function of the whole organism.

It may be a surprise to learn that cholera has anything to do with intracellular signalling. How can this signalling be related to the raging diarrhoea which can cause such lethal dehydration? Cholera still affects millions. It is caused by the gram-negative bacterium *Vibrio cholerae*, its striking clinical feature being massive diarrhoea. Several litres of fluid can be lost in a few hours, resulting in shock and death if the fluid is not replaced.

The diarrhoea appears to be caused by a toxin released by the bacterium, which has been extensively and successfully studied by the reductionists. We know that this toxin is a protein. We know its precise size and shape. And we know that it recognises specific target molecules on the surface of the cells which it attacks. The result is the generation of a chemical signal within the cell, cyclic AMP formed from ATP. This is then supposed to activate a large efflux of salt from these cells, and water then follows. Personally, I find the molecular detail fascinating. As a result of this knowledge, cholera toxin is widely used as an experimental tool throughout the world. The problem is that the connection between cyclic AMP and diarrhoea has never been established experimentally; nor is the current reductionist explanation of the diarrhoea convincing.

What good will all this hard work do for the people of South America and Bangladesh? A knowledge of the 3D structure of cholera toxin coupled with protein engineering may one day lead to an antitoxin or a really effective vaccine. But what the people in these regions really need is clean water and a proper sewage system! Some strains of *Escherichia coli*, the common bacterium in our gut, produce a similar, though less serious disease. In either case the reductionist approach has once more failed to explain and solve a real biological problem.

Signalling is central to the actions of all hormones, including one that most people have heard of, insulin. There have been at least five Nobel Laureates associated with insulin: Frederick Banting (1891-1941) and John James Rickard Macleod (1876-1935) for Physiology or Medicine in 1923 for the discovery of insulin in 1921; Frederick Sanger (b. 1918) in 1958 for Chemistry for the first primary structure of a protein, insulin, in 1954; and Dorothy Mary Crowfoot Hodgkin O.M. (b. 1910) in 1964 for Chemistry for the X-ray structure of vitamin B$_{12}$. Hodgkin was also the first to provide a 3D structure of insulin, which she completed in 1972. A year earlier Earl Wilbur Sutherland (1915-1974) won the Nobel prize for Physiology or Medicine for the discovery of cyclic AMP, the first so-called second messenger, found in 1956, as a result of investigations into the breakdown and synthesis of the glucose store in the liver, glycogen. As I write, the Nobel prize for Physiology or Medicine 1993 has just been announced. The winners were Krebs and Fischer from the USA for their discovery, also in the 1950s, of how signals like cyclic AMP work inside cells.

Yet we still don't know how insulin really works to cause a reduction in blood sugar after a meal. Significant advances in our understanding of diabetes since 1921 have been few and far between. Insulin extracted from pigs and cattle and now human insulin made by genetic engineering have saved many lives. Type I diabetes, with a collapse of the insulin-producing cells in the pancreas, is no longer an immediate killer in children as it often was a century ago. But the complications of blindness, gangrene and circulation problems in later life remain. The cause of the disease is still unknown.

Type II diabetes occurs without loss of insulin, and the beta cells which make the insulin the body needs continue to function. Yet again the cause remains elusive, and treatment has hardly improved for decades. Is diabetes really a problem of sugar metabolism at all? It is the fats which go wrong and are ultimately responsible for the death of diabetics from heart attack.

And what about traffic-lights in the brain? Surely we know how these work? To some extent we do. But does our knowledge go far enough? As a result of the pioneering work of Hodgkin and Huxley based in Cambridge but working with giant nerve fibres collected from squid at Plymouth, we know that the electrical signal transmitted down a nerve fibre comes from the movement of an electric current across the outer membrane of each axon carried by sodium and potassium ions. This is unlike a wire in a man-made electrical circuit, where current is carried by electrons. The decision to fire, and when, is made in the so-called cell-body of the nerve. If the activating and inhibitory agents on the outside of this cell body, released by neighbouring cells, summate in the right way, the nerve's traffic-lights switch to green and it fires. Yet we still can't explain what clearly are thresholds – rubicons – in the functioning of compartments within the whole brain. A yawn, sleep, hibernation, coma, an act of memory, the inspiration of Archimedes and the sudden generation of an idea, recognising an object, a sneeze – what determines these and recovery from them?

What we know about mechanisms in individual nerves will surely be required to give us the answer. But unless we recognise what the real natural phenomenon is that we are trying to explain, the reductionist path is in danger of leading to true artifacts, experimental, man-made phenomena in the test tube.

And what about the senses – smell, sight, touch, hearing, taste?

Fat is tasteless. The body is indifferent to it. But not so sugar, salt, caffeine, vinegar or chilli. Our taste buds recognise them as sweet, salt, bitter, sour or 'hot'. Sweet things give us the energy we need, and salt provides necessary minerals. We accept them. In contrast, bitter things are rejected as potentially harmful or toxic, and sour fruit is unripe, contains insufficient carbohydrate and may cause indigestion. These are some of the obvious benefits of taste. But how does it work? What is the molecular basis of these culinary rubicons? What, for example, is the cause

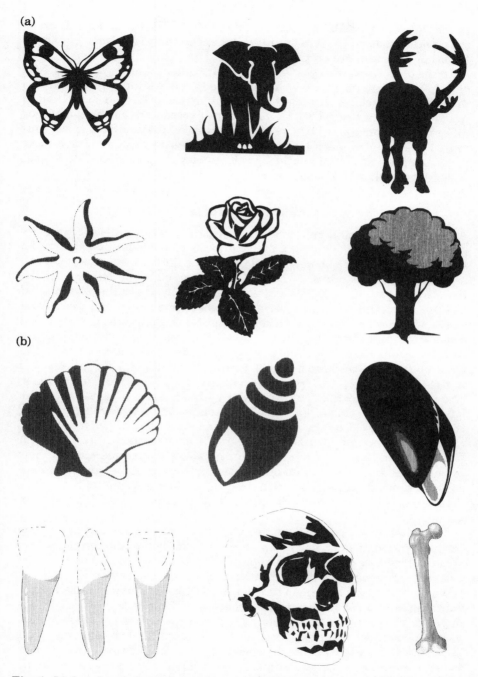

Fig. 1. Living shapes involving rubicons in development and evolution: (a) Soft shapes; (b) Hard shapes – some precipitates of Nature.

of the salty taste? Cooking-salt is sodium chloride, but is it the sodium or the chloride that makes it taste salty? Potassium chloride also tastes salty; yet other chlorides are only faintly salty.

In the days when we pipetted chemicals by mouth I once got a mouthful of sodium glutamate, which we were trying to use to stimulate contraction in barnacle muscle. At midnight I had an image of a Chinese feast, though it also tasted a bit salty! So, we may identify receptors on the tongue for different components of our food, but the rubicon that matters is recognition of the complete entity. This is what we have to explain in molecular terms. At present the conventional reductionist approach has failed again to come up with a complete answer.

Shape and form

A distinctive characteristic of each organism, organ and cell type is its shape (Figure 1). This changes as the organism develops and ages. In the window of a butcher's shop we recognise immediately the shape of a liver, a heart, a bone, or a brain. In plants, we appreciate the elegance of the different shapes of the leaves and flowers. Look closely in the mud or sand collected from the beach and you may be lucky enough to find the exquisite shells of some *Foraminifera*. Next time you walk along the beach and you come across some large brown seaweed, kelp, pick it up and see if you can find on it some *Obelia* hydroids. They look like small plants when in the water, but in fact they are animals, producing multitudes of tiny jelly-fish in the summer. Both the hydroids and the jelly-fish can flash in the dark. The minute 'flower-like' organs of the hydroid and the tentacles of the jelly-fish contain sting cells, which are lethal to tiny crustaceans, enabling them, like their close relatives the sea-anemones, to catch their food.

The list is endless for the naturalist to be excited about. The beauty of Nature depends as much on the shape of plants and animals as on their colour. Each cell even has its own distinctive shape. Look down a microscope at a blood cell, and you will see not a boring red sphere, but rather an elegant disc with a small dimple in it, as if a minute cushion has been sat on.

But what do we know about the molecular processes which determine the size and shape of a cell or an organ like the heart, the liver or a leg? What determines the size and shape of a tree or an individual flower? The extraordinary shapes of invertebrates, sometimes revealed only by looking down a microscope, are among the most breathtaking features in Nature. Our appreciation of the beauty of Nature would surely be enhanced if we understood how and why they form? Genetic manipulation experiments, particularly those involving the fruit fly *Drosophila*, have confirmed that in the DNA there are genes, the so-called homeobox genes, which appear to determine the shape and form of individual organs and thus the shape of the whole creature or plant. However, there is as yet no molecular explanation of how these genes are translated into the intricate and beautiful structures for which they are supposed to be the blueprint.

Similarly with the shapes of structures within cells, the organelles. How they are coordinated and what happens to them when a cell decides to divide also remains elusive.

Evo-crises

Evolution is a fact, as is Darwinian-Mendelian selection which is one mechanism enabling evolutionary diversity to be selected. Yet many crises are now apparent: no missing links; no convincing evidence for the origin of the three major cell types in living systems (the prokaryotes, the archaebacteria and the eukaryotes); no consensus to explain the disappearance of the dinosaurs, or the other major taxonomical catastrophes which the fossil record has revealed; no explanation for the selection of key molecular properties of life. For example, why is ATP and not GTP the energy source for powering reactions and cellular events? And what about the genetic code and protein structure? Why are there only 20 or so amino-acids in proteins, and why have particular triplet letters in the DNA been selected to code specifically for each one? Why for example does TTT code for the amino-acid phenylalanine and not for glutamate? Why does ATG code for methionine and start nearly all proteins, and TAA, TAG and TGA tell the cell to stop adding any more amino-acids to a protein and to release it to do its job?

And then there is the puzzle of chirality (molecular handedness). Molecules, like sugars and amino-acids, are three-dimensional and asymmetrical. The ones found in all living cells are designated D-sugar and L-amino-acid, D– for *dextra* or right-handed, and L– for *laevo* or left-handed. But chemical reactions in the test-tube can also generate the mirror-images of these handed, or chiral, molecules, i.e. L-glucose and D-glutamate. Yet only the D-glucose can be metabolised by cells and converted into energy and only L-glutamate incorporated into a protein. Similarly in large molecules like proteins and DNA there is another form of 'handedness'. The strings of small molecules of which they are made wrap round to form helices. Usually these have to be right-handed, like a normal corkscrew. When and why life took the decision to opt exclusively for a particular molecular handedness is a mystery. Is there a mirror-image of life on the other side of the Universe? It must be a possibility. Or is it?

The sequencing of DNA and proteins has thrown the conventional Darwinian-Mendelian theory of natural selection into crisis. Natural selection may explain some, or even most, of the macro-taxonomical events in evolution, but it breaks down at the molecular level. What is a species anyway? Even Darwin's classic text failed to address the statement embodied in its title, *The Origin of Species*. What was the origin and evolutionary significance of viruses? Why are the creative and cultural features of human civilisation – music, art, literature, sport and so on – apparently unique in the animal kingdom? Why are there no triffids?

These are some of the evo-crises that *Rubicon* intends to resolve.

Eco-crises

And what of the biosphere? There is no acceptable pathway relating the chemical evolution of the oceans, the land and the atmosphere to the evolution of life – no clear hypothesis predicting its fate. What determines its stability? What can throw it into a period of major instability and change, with the inevitable consequences to the particular species prevalent at that time? And what about man's influence? Should we accept the negative scenario of Rachel Carson in *Silent Spring*, or should we all become disciples of the positive holistic philosophy of James Lovelock's Gaia Hypothesis? What is an ecosystem anyway – just a random collection of plants, animals and microbes, or what? I have these in my garden!

So we find biological phenomena from the whole ecosystem down to individual cells which we can't fully explain. The control of cell behaviour and signalling, the development of the chemistry, shape and form in multi-cellular organisms from a single cell, communication and senses, memory and creative thinking, the appreciation of science and the arts, death and survival, the evolution of all these processes – they are all real biological *events* which we are struggling to explain in molecular terms. Once we have gone along the molecular pathway we seem unable to step back and take the holistic approach necessary to explain the natural phenomenon. Unless we remain continually conscious of Rubicon we will never achieve this ultimate goal. If this isn't a crisis I don't know what is.

And what of modern medicine and its attempts to improve the health of the human race?

'I'VE GOT A PAIN, DOCTOR'

You are standing on the platform of a railway station when suddenly the man next to you clasps his chest and collapses. He has had a heart attack. A potentially disastrous rubicon has been crossed. Fortunately, you have had a comprehensive First Aid course. No pulse. You give him resuscitation and his heart starts beating again. Eventually an ambulance arrives and takes him to hospital, where, if he is lucky enough not to have another attack, he has a good chance of survival. The internal figure of doom which struck this man down, causing immediate chest pain and rapid loss of consciousness, appeared like a thunderbolt, a flash of lightning. Yet the chemical and physical changes which led to this cataclysmic event may have taken months, even years to develop. Why now, at this point, has the blood decided to clot and the coronary artery become blocked? What determines when the pain starts?

We have all heard about cholesterol. The two main forms in which it circulates in the blood, namely LDL and HDL, enable the doctor to calculate your cholesterol index as a risk factor. We know a lot about the cells which infiltrate the heart before an attack and what changes have occurred in the wall of the artery. We know a lot about what is required to form the clot that is ultimately responsible for blocking the artery. Yet all the man on the station platform would have got if he had visited a doctor that morning pleading, 'I've got a pain, doctor', was the possible identification of angina and a bad cholesterol index putting him in the high-risk group for a heart attack. Nobody could say definitely that he would have one, and if so when. The key to understanding the biggest killer in the Western world, the crossing of a coronary rubicon, is not known.

What about some of the other main causes of pain and disease throughout the world?

Why does an alcoholic liver or a hypertensive kidney suddenly collapse? Why does a child suddenly, with no warning, collapse into a diabetic coma? What causes the body's defence system to mutiny and turn against itself, to make antibodies to its own proteins, or cause cell infiltration into tissues and painful inflammation, as in rheumatoid arthritis? How can some people carry cytomegalo-virus, herpes virus, hepatitis virus, HIV and other nasty viruses and pathogens without apparently having the disease? They haven't, for some reason, crossed the disease rubicon.

These are all examples of pathological thresholds, where the rubicon between physiology and pathology has been crossed. And pathological thresholds are not restricted to the onset of disease. Many diseases have flare-ups, having remained dormant or relatively inactive for weeks, months or even years – rheumatoid arthritis, multiple sclerosis, ischaemic heart disease, cancer, TB and malaria, to name but a few. There is as yet no cellular and molecular framework adequate to explain why these particular flare-up rubicons have been crossed.

Until the mid-nineteenth century infectious diseases – TB, cholera, typhoid and blood-poisoning – were major causes of suffering and death in the West. Cleaning up the water supply, major improvements in the handling of sewage, the realisation that infectious diseases are caused by bacteria, viruses and other microbes, the advent of vaccination pioneered in 1796-8 by Edward Jenner (1749-1823) and Louis Pasteur (1822-1895) for anthrax in sheep and rabies in man, and the discovery in 1928 of the first of the antibiotics, penicillin, by Alexander Fleming (1881-1955), have lead to an enormous reduction of these problems in this century. Smallpox is now officially eradicated from the earth, except for specimens retained in one Moscow and one US lab, for scientific purposes! Yet protozoal infections such as malaria and parasitic worms causing bilharziasis, known as schistosomiasis, remain a scourge in the Third World, affecting hundreds of millions. The World Health Organisation estimates that some 200 million people are infected with schistosomiasis, usually caught by working, bathing or swimming in water populated by snails which carry the trematode worm parasite. Similar numbers are infected with malaria.

The two together could therefore account for as much as 10 per cent of the world population. AIDS is fast catching up. Antibiotics only kill bacteria. They have no effect on viruses. There is no cure or fully effective vaccination for the common cold, AIDS and many other viruses.

In the West one in three die of a heart attack, and not only old people. One in three get cancer. Some 8 million in Britain alone have some form of arthritis, mainly osteo– and rheumatoid, causing continual pain and reducing life-fulfilment. Several of these diseases are increasing in incidence, and not simply because we are getting better at diagnosing them.

'The poison is the dose', we are told by the wisdom of Paracelsus. But is it? For several centuries chemotherapeutic agents in medicine have been based on a range of chemical poisons aimed at attacking a particular target in the sick person, either an invader or a host cell. There have been clear successes – the naturally occurring antibiotics, the anti-cancer drugs, and the cyclosporins, for example. But there have been many disasters. Hospitals in this century have been, and still are, full of patients who are there because of iatrogenic problems. The thalidomide tragedy was the tip of the iceberg. The man-made poisons are never totally selective and nearly always have some side-effects, sometimes lethal, at least in some patients. Radiation and chemotherapy have clearly been successful in curing many people of cancer, when diagnosed early enough. Perhaps the innovation arising from genetic engineering of using RNA – anti-sense so that it clings to the normal sense RNA and thus stops it working – will be an effective treatment for leukaemia. Yet we are really only scratching the surface. Aspirin, first used by the Romans, is still the most popular pain-killer. But ask someone with rheumatoid arthritis if this, or any of the chemical poisons, is any good? Most of these sufferers look in desperation to alternative medicine. The placebo effect often seems of more value than the claim of the pharmaceutical manufacturer. We still don't even know what the cellular and molecular basis of pain is.

The surgeons have done a good job, but what about the physicians? With the aid of sophisticated X-rays and MRI, pathological and biochemical investigations, they are quite good at diagnosing. But can they cure? Physician heal thyself! Are they really trying or is the medical profession in a giant conspiracy with the pharmaceutical industry to maintain the status quo and thus their jobs – and their billion-dollar markets? In spite of the current funding problem in university and research institutes many of us have cause to be grateful that governments, charities and the pharmaceutical industry have poured money into so-called medical research during this century. Without it I would have been unable to carry out my research since I chose this career over twenty years ago. But what real success has been achieved? Most people only enter the doctor's surgery when they have a pain or problem, often too late.

In the United Kingdom great efforts are being made to live up to the vision of the National Health Service, and prevent it being simply a National Sickness Service. But the fact remains that in diabetes little real progress has been made since insulin was isolated by Banting and Best in 1921. As we saw earlier, in spite of more than sixty years work on the fundamental properties of insulin we still don't know the cause of either type I or type II diabetes, or why the eventual arterial blocking occurs which can cause blindness and gangrene in diabetic patients after several years on insulin. Several abnormal genes, thought to be the cause of certain inherited diseases, have been isolated. Yet we still don't know how they cause the disease. The amino-acid abnormalities within proteins in the haemoglobinopathies have been known for several years. The abnormal genes in people with cystic fibrosis and Duchenne's muscular dystrophy have been isolated by modern DNA techniques, and the precise abnormalities in the DNA have been defined. Yet researchers are still struggling to explain how the mutations in the DNA result in the disease. And what of the less serious afflictions, which all the same can affect the enjoyment and fulfilment of life – back pain, the major cause of time off work, gut problems of indigestion and constipation, premenstrual tension, menopause, migraine, morning sickness in pregnancy, geriatric problems and mental illness, a problem poorly coped with by society? Is manic depression really a disease? What causes the brain to cross the elation or depression rubicon? Aren't we all susceptible to cyclothymic moods?

Let's face it, we are much better at diagnosing diseases, using a range of sophisticated imaging and biochemical techniques, than we are at curing them. Even so, we still have no definite test for rheumatoid arthritis or multiple sclerosis. The major diseases of the world have remained virtually untouched for a century or more, and many are on the increase. So what can we do about it? Much of the knowledge that has been accumulated will be vital in helping us eventually to conquer these afflictions. However, if we are to design an effective experimental approach to discovering the cause of disease, and achieve a really effective cure, a change in philosophy is required.

Where then does physiology end and pathology begin? Should we think of medicine as a separate discipline from biology at all? Only when we can define such rubicons in cellular and molecular terms will we have a real chance of conquering the diseases that cause so much suffering in the modern world. But to do this we must first understand what the science of biology is actually trying to achieve.

BIOWHAT?

Biology, biochemistry, biophysics, biometry, biogeochemistry, biogeography, biogenesis, biotechnology, the biosphere, the biosciences – these are all scientific disciplines or terms which are prefixed by *bio-*, because in each life-forms are involved. Yet in ancient Greece the word *bios* ('life') had a much narrower meaning, more anthropomorphic, meaning an individual's 'life-span', for example when found in terms such as *biography*. Likewise the word 'biology' was first used in 1800 by Karl Friedrich Burdach

(1776-1847) to embrace the whole study of man, a synthesis or combination of morphology, physiology and psychology. But it was two seminal works, published two years later, which established the new word *biology* in its modern form: the science of all living things.

The German botanist Gottfried R. Treviranus (1776-1837) in his treatise *Biologie* defined biology as 'the science of life'. Likewise the French scientist Jean-Baptiste de Lamarck (1744-1829), famous for what is now regarded as a major mistake he made in his hypothesis of the process of evolution – namely, his belief in the inheritance of acquired characteristics – defined biology in his *Hydrogeologie* of 1802 as a new scientific discipline for the study of the living world. Lamarck wanted to get away from the Linnaean approach of simply cataloguing animals, plants and minerals. The new science of biology was to address the question how they worked.

Lamarck took the holistic view that a sound physics of the earth must include all the primary considerations of the earth's atmosphere, the characteristics and continual changes of the earth's crust *and* the origin and development of living organisms. Thus the study of the physics of the Earth was divided naturally into three interacting disciplines: (a) the theory of the atmosphere, or meteorology, (b) the theory of the earth's external crust, or hydrogeology, and (c) the theory of living organisms, or biology. Lamarck's new science of life embodied the premise that organic and inorganic phenomena were fundamentally different. However, as we shall see again in Chapter Eight, he rejected the vitalist ideas of his day. To Lamarck, 'biologie' had to use physical and chemical processes to explain how plants and animals functioned and evolved. It is thus perhaps surprising that this great thinker, who is underrated today and often remembered only for his evolutionary 'mistake', did not also think of using the terms biochemistry and biophysics. These were not introduced until after his death.

The last fifty years have seen the publication of many distinguished textbooks of biochemistry, which have influenced generations of students. The works of Baldwin; White, Handler and Smith; Mahler and Cordes; Stryer; Watson; and others come to mind. The origin of the discipline of *biochemistry* can be traced back to the chemical analysis of living tissue described in 1842 in the *Animal Chemistry* of J.J. Liebig (1803-1873). But the word biochemistry itself was first used in print by Ernst Felix Hoppe-Seyler (1825-1895) in the first edition of *Zeitschrift für physiologische Chemie* published in 1877. This was well before Carl Neuberg, who was quoted by White, Handler and Smith as being the first to use the term in 1903. However, biochemistry had to wait until the early years of this century before establishing itself as a new discipline in its own right. After the German chemical school, chemical physiology or physiological chemistry began to be studied and taught in many university departments of physiology in Britain and other European countries. It was the University of Liverpool which in 1902 appointed the first Chair in Biochemistry in the United Kingdom, the Johnston Professorship. This was awarded to Benjamin Moore, later FRS and founder of the *Biochemical Journal*. In 1912 the University of London appointed Sir Arthur Harden FRS to a Professorship in Biochemistry at the Lister Institute. But it was to be the third chair of biochemistry, given by the University of Cambridge, after typical wranglings, to Frederick Gowland Hopkins (1861-1947) (Plate 13(c)) that was to be the most significant. For it was Hopkins who established, from the William Dunn laboratory in Tennis Court Road, Cambridge, a school of biochemists of world-wide influence on the biologists of this century, whose impact and approach to the chemistry of living things is still with us.

Biochemistry is the study of the molecular basis of life and its evolution, including all animals, plants, microbes and viruses. White, Handler and Smith in their *Principles of Biochemistry* first published in 1959, list some fifteen chemical aspects of life which should be embraced by this discipline. These boil down to six main questions:

1. What are the chemical substances found in living organisms?
2. How much is there of them?
3. Where, in and out of cells, are they found?
4. What do these molecules do and how do they work?
5. How did they evolve?
6. What goes wrong with them in disease?

The answers to these questions should provide an explanation, at the molecular level, of how organisms and individual cells maintain themselves alive, how they do the things they do, how they develop, how they reproduce, how they defend themselves against physical, chemical and biological attack, how they die, and from whence they came.

Most of the main chemicals of life have now been identified, or so we believe. The clinical biochemist is able to analyse many of them in various body fluids and search for diagnostic abnormalities in them. Two new schools have emerged from biochemistry, *molecular biology* and *cell biology*. Molecular biology was first used in 1938 by Warren Weaver (1894-1970) to describe a research programme, supporting some of the pioneers of this new discipline as he saw it, including W.T. Astbury (1898-1961), Linus Pauling (b. 1901) and Max Perutz (b. 1914). Astbury, a co-discoverer of the real significance of DNA, apparently first called himself a molecular biologist in 1939. However, only after the setting up of a few, now famous, laboratories of molecular biology in the USA, UK and France, and the foundation of the *Journal of Molecular Biology* in 1959, did the term become fashionable. Now everyone wants to be a molecular biologist. So what do they do?

Molecular biology aims to define the structure and function of biological macromolecules: proteins, DNA, RNA, membranes and so forth. It uses X-ray crystallography and nuclear magnetic resonance to find the 3D shape of proteins and DNA. It uses genetic engineering and chemical analysis to discover how the blueprint for the chemistry of the cell, the DNA, is expressed and translated into structure and function within the cell. X-ray crystallography has to use crystals. In this form the proteins and nucleic acid structures may be similar to those in the cell, but they can never be identical with them. In the cell these molecules interact closely with ions, metabolites and other macromolecules. A tiny concentration of calcium (a few μmoles per litre), less than the concentration in many sources of fresh water, can change the behaviour of an entire cell for ever. So where does the energy come from? In molecular biology, as in its parent, biochemistry, we have learnt a lot about the bricks from which macromolecules are made, and how the bricks are joined together to support a function. But we have yet to be able to use this reductionist knowledge, elegant and exciting as it is, to explain how a cell really works, divides or dies.

Likewise with cell biology. In 1974 the Nobel prize for Physiology or Medicine was awarded jointly to Christian René de Duve (b. 1917), Albert Claude (1898-1983), whom we met earlier, and George Emil Palade (b. 1912). These three innovators are often described as cell biologists. Their work was of considerable significance in the unravelling of the sub-cellular organisation of the cell, the organelles. Yet all studied *dead* cells, Claude and de Duve homogenates of tissues, and Palade fixed sections of cells under the microscope.

Heresy! Or is it?

I am not denigrating the brilliant work of these pioneers. On the contrary, without it I would not have the knowledge to put together the arguments in this book. All I ask is, 'Can we, please, put the *bio-* back into *biology* and *biochemistry*, whatever form they may take.'

THE UNIT OF LIFE

Bio-, or life, depends totally on cells. There are some one hundred million million (10^{14}) cells in a human body one and half metres tall. Yet only some 800 cells are required to make a complete nematode worm a few millimetres long. These tiny chemical factories process and make everything we see in the biosphere. Well, almost.

The word cell comes from the Latin '*cella*' connected with *celare* ('to cover') and meaning 'cell' or 'small room'. Today any student of biology or biochemistry can give you a detailed description of the structure and chemical processes of cells, but this would be a far cry from the original concept, whether lay or scientific. In 1665 Robert Hooke (1635-1702), a co-founder of the Royal Society, described in his *Micrographia* the cavities in cork as *cells*. This everyday meaning remained until well into the nineteenth century. To most scientists between 1600 and 1800 'cellular tissue' referred to tissue with holes in it, now usually thought of as connective tissue.

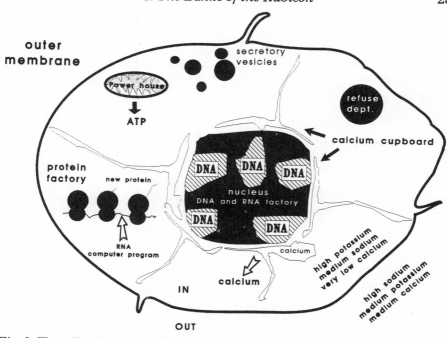

outer membrane

secretory vesicles

Power house

ATP

refuse dept.

calcium cupboard

protein factory

new protein

DNA DNA DNA

nucleus
DNA and RNA factory

DNA DNA

calcium

RNA computer program

high potassium
medium sodium
very low calcium

calcium

high sodium
medium potassium
medium calcium

IN

OUT

Fig. 2. The cell – the unit of life and the ultimate source of rubicons.

What we now know to be single-celled organisms had been observed by the Dutch pioneer of microscopy Antonie van Leeuwenhoek (1632-1723). In 1677 he described for the first time sperm from several animals, including man, and he produced the first accurate description of red blood cells in 1684. Ten years before he had observed bacteria and protozoa, but they were given the name 'animalcules', 'microbes' or later 'vibrionia', and were often confused with each other and with other single-celled organisms. In 1702 he pointed out that 'In all falling rain, carried from gutters into water-butts, animalcules are to be found ... For these animalcules can be carried over by the wind.'

The early micro-anatomists of the eighteenth century thought of living tissue as made of *fibres* which were formed from small *globules*. Globules then took over as the main focus of attention. Some we now recognise as the nuclei within cells, others were particles or acellular illusions of various sorts, but only sometimes a real cell. Important scientists of the eighteenth and early nineteenth century now forgotten – such as Lorenz Oken (1779-1851), the German anatomist Johann Friedrich Meckel (1781-1833), the French botanist Charles-François Brisseau de Mirbel (1771-1854) and his compatriot physiologist Henri Dutrochet (1776-1847), the Czech experimental physiologist Jan Evangelista Purkinje (1787-1869), Valentin, and the Frenchman Raspail – did not think of organisms, as we do today, as being composed essentially of cells and their products.

Living cells had been observed ever since the invention of the microscope, but either they were ignored or their significance to life was misunderstood. The cell theory has its origins in plant anatomy, in the early nineteenth century. By 1809 Brisseau de Mirbel had shown that all plant structures consisted of cells and developed from cellular tissues. And in his *Philosophie zoologique* (1809) Lamarck extended this generalisation to all living organisms. Both Lamarck and Mirbel recognised the universal presence of cells and believed them to be bound together by continuous membraneous tissue. Then in 1824 Dutrochet showed, using maceration techniques, that the single cell is the fundamental structural and physiological element in all animal and plant tissues. Schleiden (1838) and Schwann (1939) elaborated on this principle, their main original contribution being to highlight the importance of the nucleus.

The Scottish botanist Robert Brown (1773-1858), immortalised in the phenomenon now called 'Brownian motion', was a shy yet brilliant botanist and microscopist. In 1831 a young, inexperienced, but enthusiastic Charles Darwin visited Brown at the British Museum. Brown advised him which microscope to buy, and in return Darwin promised to send him some orchids from Patagonia during the *Beagle* expedition. Brown, now Darwin's friend, succeeded in convincing him on his return of the importance of the movement inside live cells. In 1830 he realised that all plant cells had a nucleus. It was this observation that led another botanist, Matthias Schleiden (1804-1881), to propose that the cells of plants form inside existing cells, either from cell nuclei or from cytoblasts already formed. Theodor Schwann (1810-1882), looking at the embryonic tissues of animals, thought he saw a striking similarity between the notochord, the embryonic origin of the spinal chord, and plant parenchyma, the cell layers in plants. In 1839 Schwann published his *Mikroskopische Untersuchungen* in which he proposed a universal *Zelltheorie* of living tissue. Everything that lives owes its origin to cells. And by 'cell' Schwann meant a layer, or *Zellenschichte*, surrounding the nucleus. So far so good. Unfortunately he went further, developing from his friend Schleiden the proposition that cells form around the nucleus, inside a blastema of amorphous material which could be inside or outside the mother cell. Schwann's mistake was that he thought that animal cells usually formed a cytoblastema, which was outside pre-existing cells.

The modern version of cell theory comes from Robert Remak (1815-1865), and was generalised and publicised by the anatomist Rudolf Virchow (1821-1902). In his *Cellularpathologie* of 1858 Virchow established the cellular basis of modern physiology and pathology. *Omnis cellula e cellula*, 'all cells from cells', he wrote. Virchow acknowledged Schwann's vital contribution to the cell debate, recognising as he did the universal cellular origin of tissues. But it was Virchow's dictum which established that every cell in existence today has come from another cell. Life – cells

– cannot occur spontaneously. *Spontaneous generation* of bacteria and other life forms had been a belief of many notable scientists for several centuries, including Lamarck, who thought it was still happening. Inoculation of a sterile culture showed that a small number of bacteria could generate many bacteria. It was this approach that led Johann Florian Heller, Professor of Medicine in Vienna, to conclude in 1843 that luminous bacteria were responsible for the shining flesh which had puzzled laymen and scientists alike for centuries. Needy (1713-1781) had claimed that microbes appeared in sealed flasks containing boiled broth. But Lazzaro Spallanzani (1729-1799), whom we shall meet again in Chapter Six, showed that this was a mistake. Microbes would only appear if the broth had been inadequately heated or if air was admitted. The controversy over spontaneous generation was finally resolved by the careful experiments on sterilisation of F.J.Cohn (1828-1898), Louis Pasteur (1822-1893) and John Tyndall (1820-1893).

So all life originates from, and is dependent on, cells. Life may depend on DNA, but a piece of DNA, even a complete set of chromosomes, is sterile if it is not inside a cell. Nowhere on this Earth do we expect to find a Jules Verne version of the primaeval soup, in which cells are forming from inanimate chemicals.

What then is a cell? How is a cell structured? How does it work? Indeed how many different types of cell are there in Nature and what can they do?

Cells vary considerably in size. The smallest in our body, the red and white blood cells, are just a few millionths of a metre in diameter. You could fit several thousand onto the head of a pin. But there are other cells in Nature which are enormous. Our largest nerves have a cell body the same size as most of the rest of the cells of the body. But emanating from this cell body is the axon which conducts the electrical impulses to the terminal, which then communicates this to the next nerve, or a muscle. The longest of these is a metre or so. Just think of that when you next wiggle your toes. Similarly, some of my leg muscles are 0.5-1 metre long, but in this case they have been made by fusing thousands of tiny precursor muscle cells into one giant fibre. Invertebrates too can have very large cells. The muscle cells responsible for closing the plates of barnacles can be a millimetre or so in diameter, and several millimetres long. However, these giant cells are exceptional. Most cells are between 5 and 50 millionths of a metre in diameter. All cells consist of a gel containing proteins, salts and small organic molecules enclosed within a membrane. This membrane is no passive bag, simply holding the cell together. It is in its own right an active chemical machine, even though it has to be supplied with material from both inside and outside the cell to enable it to function. The membrane is semi-permeable, being permeable to some substances but not to others. It contains pumps and catalytic proteins. It can change shape, enabling some cells to move. Some cells have a more rigid structure outside this membrane, the cell wall. In plants, yeasts, fungi and bacteria this is made of carbohydrates, i.e. sugars. Other organisms and some individual cells have a crystalline wall protecting them made of calcium carbonate or silicate. The structure within cells also varies considerably from cell to cell, some being very simple while others contain a conglomerate of internal structures known as organelles, each with its own special functions contributing to the whole.

But what about DNA? All cells have DNA as the blueprint for manufacturing and controlling all the cell constituents, though as often with general rules there are a few exceptions. We have red cells in our blood, carrying the oxygen to the tissues of the body. The red cells of mammals have lost their DNA and therefore their ability to divide or make proteins from the blueprint. Similarly, platelets in the blood, required to form a blood clot, are tiny fragments from a mother cell which has the main DNA. Interestingly enough, fish, bird and amphibian red cells still have DNA, though it seems to be inactive. These few exceptions apart, all cells contain DNA, which is the blueprint for making proteins.

What about cell types?

Take a look down a microscope at some pond water. You will see, just as Leeuwenhoek did three hundred years ago, many amoebae moving along the surface of the vessel and the flagellate *Paramecium* rushing round as it bumps into things. Protozoa, as these are known ('first living things'), are usually regarded as animals. There are also unicellular algae. Dinoflagellates are more of problem, being apparently half plant and half animal. The rest of the single-celled microbes are bacteria. Most people think of three types of cell: animal, plant and microbe. Animal cells can move either like an amoeba or a sperm, if they have a tail known as a flagellum or cilium. Plant cells contain chlorophyll which traps the sunlight, making them green. Some, like algae have other light-trapping pigments as well, so they can be red, pink, blue-green or brown. Both animals and plants are made up of many different kinds of cells, each with a particular function.

But there is a more fundamental classification of living cells, now possible because of our detailed knowledge of the inner structure and chemistry of cells. *Karyon* in Greek means nucleus (literally 'nut' or 'kernel'). The eukaryotes are nucleated cells, just like those observed by Schleiden and Schwann. They include all plant and animal cells, fungi, protozoa, algae and dinoflagellates. The other major group of cells are the prokaryotes, containing no nucleus. Prokaryotes include the bacteria and blue-green algae. And this is not the only major difference between these two basic cell types.

The eukaryotes contain all sorts of internal structures (see Figure 2) enclosed within a membrane similar to, but not the same as, the one enclosing the whole cell: mitochondria, chloroplasts, peroxisomes, lysosomes, secretory and storage vesicles, endoplasmic reticulum, the Golgi apparatus. All eukaryotic cells have these organelles. Some have additional special ones – flagella in sperm and other cells enable them to swim, nematocysts in the sting cells of jelly fish are the micro-syringes injecting poison into their prey or an enemy, trichocysts are hair-like structures in protozoa which shoot out to attach the cell to something, and the fluid containing vacuoles in plants are just some examples. Prokaryotes have none of these, though some do have a flagellum. But this is quite different in structure from that in eukaryotes. In eukaryotes the chromosomal DNA is housed in pairs within the nucleus, with a single copy of a small piece of DNA in the mitochondria and chloroplast. In prokaryotes, on the other hand, the DNA is single and circular, and is not enclosed within a membrane. One organelle is common to both types, the ribosome, whose function is to manufacture protein. But even here there are fundamental differences in the structure and composition of this minute protein factory between the eu- and pro-karyotes. Analysis of a particularly interesting group of bacteria which can live in extremely high salt, or can make methane, led Carl Woese in 1977 to argue that the prokaryotes should be divided into two basic cell types, the eubacteria and the archaebacteria. In the latter, some characters are more like those of eukaryotic cells than the prokaryote group into which they were originally assigned. We shall hear more about taxonomy in Chapter Two, but for now, in line with Woese's classification of 1990, we will consider there to be three fundamental cell types: Prokaryta (Bacteria), Archaea, and Eukarya.

What can cells do?

Eukaryotes can do more than the other two groups, but all cells, from whatever group, maintain gradients of salts and other substances across their outer membrane. All contain active chemical reactions, metabolise food, make proteins and other substances, some for internal use, some for export. Some can respire using oxygen, some not. Some can divide, some not. A bacterium can divide into two within half an hour. This means that one bacterium, allowed to go rampant, can generate over a hundred million million (10^{14}) cells within 24 hours. By contrast it takes nine months or more for one fertilised human egg to form the same number of cells, the full complement of the body. Many cells, including bacteria, can move. They can be attracted or repelled by light, by chemical gradients and by touch. Although bacteria can form conglomerates of cells, they do not form the highly differentiated structures of animals and plants. Not only can animal cells move but they can also communicate with each other or with other organisms electrically and chemically. Clusters of cells can produce sound, and some cells in luminous animals can produce light. There are even bacteria that can produce light. They exist worldwide in the sea and in soil. They are the explanation of the remarkable stories of luminous cadavers on battle fields, and luminosity on meat or dead fish (see E.N. Harvey, *A History of Luminescence*).

Eukaryotic cells can secrete or ingest soluble and particulate matter. They can construct the most incredible and elegant extra-cellular structures made of mineral and protein: bone, teeth, shells, coral and so on. They can act as energy converters, processing and producing light and electricity. They can all defend themselves against attack and repair damage, whether chemically or physically induced. Some have the special function of killing invaders. Some cells only survive a few minutes or hours after their formation; others, like nerve cells, can survive for decades, in fact for the whole of the organism's life, without needing to divide or differentiate. During development cells change their appearance. Three embryonic cell types, the endo-, ecto- and meso-derm, are the precursors of all the organs of the body. On the other hand, in plants it is the tissues known as xylem and phloem which differentiate into the familiar structures of a plant or tree.

Although the problem of searching for universalities to define life at the chemical level remains, one universality is clear. The unit of life is a cell, not a piece of DNA. Viruses are not alive; they have to invade and take over the machinery of a live cell in order to reproduce. They cannot do this on their own, nor can they do it outside a live cell.

What we now need to know is how all these cells do what they do, and how these functions evolved.

Among all this diversity of classification, structure and function there is one universality which embraces every 'unit of life'. At some point or other they have crossed the Rubicon. Some have crossed many rubicons, others apparently only one. In birth, in life, in death and in their ancestry thresholds abound for every cell. The question we must ask therefore is: when and how are these rubicons crossed? Also, when was the decision made that there should be three fundamental cell types – the Prokaryta, the Archaea, and the Eukarya – and what determined this? What are the molecular mechanisms responsible for converting particular cells in the amorphous cell cluster which first forms from a fertilised egg into one of the three embryonic cell types and then into a specialised cell type in an organ, with its characteristic shape and functions? In other words, what decides if and when an embryonic cell becomes ecto-, endo- or meso-derm, and then becomes a skin cell, a nerve cell or a liver cell? A cell moves or it remains stationary, a cell divides or it remains single, a cell releases or ingests something or it does not, a nerve cell fires or it remains asleep, a luminous cell flashes or it remains invisible, a cell dies following attack or it survives. What are the chemical and physical reactions which take a cell to the edge of these thresholds, the banks of the Rubicon, and when, why and how does it then take the decision to cross? What then happens when it reaches the other side? Although we know a lot about the machinery responsible for these phenomena, the answers to the questions when, how and why remain elusive.

It is in the cell too that we must look for the molecular basis of disease. Platelets aggregate (clot) causing a heart attack. Bleach-producing cells invade the joints in rheumatoid arthritis. And insulin-producing cells are killed in diabetes. Even when the damage appears to be outside the cell we must still examine the inside of cells carefully to see if the real problem lies within. The insulation round the outside of nerves in the brain, called myelin, breaks down in multiple sclerosis. But it is actually made by another cell, the oligodendrocyte. It is inside this cell that we must look for the rubicons responsible for the loss of nerve conduction in this disease.

CONCEPT OR METHOD?

So do we need a new concept, or is the problem that we haven't done enough experiments yet? Or is it simply that we aren't measuring things in the right way?

Yes, yes and yes!

The new principle underpining the Rubicon Hypothesis is that the unit of life, the cell, behaves in a quantal and not a graded manner. Like the electron in an atom, a cell can be excited, both by external and internal agents. In an excited state the cell is able to do things which in the ground state it cannot. When the cell drops back to its ground state further events occur. This principle applies to all cells, whether bacteria, archaebacteria or eukaryotes.

To test the validity of this principle we shall have to develop new methods, as well as extending ones already in use. In particular, we shall need ways of lighting up the chemistry of living cells. We shall have to find a way of measuring, manipulating and locating chemical events inside individual live cells and those within intact organs. And we shall need to do this in defined compartments of the cell, in other words inside each organelle as well as the cytosol. This is because a fundamental feature of the Rubicon Hypothesis is that the rubicons in life and death can only be identified by studying cells while they remain alive.

THE RUBICON HYPOTHESIS

The Rubicon Hypothesis is a unitary hypothesis, applicable to all living cells and all biological phenomena. It takes as its central theme the fact that all real biological phenomena occur through leaps or quantal events, by cells crossing thresholds. It states the following:

All biological phenomena are explicable by individual cells or groups of cells crossing a series of chemical and physical thresholds, henceforth called rubicons. The timing and magnitude of the complete phenomenon are dependent on the number of cells which have crossed each rubicon, together with the size and timing of these events in each cell. A cell rubicon can occur as the result of a threshold crossed by just one molecule in the cell, for example a gene, or one organelle, for example the fusion of a secretory granule. It may require a molecular sequence and chemisymbiosis involving several metabolic pathways and internal structures, which must take place at the right time in the right place in the cell if the final rubicon is to be crossed. The complete sequence may require a matrix of cellular rubicons, for each cell has its own rubicons to cross. Once a series of rubicons is achieved the cell can never be the same again, even though it may apparently be able to return to the territory from which it came.

The path of a cell to its ultimate end-point rubicon, when a biological event occurs, often involves a series of mini-rubicons within the cell. But, the path to, and between, the banks of each mini-rubicon involves a combination of *continuous* chemical and physical change. The role of the molecular biologist is to define these chemico-physical changes and provide a molecular explanation of the crossing from bank to bank. Let me illustrate this principle with three examples.

You are looking out of the window when the door opposite is pushed open. There, much to your surprise, stands a man-eating tiger. Many cells will be crossing rubicons at this crucial moment in your life! Let's consider just one tissue, the liver. So that you have enough energy to run like hell out of the room and shut the door, your leg muscles and heart need fuel. The liver can supply the glucose they will need. Your brain has already sent signals down various nerves to tell the adrenal gland to release adrenaline into the blood stream. Several other hormones will also have been released by other tissues. Some of these will stimulate release of glucose from the liver. If this were an animal experiment the biochemist would make a pâté by grinding up the liver in order to measure various enzymes in the hope of finding out how they have been activated to cause this release of sugar. But these biochemical measurements represent mean values from millions and millions of cells, preventing an answer to the crucial question which Rubicon now presents: *When the glucose released from the whole liver has reached half the maximum level it will eventually achieve, have all the cells been activated to half their maximum or have only half the cells been switched on?*

This *obvious* question has been ignored mainly because of the nature of the experimental approach to biochemistry which has developed over the course of this century. The answer is fundamental to the description of how hormones and neuro-transmitters work. Rubicon predicts that only some of the cells will have crossed the glucose-releasing rubicon. Unless one is able to follow the timing as each cell goes though its sequence of rubicons the molecular mechanism of this phenomenon can never be fully elucidated.

The major *white* cell in the blood is called the neutrophil, really green because it has the ability to produce bleach. As a result, like the bottle of bleach under your kitchen sink, these cells really can 'kill all known germs'. This is crucial to their job in the body's army of defence against microbial invaders. The amount of bleach produced by each cell varies according to the size of the instructions, the amount of stimulus received. But critically important to Rubicon is that the time-course and amounts of bleach produced by cell populations depend on how many cells have been switched on. With some stimuli, even at a maximum dose, only a proportion of the cells produce bleach. Some produce no bleach at all. This can of course only be demonstrated by measuring the timing and amount of bleach produced by each cell, one at a time. The internal mechanism responsible for this starts with the generation of a signal inside the cell. Only when this signal has reached its target will the cell switch its traffic lights from red to green, and GO!

A third example of Rubicon in action can be found in another component of the body's defence system – in the Navy this time. In the plasma of the blood – that is, the fluid part which surrounds the red and white cells as they flow around the body – is a system called complement. Like bleach it also can be a killer, though as we shall see later it is its non-lethal actions which may be particularly important in diseases such as rheumatoid arthritis. But it kills cells in a different way, by firing chemical 'shells' at the invading cells. Under appropriate experimental conditions you can also get these shells to kill red blood cells. As a result they release all their red haemoglobin into the surrounding fluid. Read the description of this process in a standard immunology or pathology textbook and you are given the distinct impression that after attack the haemoglobin gradually leaks out of the cells as they swell. This is not the true story. If you watch one cell you will see that the actual release of the red haemoglobin is in fact very rapid. The red colour in the fluid phase of the cell suspension only increases with time because the *number* of cells which have been killed increases with time. The shower of shells may hit many cells at the same time, but while some cells cross the cataclysmic rubicon very early after attack, perhaps within a few minutes or even seconds, others take up to 30-60 minutes to die. Yet the death event itself takes only a fraction of a second.

We shall be re-examining many such phenomena as examples of Rubicon in action throughout this book. But the validity of the hypothesis and whether it really does give us a new perspective on biological phenomena first depend not so much on the novel questions it raises, though these will be very important in the future, but rather on the answers to six specific questions:

1. What is the evidence already available to support the hypothesis?
2. What predictions does the hypothesis make, which will lead to new discoveries?
3. What experimental strategy and new methodology do we need to test these predictions?
4. Does the hypothesis really give us a new perspective enabling us to understand biological phenomena better – in health and disease, in the earth as a whole, as it is now and as it was through nearly 4,000 million years of evolution?
5. Does the hypothesis provide the fine detail of molecular and physical mechanisms necessary to explain a threshold, whether in a cell or in a whole ecosystem?
6. Can this quantal hypothesis lead us to a theory, a law of biology, which

enables biological phenomena to be described quantitatively in simple, mathematical terms?

It is important also to realise the limits of the hypothesis. I may be claiming that it applies to all living things, but that does not mean that it is omnipotent. Rubicon will not explain everything. It will not resolve all the problems and crises in contemporary biology. Nor does it attempt to destroy previous reductionist discoveries. One does not need quantum theory to calculate the time a car takes to move a particular distance at a measured velocity. Quantum theory did not destroy Newton's laws of motion. So with Rubicon and biology. One of my aims in this book is to identify when we need to use the threshold principle embodied in Rubicon and when we do not.

So what is Rubicon about? What are we going to learn from it? Is this hypothesis really saying anything new, or is it simply stating the obvious? Some phenomena clearly involve cell thresholds: nerves and muscles firing, for example. We knew that already. But surely not *all* biological phenomena?

Let's reconsider the man we met earlier who dropped down on the station platform. The day beforehand he had a complete medical check up. He was not a smoker, but several relatives had died of heart attacks and he had a high blood cholesterol. The risk factor calculated by his doctor gave him a 30 per cent chance of a heart attack. That is the way medicine works. It is all down to probabilities. But 'God did not play dice with the Universe'. Having to resort to probabilities is an excuse for ignorance. Rubicon aims to transform our understanding from probability to certainty.

Another key feature of Rubicon is that it shows us that a biological phenomenon should be viewed not as a single event but rather as a pathway. This pathway is a sequence of phases, each phase involving gradual physical and chemical changes leading to the banks of a rubicon. The biological system then crosses and the next phase begins. This will be particularly pertinent when we examine what we mean by death and extinction. Rubicon argues that we must reconsider them as a sequence of events rather than a single one.

To uncover each rubicon – how it is reached, how it is crossed and what is the next stage in the pathway – is our goal. But please do not reject the principle just because we have yet to find the rubicon, or because there is as yet no credible molecular mechanism to explain how a rubicon is reached or crossed.

Earlier we met Peter Mitchell, who discovered how the energy from our food is converted into the inner fuel of cells, ATP. The key steps occur inside a particular room inside the cell, the mitochondrion. In each liver cell there are a thousand or more mitochondria. But Mitchell's analysis considers them as one, a giant. But is this the right way to look at them? No. To explain the synthesis of ATP, and damage to this in cell injury, Rubicon insists that we find out how many mitochondria are working at any one time in a particular cell. The first question Rubicon asks is: When the ATP production in a cell is 50 per cent of maximum, have all the 'mitos' increased their production by 50 per cent, or has the cell switched on another set of mitos previously at rest? A similar question can be put when the ATP drops to 20 per cent in cell injury. Have 80 per cent of the mitos stopped working? You will have guessed that Rubicon predicts that the answer will be the threshold one. In which case we need new mechanisms, and we need new spectacles to view them!

Rubicon provides a new conceptual framework and a new experimental strategy at the interface of reductionism and holism. It recognises the value and the fascination of the knowledge and understanding which arises from both philosophies. Rubicon needs to know the components in and out of cells that are involved in a biological phenomenon. Then, like the reductionist, it needs to identify the molecular and cellular sequence on each bank of the Rubicon. This includes the signals that start a cell, organism or whole ecosystem on the route to the Rubicon.

But not all thresholds should be considered as rubicons. Nor need all stages between rubicons be continuous and smooth. The breaking or formation of a single chemical bond is clearly a threshold, but it is not a rubicon unless it causes a biological step to be taken.

Rubicon is about presenting natural phenomena in a way that makes them susceptible to penetrative investigation. Only when the rubicons in a phenomenon are defined can we understand the cause, the molecular basis, the true function, the evolutionary origin of the phenomenon and all its facets. Rubicon focuses on what we are really trying to explain. In physiology, pathology, disease, ecology and evolution the aim is to describe *natural* phenomena, and then try to explain how they work.

The thrill of seeing the beautiful colour of butterfly wings or the penetrative greenish glow of a glow-worm with her amorous fire should be enhanced, not diminished by our scientific excursions. Only when we see molecules and even cells through the eye of the naturalist will we understand that there is a real alternative to the pure reductionist's perception of Nature!

In spite of the inglorious shift of modern railways from the romance of steam to diesel or electric engines, train-spotting remains an active pastime for many enthusiasts. As a boy, I remember encountering one of my first puzzles in physics while on a train-spotting trip with my cousins. Standing on the station platform we were urgently instructed to move back as a non-stop express was about to pass through the station. Sure enough within a few seconds we heard the noise of the engine's whistle as it approached the station at great speed. Being a musician, the pitch of noises in the environment, whether from birds and animals or from trains and other artefacts, has always been something which I notice particularly. As the train passed, the whistle went *whee-aah*, dropping in pitch after it had passed. The immediate question in my mind was how could they design a whistle with such an unusual control of its pitch. But then I realised that

I had heard a train whistle when it was stationary, and the pitch was constant. Was there something about the physics of sound which caused an apparent change in pitch when the train was moving at speed? It was not till some years later that I learnt about Doppler and his experiments. The point of this example is that it illustrates how easy it is to assume the wrong explanation of a phenomenon when the question is not presented in the right way.

The problem with biology is that, because fundamental laws and incontrovertible universalities are scant, we have to rely on mental images and cartoons to convey the essentials of a biological process. How can I talk about thresholds and 'rubicons' without giving a mental picture of the 'crossing'? I do intend to deal with that problem, but first we must concentrate on 'The Banks of the Rubicon'. Only when 'the banks' are described in the right way will we understand precisely how a living system has reached this point, what the consequences of the crossing may be, and whether there is any path to a true return to the status quo afterwards.

The real Rubicon is a stream in central Italy (Figure 3). It was the demarcation line separating Julius Caesar's province of Cisalpine Gaul from Italy proper. On 10-11 January 49 BC Caesar and his army crossed the Rubicon, thereby declaring war against the Republic. Although 'Rubicon' in French still conveys such undertones, this book, I trust, does not have such aggressive intentions. However, its central thesis is the idea that cells, the structures within them and even individual molecules take decisive and irrevocable steps. These are necessary for any biological event to occur, in health or sickness. Rubicon will help us understand what goes wrong with tissues in disease, and provides an opportunity to resolve some of the crises in evolution, both at the whole-organism and at the molecular level. Living things, their evolution, their reproduction, their specialised functions, and their eventual death, depend critically not on gradual chemical and physical changes but on events, thresholds. It is this concept that this book tries to develop by making use of a common phrase from the English language, 'crossing the Rubicon'.

Should we worry about how the crossing occurs? We shall look at this, but I believe it is secondary to the main thrust of the argument and at this stage may even be a diversion. The science of photochemistry and luminescence has been critically dependent on the ability to use Einstein's equation Energy = $h\nu$ to describe the transformation of electrons within atoms and molecules from ground to excited, and thus 'reactive', states. When an electron *jumps* to a higher energy level it 'crosses the Rubicon', and as a result enables the atom of which it is a part to do something. The excited atom may react with another atom; it may split from its neighbour if it was in a molecule; it may transfer its energy to another; or it may simply emit the energy as light. Physics and chemistry were not initially bothered by the perplexing problem of how the electron 'physically' crossed these rubicons, but rather on defining, both qualitatively and quantitatively, each different state, i.e. the 'banks' of each rubicon. Particle

Fig. 3. The location of the Rubicon.

physicists are only now able to address the question of what is happening to the electron during the crossing.

Are the banks running a legalised usury? Every month money is transferred from my bank account to my sons' building society accounts. The distance between these two buildings used to be about one kilometre. Yet it often took as long as five days for the money to reappear in their accounts after it had disappeared from mine. We are forbidden to ask where the money has disappeared to! So also with an electron buzzing around the nucleus of an atom, as it leaps up to a new orbit when excited, for example in a glow-worm after its light-generating chemical reaction has taken place. The time between the ground and excited state is very, very short, a thousand million millionth (10^{-15}) of a second. It then takes about a hundred millionth (10^{-8}) of a second to drop down again – minute time-scales in terms of human experience, but finite all the same. But where is the electron in between? We are not allowed to ask. Yet this is anathema to a biologist who demands pictorial images of the pathway.

We shall have to address the problem of how to cross the Rubicon. But let's not worry about this immediately. First, let's convince ourselves of the validity of the principle of thresholds embodied within the concept of Rubicon. Even if our initial attempts to explain how the crossing occurs turn out to be wrong or without mechanism, as was the case for Mitchell and Darwin, we must not reject the concept itself! To the banks!

2

The Rubicons of Life and Death

EVERY ONE'S A RUBICON

You are lying in bed staring up at the ceiling, thinking about work as usual! But your partner has other ideas. You sense the gentle caress of a hand moving down your body. Rapidly both of you move to the banks of an exciting rubicon. A Rubicon pathway is set. The penis becomes erect and the vagina is secreting. Some minutes later you have both crossed the ultimate rubicon, and each enjoyed a fulfilling orgasm. You both soon slip into a beautiful post-coital sleep.

Sexual interaction between male and female is a wonderful thing. Love-making has evolved for us to procreate our species. This requires both the rubicon of the fertilisation of the egg by the sperm, and the maintenance of the pair-bond to provide the protective environment needed for children to survive and flourish into adulthood. As we dissect such processes into the constituent stages of the Rubicon route, we must take care not to destroy their inherent beauty.

It is August and the following morning you wake up, jump out of bed and walk out into the garden. Stopping for a moment by the French windows you sense the smell of honeysuckle. It has bloomed for a second time this year. The succulent plum you noticed on the tree last night has fallen to the ground and has already been half devoured by buzzing wasps and slimy slugs. Also, on the flower bed are the brown remains of a dead apple. A couple of blue tits are titzzing in the plum tree. Suddenly you have a great idea, and rush inside to write it down before you have a chance to forget it.

These are all clear examples of natural phenomena where you or another organism have moved to the banks of a rubicon and then been taken across. How the crossing occurs will be addressed in the next chapter. But for the moment I want to concentrate on convincing you of two things: first the universal occurrence of rubicons in virtually every biological phenomenon, and secondly that to explain the ultimate rubicon we must look for the pathway of mini-rubicons which lead to, or combine together for, the real biological event. In some we may find a single rubicon, while in others there may be many thousands or even millions.

You are born, take your first breath, and die only once. But in between, if you live to be eighty, your heart will have crossed something like three billion rubicons (3×10^9). At rest the heart has to beat just over once a second and when running nearly twice a second, with millions of tiny muscles cells contracting in synchrony. You need these rubicons to remain alive, to think clearly, to run and do what you want to do.

Consider the following scenario. You are late leaving work to collect your children from school. When you arrive most of the other children have gone and there are two lonely figures standing on the other side of the road, your daughter carrying her violin case. As you get out of the car, they see you and in great excitement run to greet you. To your horror you see a large lorry travelling fast, which the children have clearly not seen. As they turn to charge across the road your heart is in your mouth. Your daughter has tripped over her violin case and looks set to fall into the path of the oncoming lorry. The lorry screeches to a halt, misses the children, but not before your daughter has fallen over and grazed her knee. After some tears and cuddling the bleeding stops, and thankfully you shepherd the children into the car and drive off home, trying to decide how you are going to explain things to your wife!

During this scenario literally dozens of rubicons have been crossed by various components of your body and those of your children: the eyes have observed and the brain recognised, legs and arms have moved during the running, bodies have stopped and fallen, wounds have been opened and bled and the blood has clotted. The brains of all participants have recorded fright and pain at the whole-body level. Then at the cellular level nerve cells in the brain and the periphery, including those responsible for pain and the photoreceptors in the eye, have transmitted signals back to the part of the brain which processes them into a feeling or a picture. Muscle cells have contracted and relaxed for movement to occur. The muscle cells of the heart have beaten stronger and faster in response to adrenaline released by cells in the adrenal gland, thereby increasing blood flow to the muscles. The adrenaline has also instructed cells in the liver to release sugar, and cells in fatty tissue to release fat, into the blood, both to supply the extra energy needed by those cells faced with an increased work load. Tiny platelets in the blood have helped to form the clot with a blood protein called fibrin in response to thrombin released from damaged tissue at the site of the wound. And your daughter's defence system has been conscripted into action. White cells from the blood have been attracted into the cut to try to kill any invading bacteria and thus prevent the wound becoming septic. Her mother will not be happy if this latter rubicon is crossed, particularly if she has to have another dose of antibiotics to prevent the dangerous rubicon of blood-poisoning.

Quite a list of thresholds which are rubicons, and it is far from exhaustive. But there are thresholds which are not rubicons.

IS IT OR ISN'T IT?

Let's return to the scenario at the beginning of this chapter, at the point when you have just woken up, your first rubicon of the day. You turn on the light, a physical threshold occurs in the filament of the bulb, heat generates light. But the biological rubicon is in your perception of the light. You see *Rubicon* lying on the bedside table, open at the page where you finished just before going to sleep last night. You close the book. Another rubicon? After returning from the garden, inside you find that your daughter is doing her violin practice before breakfast. After a few minutes you have lost count of how many rubicons have been crossed as each note was received by your ears and processed by your brain. The post and the morning newspaper arrive through the 'rubicon' in the front door, the letter-box. As you open one of the envelopes you see a blue flash of light from the self-sealant. Inside is an invitation to a family golden wedding, while on the back page of the newspaper there is a detailed description of an exciting cricket match. England's star batsman has reached 300 runs for the first time. A record rubicon! And so it goes on throughout the day. Threshold after threshold. Rubicon after rubicon? Let's examine some of these apparent rubicons a little closer, for I am trying to make two serious points.

First, some of these thresholds are of genuine scientific interest, while others are either too trivial or artificial. Secondly, this book is about biology, so we want to select events which are relevant to the survival, reproduction and evolution of living things. Thus to be a *rubicon* a *threshold* must be part of a genuine biological event. By using the Rubicon framework we hope to gain a better understanding of life and death and the physico-chemical processes responsible for them. But, as we shall see, this means that we must also examine physical and chemical phenomena which have an impact on living systems. In one light the phenomena may appear to lack thresholds; yet, when examined in the light of the living organism or cell experiencing it, we see rubicons being crossed. For example, we shall see in Chapter Six the necessity of water remaining in its liquid state for life to survive and continue. Yet phase transitions, gas-liquid-solid rubicons, play a vital part in life and in determining death: the exchange of gases in the lungs and between special cells in the leaves of plants known as guard cells, the emission of pheromones by insects, and the gel-sol conversion of the cytoplasm in an activated cell are but a few examples. Everyone knows what happens when you boil an egg. A similar thing happens to the fluid inside a cell when it dies.

So how are we going to tell whether we are dealing with a true rubicon crossing or not, and whether it is worth a second thought?

Rubicon goes decimal

The obsession with tens obviously originates from a natural phenomenon, the fact that we have ten fingers. But events such as fifty years of marriage, a century in cricket, the media-hype of the *event of the decade* are artificial. There is nothing biologically-special about 100, as opposed to 99 or 101, or 10 as opposed to 9 or 11, except in the way that we as a society have chosen to view them. The appearance of your morning post through the letter-box is too trivial to warrant serious scientific thought. The boundaries created by many scientific units are also artificial, developed by man for a reason, yet arbitrary all the same: the units of time, length, weight and volume – seconds, minutes, hours, metres, miles, grammes, pounds, litres or pints and so on. 100°F has no particular significance scientifically, but 100°C has, being the temperature of the phase transition between liquid and gaseous water. The latter is a true scientific rubicon, the former not. Similarly certain units of time are arbitrary, while others indicate that a rubicon has been crossed. Examples of time intervals which generate genuine biological rubicons are 24 hours = 1 day + night cycle, the time it takes the Earth to complete a rotation, approximately at least, generating various physical and chemical rubicons from the clock in our body; and a year, with the inevitable four rubicon seasons so obvious in the plant kingdom.

So there are rubicons which we come across in everyday life which are outside the scope of the present argument either because they are true artifacts, man-made, or because they belong solely to the realm of physics or chemistry. The physical and chemical world is full of thresholds. The transition between the three states of matter, the formation of a snowflake or a drop of water in a cloud, a flash of lightning or a clap of thunder, the decay of a radioactive element, the flame in a fire, the appearance of rust on a nail, the explosion of methane gas in a coal mine, the formation of a white dwarf or black hole millions of light years away, are just a few examples. Yet we must not put all of these physical and chemical thresholds aside. Several will be vital for our understanding of how biological rubicons can actually be crossed. Even those which appear to fall within the realm of the physicist, astronomer or geologist, rather than the biologist, need to be looked at closely before passing on.

Physics crosses the Rubicon

There is but one science, natural science. A crack in a pane of glass or the crumbling of a rock face, an earthquake or a tornado's vortex are for the geologist to explain. But the separation of the major land masses on the earth by plate tectonics, the first rubicon for which was crossed some 600 million years ago, with its subsequent exposure of living organisms to new physical conditions such as temperature and radiation, must be considered when we look for explanations of evolutionary rubicons. The breaking of a wave on the beach is of importance not only to the surfer, but also to the inter-tidal organisms which have had to evolve ways of surviving this onslaught week-in week-out. Similarly, the chemistry and weather in the atmosphere has a vital impact on the rubicons of the biosphere. If the temperature of the Earth's surface had not dropped to less than 100°C some 4,000 million years ago there would be no sea, no rivers, no rain, no liquid water for life to exist.

But what about a rainbow, or the *Aurora borealis*? Measurement of the scattering of light by raindrops or the impact of particles from the sun on the atmosphere may help to explain why a particular spectrum of light in this region of the electromagnetic spectrum has been generated, but it does not explain the colour we see. Unlike the physicist's spectrometer, which sees the spectrum with no colour discontinuities, our eyes see at least seven rubicons in the spectrum defined by Newton: violet, indigo, blue, green, yellow, orange and red. The boundaries between them may be a little blurred, but the colours of a rainbow resulting from our retina having cells each with pigments sensitive to one of three colours (blue, green, red) means that we have colour rubicons. Without these there would have been no art, and no appreciation of the beautiful colours in nature. Many animals, plants and microbes have pigments which only respond to one particular region of the electromagnetic spectrum. As with the human eye coupled to the brain, these photoreceptors also generate thresholds which determine the behaviour of the organism. Bioluminescence in the deep sea, where there is very little penetration of light from the surface, plays a similar role to colour for surface organisms. This is a wonderful phenomenon. I hope you will excuse my indulgence in it throughout this book. But more of this anon.

As was pointed out by Alfred Russel Wallace (1823-1913), co-discoverer with Darwin of evolution by natural selection, colour has played a vital part in animal and plant recognition throughout evolution. And it matters whether the organism perceives blue or red, yellow or green. It is the threshold of colour perception, not the precise wavelength at the peak of the emission or the absorbance spectrum measured by the physicist's highly precise spectrometer, that matters. The very similar spectra measured thus from a firefly or glow-worm do not explain why one appears yellow and the other green.

Molecules cross the Rubicon

Every time a molecule is cleaved or combines with another a threshold has been crossed, but it should not necessarily be considered as a rubicon. Consideration of chemical or biological reactions as individual molecules reacting is relevant if we want to understand the switching on or off of a gene, or the cleavage of a single chromosome in an irradiated cell, or the opening of a channel in the membrane of a cell. But for reactions involving millions of molecules, and obeying the laws of mass action, it is not helpful to think of each molecular threshold, unless of course one is concerned with the electronic mechanisms responsible for bond-breaking or bond-forming. Nor is the individual molecule necessarily the right starting point to explain a biological rubicon. Rubicon starts with the natural phenomenon, whether physiological, pathological, psychological, ecological or evolutionary. The Rubicon has been crossed when experience of the phenomenon begins.

To decide whether we are really looking at a natural, biological rubicon or not we need a classification. As to the Swedish founder of modern taxonomy Carl von Linné (1707-1778), better known by his Latin name as Linnaeus, what matters is whether we are dealing with an animal, plant or a stone! We shall attempt this at the end of the chapter. A key question will be: At what point does experience begin?

RUBICON ILLUMINATED
Living light

All animals and plants respond to light. A white etiolated seedling grown in the airing cupboard becomes green within a day or two once it is brought out into the light. This rubicon involves signalling specific genes to make chlorophyll. Plants grown inside on a window sill lean towards the light in a few days. Animals have eyes or photoreceptors which can be more sensitive than the best photographic film. A silver grain in a photographic film requires a cluster of light particles to hit it within a short time interval if its threshold is to be crossed, enabling it to form part of the latent image which will appear once the film is immersed in the developer. Go into a dark-room after being out in the sunlight. Your pupils will dilate, but you still can't see a thing. But wait a few minutes and your eyes will dark-adapt, enabling you to see faint images. The rubicon pathway has been sensitised. At this maximum sensitivity the individual light-sensing cells in our retina are incredibly sensitive – much, much more senstive than photographic film. In fact they seem to be capable of detecting individual light pulses. Einstein called these packets of light energy 'photons'. But this does not necessarily mean that you will perceive an image. If the brain is to recognise an image, the light intensity has to be high enough for large numbers of individual cells to cross their rubicons simultaneously. Even unicellular organisms including bacteria can respond to light, some being attracted, some repelled. Once again there is an intensity or colour threshold. But there are far fewer animals that actually produce their own light (Plates 2 and 3). Yet these offer some of the most spectacular and wondrous examples of Rubicon you could imagine!

There are some million or more species of beetle on the Earth. A few hundred of these are luminous. They belong to four families: the *Phengodidae*, the *Homalisidae*, the *Elateridae* and the *Lampyridae*. They are the fireflies and glow-worms. There are also a few luminous earthworms and centipedes. And there are some spectacular luminous rarities, such as the New Zealand glow-worm, really a fly, a rare luminous millipede living 1,500-2,000 metres up in the Sierra Nevada mountains, and a freshwater limpet from New Zealand. Living light is rare on land, but in the sea it is a different matter. Three-quarters of the Earth is covered by sea. Here we find luminous animals and bacteria in abundance. Delve into the twilight zone some 1,000 metres down which covers half the Earth's surface, and virtually everything is luminous: jelly fish, shrimp and many other crustaceans, squid, octopods and fish. In order to see them you need either to have a submersible or to be lucky enough, as I have been, to use specialised nets from research ships such as RRS *Discovery* to bring them to the surface. The nets at night are aglow with flashing specimens.

The taxonomist classifies animals, plants and microbes first into kingdoms and then into the major groups, or phyla. After several sub-divisions we reach the genus, and the individual species. Living light can be found in some 700 genera from 16 phyla. It is a major means of communication on the Earth, or the sea to be precise! Yet there are no luminous plants and no luminous spiders, lobsters or crabs, except those infected by cultures of luminous bacteria. Most luminescence in the sea is blue or green. On land some fireflies emit yellow and occasionally orange light. But red bioluminescence is very rare. It is restricted to a few beetles, the most famous being the South American rail-road worm, and a group of deep-sea fishes with two pairs of major light organs, one emitting blue and the other red light. Red shrimp down where these fish live are normally black unless illuminated by a red torch, because the sea-water above has scattered or absorbed the red component from the sun's rays. Only the blue component is left. As a result, evolution has lead to these shrimp and virtually all other deep-sea animals being able only to see blue light. The exception is our luminous fish with its red torch. It can see its own light, but the prey, the shrimp, cannot. A wonderful example of Rubicon in action!

There are other extraordinary examples of luminous rubicons in various parts of the world, the red tides and a luminous ship's wake resulting from dinoflagellates, the flashing of a jelly fish, 'phosphorescent bays', milky seas and the 'Christmas tree' displays in the forests of New Guinea where thousands of fireflies flash in Rubicon synchrony with one another. In Bermuda there are marine worms where the females spin round producing a luminous trail which tells the male to release its sperm. The krill eaten by whales are luminous. A swarm containing thousands and thousands of these is a spectacular sight, especially when they fill the filters of a ship's engine choc-a-bloc with luminescent bodies!

Living light has invaded most of the habitats of the earth. Luminous worms live underground, luminous fungi grow in the forest, fireflies flash in the air, hydroids and starfish sparkle in rock pools, and hundreds of invertebrates and fish flash or glow in the sea. The extraordinary piddock *Pholas dactylus* lives all its life inside a rock – a boring, but to some a very interesting, mollusc! Bang the rock at night and the sea is lit up with a starlit display underwater as each piddock crosses its own rubicon and secretes a luminous cloud from its siphon out of the burrow. Many luminous animals have amazing appendages associated with the luminous cells or organs – lenses, fibre optics, reflectors and colour filters – so that they can induce the right Rubicon response in the observer.

Some luminescence has evolved to prevent a rubicon. Many deep-sea fish have a spectacular pattern of luminous cell clusters on their stomachs, or ventral surface. These clusters produce a sparkling array of light of the same colour as the ambient light at the depth they live. Why? Dive off a boat at night, look up underwater and you will see. The boat's silhouette is obvious. But put a few lights on the keel and it becomes much more difficult to pick out. So with the luminous fish who use it to camouflage their shape against predators looking upwards.

As you will have gathered, some luminous animals produce their light from within their cells, while others are squirters: for example, shrimp squirters and squid, emitting brilliant clouds of light or cylinders of luminous toothpaste. These can act as a luminous 'smoke screen' or dazzle a would-be predator. So a rubicon in one animal triggers a rubicon in another, which prevents a combination rubicon between them. Living light can have one or more function in a particular species, each a rubicon: reproduction, defence, obtaining food and communication. Rubicons all over the place. Flash frequency and colour can matter, providing for one species a recognition rubicon but in another camouflage. Each species has its own recognition pattern. An infamous 'femme fatale' in the US fools males of another species by flashing like its own female. Having attracted it, the 'femme fatale' then kills the unsuspecting male!

Living light also exhibits cycles and circadian rhythms. The British species of luminous beetles, the glow-worm, glows mainly during July. The female is the big glower, being wingless, and the male flies in to her beacon. Sea-water containing luminous dinoflagellates will start flashing when disturbed about an hour before sunset, and stop again an hour or so before sunrise. The control of the luminescence is thus also a nice example of Rubicon, particularly elegantly illustrated in certain bacteria.

Sea water throughout the world contains individual bacteria. Some are pathogens from sewage effluents. But many are harmless, and some have the capacity to produce their own light. Free-floating in the sea, however, they are non-luminous. But when they infect a host – for example, a bit of decaying fish, a dying invertebrate, or the luminous organ of a deep-sea angler fish or a squid – they become luminous. The point of course is that the colony is now visible, whereas individual bacteria are too small to be seen even when they are luminous. This would be a waste of energy. Once again the coordination of this rubicon is uncanny. The cause of the rubicon is the production of a signal, a so-called auto-inducer, by the bacterial colony itself. This switches on the genes necessary for producing the light-emitting reaction. Once the colony reaches a critical size it produces a blue glow, easily seen by a predator, which then carries it away to spread the bacteria far and wide, whereas, in the case of the angler fish, its luminous lure is the envy of all fishermen for its efficiency at attracting prey. In fact fishermen in some parts of the world actually use bits of luminous squid or colonies of tiny luminous crustaceans to catch fish. Synthetic luminous lures now available in fishing shops have been banned from competition. Nature knows best!

Man has found some ingenious uses for luminescence, of which we shall see more in Chapter Seven. There is an interesting apocryphal story about Florence Nightingale (1820-1910) and luminous bacteria. A species of luminous bacteria is found in the soil, which is distinct from those found in the sea. Remarkably, there is a nematode which carries a colony of these light-emitting bacteria within it. A pigment makes it red during the day, and when a host is infected the luminous bacteria make it blue by night. Such bacteria are known to infect cadavers on battle fields and, before refrigerators, caused frightening rubicons in housewives and maids entering the unlit pantry at night to find a large carcass of meat glowing in the dark. One night Florence Nightingale is said to have been walking down the wards in the Crimea, where between 1854 and 1856 she was in charge of nursing in the military hospitals. She noticed that some of the wounds were glowing in the dark. Consulting the orderly she discovered that he had observed that soldiers with glowing wounds tended not to get gangrene. So, not being restricted by a local ethics committee, they did the obvious experiment. They made sure that the glow crossed the rubicon from patient to patient, by transferring it with swabs. They were unaware that the light was caused by live bacteria, for Johann Florian Heller (1813-1871), professor of medicine in Vienna, had only just published his observations that bacteria were the cause of shining flesh in 1853. Crazy? Recently it has been reported that these bacteria can produce a potent antibiotic, giving some credibility to this apocryphal story, which was told me by an authority on bioluminescence, Professor Woody Hastings of the University of Harvard. Unfortunately I have been unable to substantiate this anecdote, in spite of several hours spent reading through Florence Nightingale's fascinating correspondence with Lord Cardigan, almost illegible because of her atrocious handwriting. Nevertheless it is a nice and believable Rubicon story. It certainly throws new light on the legend on the 'Lady of the lamp'! Even as I write, reports have been published about luminous bacteria isolated from human wounds and an extraordinary luminous baby in France who gave her mother a real fright (Figure 4).

All such living light is chemical light and requires oxygen. We now know a lot about this chemistry. Precisely how the chemical components are consummated to produce a rubicon with the right flash or glow will be addressed in the next chapter. But can this detail explain why the flash of a particular firefly is yellow, whereas the glow of the British glow-worm is green? Meticulous scientific measurement has given us details of the spectrum, flash patterns, chemistry, biochemistry and molecular biology of dozens, if not hundreds, of luminous species and yet failed to explain

BABY GLOWS IN DARK, BAFFLES DOCTORS

A BABY WHO glows in the dark has scientific experts baffled — they think she may have a skin pigment and the same enzyme that allows some fish and other marine life to produce light.

STORY by JOHN COFFIN

"It's eerie," says Bernadette Boulle, mother of the baby, three-month-old Regina. "She glows in her crib at night like one of those luminescent statues or rosary beads."

Regina did not begin glowing

BABY WHO GLOWS IN THE DARK BAFFLES DOCTORS

until she was three weeks old, adds Bernadette, 29.

"One night I went into her room and she was lying there with a yellowish-green light surrounding her," she says.

"I ran from the room, screaming."

The Boulles, who have a farm in the north of France, called their doctor.

"Except for the fact that she glows in the dark, Regina seems to be a healthy, normal baby," says Dr. Ferdinand Ferroule after examining the baby.

Although Dr. Ferroule believes Regina is normal, the feeling is not shared by the Boulles' farming neighbors.

"It's scary," says Alain Boulle, Regina's 31-year-old father. "Farmers are sometimes a superstitious lot. Some of our

neighbors think Regina is a witch, while others say she is a saint." Neighbors surrounded their farm house last month and, with candles lit, singing religious hymns and chanting prayers.

"They were led by the village priest, who said he was trying to exorcise the house and Regina," Bernadette says.

Theory

Frustrated, the Boulles took Regina to a hospital in Paris where doctors examined her and found traces of luciferin and luciferase in her blood.

Both luciferin and luciferase are present in certain marine animals that have the ability to glow in the dark, including micro-organisms, fish and certain squid, says Dr. Charles Le-

Master, a French biochemist. Bioluminescence takes place when luciferin is oxidized in the luciferase. "We have found traces of both in little Regina's blood," he says. "But we have no idea as to how it got there.

Dr. LeMaster and other specialists believe a recessive gene may be responsible.

"At one point in our evolution we lived in the sea, and may have had the ability to glow in the dark," he says, admitting his theory is a guess. "Perhaps that gene is still in Regina's gene bank. But quite frankly we're all baffled by this.

"There is mention in medical literature of humans who could glow in the dark, but apparently no one has studied the phenomenon in any depth."

April 20, 1983 — SUN — 23

Fig. 4. A report of a luminous baby almost certainly caused by infection by luminous bacteria.

what really matters. After fifty years of intense biochemical investigation we still don't understand how the firefly produces a flash or the glow-worm a glow. Colour and flashes are pattern-recognition signals and demand a more holistic description.

On land living light is relatively rare, but in the sea its rubicons are a major communication mechanism. So let us now look at the rubicons generated by those receiving light. The common feature is excitability: in light-sensitive cells, nerves and muscles.

Excitability

Nerves are chemical conductors of electricity. Each nerve cell is really three cells stuck together: the cell body, the axon and the terminal. All exhibit rubicons. A nerve either fires or it does not. Each nerve cell body may interact with the terminals of dozens or even thousands of other nerves, some positive others negative. Only when the positives beat the negatives by a critical margin does the cell body cross its own rubicon and generate an electrical signal. This then travels down the axon at breakneck speed. In a few thousandths of a second it arrives at the terminal and the next rubicon here releases a chemical package, the transmitter, in sufficient quantity and fast enough to trigger the next nerve or muscle.

In the case of a nerve-muscle junction, the arrival of the package of chemical at the precise point at one end of the muscle, the so-called end-plate, generates another electrical signal, which then travels down the muscle signalling it to contract. Nerves and muscles are the longest cells in our body, some being several feet long, i.e. 30 or more cm. But how does a squid squirt, or the leg of the little girl described at the beginning of this chapter move faster or slower? How can Rubicon explain the strength in our arms when we lift something? Very well, actually.

We increase our muscle strength by increasing the number of muscle cells contracting, not by increasing the strength within each one. By contrast the increase in blood flow when the father had his heart in his mouth and the increase in the children when they were running was caused both by increasing the frequency of rubicons in each heart muscle cell *and* by increasing the size (i.e. the strength of the contraction) of each rubicon. All the cells of the heart contract each time the heart beats. Changes in heart-beat are not caused by recruiting more or fewer cells, unless a pathological rubicon has been crossed.

Yet the interesting thing about light-receiving cells is that in some animals absorption of light excites them, while in others it appears to inhibit excitability. In the latter case the possibility exists that the photo-receptors are continuously chemically switched on. Light actually switches them off, stopping the chemical reaching the adjoining nerve cell, which then fires to communicate through the optic nerve that light has been received. It is still not entirely clear whether this is the way our own eyes work. Colour sensitivity is controlled by rubicons in three different photo-receptive cells, containing one of three pigments sensitive to blue, green or red light.

Sensory cells, either nerves or nerve-like cells, are responsible for the sensing of light, heat, touch, sound, and chemicals in the mouth and nose. Similar cells are responsible for sensory processes in insects. Some are attached to appendages, e.g. hairs, enabling the sensory cell to cross the rubicon without having to be in direct contact with the stimulus. Yet the firing of one rubicon is not responsible alone for an idea to be generated, or for pain to be sensed or for a shape to be recognised. These require a network or matrix of rubicons. Nevertheless let us continue on our cell rubicon route to emphasise the universal requirement for a pathway of cell rubicons if a biological event is to occur.

Cell rubicons

Cells cross a rubicon when they move, secrete, ingest, sense, divide, transform, defend themselves or die. These are also events which occur at the whole organism and tissue level. The chemistry and morphology of cells also exhibit rubicon pathways, cycles, oscillations and waves. A bacterial cell may take just half an hour or so to divide into two cells, while the cells in our body may take 24 hours or more to do so. Some – for example, our nerves – will never be able to cross this rubicon once they have formed within the embryo, while others, such as those lining the gut and in our skin, are dividing continuously many times a day.

The pathway leading to the ultimate rubicon of two of our cells formed from one can be divided into four phases. These are known as G1, S, G2 and M, each separated by a rubicon. This is usually referred to as the 'cell cycle'. But it is really a rubicon pathway rather than a cycle. As tissues develop or are repaired the two cells formed at division do not behave as 'identical twins' – they become heterogeneous. During development one cell can even develop into one tissue and its sibling another. G1, S and G2 normally constitute some 90 per cent of the cell cycle time. Thus the M, or mitotic rubicon, where the nuclei divide into two may take just 1-2 hours for a cell in which the whole cycle lasts 24 hours. DNA is only made during the S or synthesis phase. This type of mitotic cell cycle leads to a doubling of everything, whereas to form a gamete, i.e. an egg or a sperm, the number of chromosomes must be halved: a meiotic rubicon. The reason is that, while a bacterium only has one copy of the DNA template containing the architect's building instructions for making all the components of the cell, our cells contain duplicate copies. In fact all animals and plant cells contain two sets of chromosomes, except the gametes which only contain one. Thus, once the rubicon of union of an egg with a sperm has occurred, the fertilised egg now contains the duplicate set of chromosomes it needs to develop into a mature animal or plant.

Before fertilisation several rubicons have thus been crossed by both egg and sperm. First, mitosis, followed by meiosis to form the gametes. Then fertilisation of an egg by a sperm requires the movement of the ejaculated sperm. Attracted by chemicals released from the egg, the sperm in their thousands use their tail, the flagellum, to wiggle their way up the vaginal tract. On the way they encounter other chemicals released by cells in the tract. These mature the head of the sperm, a process known as capacitation. The expectant egg has already been matured by a hormone before being released by the ovary. Without crossing these maturation rubicons the sperm cannot fertilise an egg. Even invertebrates such as starfish and sea urchins have to mature their eggs before fertilisation. The rubicon principle is the same, but the hormone is different.

This particular rubicon pathway, which began with a soft caress and the crossing of an arousal rubicon, increasing heart beats and blood flow through key parts of the anatomy, ends in the union of one cell with another. A new rubicon pathway begins, leading to the birth of a new human being.

Let's look now at some examples of rubicons in cells where the cell itself is the organism.

Next time you are near a pond collect some water in a jam-jar, take it home and examine it under a microscope. With any luck you will see numbers of the energetic unicellular protozoan *Paramecium* darting about. Instead of having one flagellum, like sperm, *Paramecium* has hundreds of cilia on its outer membrane which beat so that the organism can move. When the protozoan hits an object, a rubicon is crossed. An electrical signal is generated at the point where the cell hits the object.

This signals the cilia to beat in the opposite direction, enabling the protozoan to move backwards away from the object it has hit. But there are other single-celled organisms in the pond water. Amoebae require a surface to move along because, not having flagella or cilia, they move by sending out protuberances, little feet, which allow the cell to 'walk' along the surface of a stone or the collector's glass jar. These then are the two fundamental types of rubicon movements – flagellate and amoeboid. Some cells can do both. Some can transform from amoeboid to flagellate, others can never do it. Cell movement plays an important role in the defence of our bodies against attack, and in development when cells generated in one part of an embryo are 'moved' to the correct site.

Dinoflagellates are another unicellular organism exhibiting clear examples of Rubicon. The luminous ones are responsible for some dramatic red tides in certain parts of the world, and for the well-known luminous trails seen from boats and the brilliant flashing caused by swimming in the sea on a summer's night. The luminous reaction is housed inside a special granule within each cell. But touching the outside of the cell causes the luminous reaction inside these granules of each cell to fire. Because of a circadian rhythm in each cell, the luminous reaction can only be triggered mechanically between the hours of dusk and sunrise. Quite sensible really. So about an hour before dusk the dinoflagellates are able to flash. But an hour or so before sunrise they cease, even when the cells contain all the components necessary for light emission.

Bacteria also exhibit rubicons, even sexual ones! Bacteria contain small circular fragments of DNA called plasmids. When a union between two bacterial cells takes place a plasmid can be transferred from one cell to another, taking with it genetic information not previously found in the recipient. It is this process which has played a central role in the development of genetic engineering. And many bacteria can move. Ones with flagella will swim towards nutrients such as sugar and amino-acids, but be repelled by toxic agents. Place a small capillary tube containing the amino-acid serine into a suspension of the human pathogenic bacterium *Salmonella* and within a few minutes the bacteria will all be clustered around the tip of the tube. Serine and several other amino-acids are chemo-attractants. In contrast phenol repels these bacteria, and so the region close to the tip becomes completely clear and devoid of bacteria. *Escherichia coli*, the common bacterium in our gut, behaves similarly. These bacteria are flagellates, and have evolved an extraordinary rubicon to enable them to move up or down chemical gradients. The gradient across a single cell would be far too small for an individual bacterium to realise that its front end is exposed to a different concentration from the back end. So the bacterium swims in a straight line for about a second, equivalent to about 15 body lengths, and then tumbles rapidly and moves off again in a different direction. The tumble is of course their rubicon. But a chemo-attractant lengthens the time between each tumble or rubicon, whereas if the bacterium moves away from the high concentration of the attractant the time between tumbles is reduced. Thus movement up the gradient is favoured, when in a few minutes the number of tumbles is several hundred for any one bacterial cell. The converse is true for a repellent.

Many uni- and multi-cellular organisms are attracted by various chemical and physical gradients, including light (phototaxis), though the mechanisms are usually different from the tumbling bacteria. Here we see an example of the crucial nature of timing and positioning of rubicons if the necessary end-result is to be achieved.

There are plenty of rubicons to be found too in plants. The germination of a seed, which could have remained dormant for years and years is a remarkable example of how long cells can remain on the banks of the rubicon before being provoked to cross. The new seedling, of course, forms in the soil, where it is dark. Not much point, then, in having green chlorophyll yet! But once the etiolated, white shoot appears above ground the seedling crosses the rubicon, the genes responsible for forming chlorophyll are switched on and the plant becomes green.

The oxygen/carbon dioxide ratio in the atmosphere is determined by cyanobacteria and plants, or was until man's factory chimneys made a mess of it. Like animals, plants have their own little lungs controlling the release of these gases. Each leaf has a cluster of guard cells which swell to shut off gas exchange, and contract back down when the leaf wants to cross the exchange rubicon. Plants are attracted towards the light, and their stems thicken and develop in the wind. Plants also have sex: that is, they release DNA which fuses with another gamete eventually to form a seed. As with animal cells, so the development, maintenance and reproduction of plants involves rubicon after rubicon.

Rubicons outside cells

Although I have argued throughout that life depends on cells, this does not mean that rubicons outside cells are not important. We have already seen how an apparent gradual chemical change in blood glucose can provoke rubicons in tissues such as the liver. Anyone who washes regularly in a hard-water area will be familiar with the insolubility of many calcium salts. In the case of soap one is the calcium stearate which comes out of solution to form the scum. Precipitates are a good example of a chemical rubicon, and those of calcium with phosphate, carbonate and sulphate are particularly important in living systems. The extra-cellular precipitates of calcium phosphate form round the collagen protein to form bone and teeth. The shells of invertebrates are made of a precipitate of calcium carbonate. The White Cliffs of Dover bear witness to the vast numbers of organisms in the past which have used this form of calcium to make their skeletons. Some organisms use precipitates of silicate, rather than calcium. The beautiful shapes of many small and large animals are critically dependent on the organised deposition of these precipitates.

And there are important organic compounds which are insoluble in water and are crucial to forming the shape of animals, plants and microbes. Sea firs (the hydroids), insects and bacteria are just a few examples of organisms that use a complex carbohydrate to protect and shape them, while plant cells surround themselves with a relatively simple carbohydrate macromolecule, cellulose, without which you would not be able to read; there would be no paper on which to put these words. Our stomachs cannot digest cellulose. But the ruminants can, for they house massive cultures of bacteria which produce an enzyme, cellulase, which can break cellulose down into simple sugar, and eventually its principal sugar, glucose.

Proteins can also come out of solution and cross the rubicon outside cells. Without the formation of the fibrin matrix, formed by chopping a bit off the soluble molecules of fibrin flowing around in our blood plasma, the little girl tripping over her violin case at the beginning of this chapter would have bled to death. For a blood clot is an insoluble complex of fibrin, encapsulating the tiny cells known as platelets that I mentioned earlier.

But what triggers these cellular and extra-cellular rubicons? There has to be a signal setting the rubicon pathway in motion.

FROM RED TO GREEN FOR GO!

In normal parlance the word *signal* conjures up images of railways and road junctions. But in modern cell biology it has become the key to understanding cell behaviour. Signals are intelligible signs seen at a distance which instruct a living entity to do something. Imagine therefore that you are at a set of traffic lights on RED. You are at rest. The lights change to RED-AMBER. The adrenaline starts to flow. You put the car into gear and your foot gently on the accelerator and get ready to release the hand-brake. A lot of rubicons have already been crossed in your body and in the car. After a few seconds the lights change to GREEN for GO!! You accelerate, the hand-brake and clutch are released, and the car moves off. At the next junction the lights change to amber just as you are reaching them. You have to decide whether to jam on the brakes or carry on through. In the event, the presence of your precious children in the back gives you the wisdom not to try jumping the lights. You stop the car before the red light comes on.

This *traffic-light* response is happening all the time in various cells within your body. At rest they are just ticking over. They are then signalled to be ready and then switched to green for GO, and as a result a cellular rubicon is crossed. The cell may move if it is a defence cell, contract if it is a muscle, secrete if it is a hormone-producing cell, ingest if it is a phagocyte, transform if it is an embryonic or developing cell, divide if it is multiplying, defend itself if under attack, or die if it is to cross the ultimate rubicon. All these cellular events have to be signalled, even death. And the cells must first be primed for them to get to RED-AMBER.

The instruction for a cell to GO can come from outside, or may be generated inside as the result of internal programming. The external stimuli may be physical, chemical or biological. For example, light, touch, heat or electrical stimuli are physical. Hormones, and transmitters released from nerve ends, are examples of chemical stimuli. Plant hormones are responsible for signalling growth and development, and for the falling of leaves in autumn. And these need not necessarily be in solution. They can be gaseous; for example, insect sex hormones, known as a pheromones, are released into the air and attract insects to each other. On the other hand chemicals responsible for the smell of honeysuckle trigger sensory cells in your nose. Ethylene, a simple gas, is a plant-ripening hormone. Tomatoes produce a lot of it, which is why some fruit can cross the ripening rubicon by being kept for a few days next to tomatoes. Nitric oxide has been discovered recently as an important local regulator of the muscles which control tension in our arteries, and thus blood flow and blood pressure. Biological stimuli include bacteria and viruses, and host cells themselves.

How these stimuli work to switch the traffic-lights from red-amber to green, how priming agents get them to red-amber, and how the traffic-lights are put into the right position in the first place during development, will be discussed in detail in the next chapter.

Signalling is essential to sex in all organisms, whether it be the fertilisation of a human egg or the formation of pollen in a plant. It is required for germination of a seed, for the development of all animals and plants, for birth, reproduction, maintenance and death of all forms of life, whether animals, plants, fungi or microbes. The amount of external signal required is often tiny in absolute terms, but may be large in fractional terms. Thus, when you run, the amount of adrenaline in the blood plasma rises perhaps a hundred times but is still a thousand times or more less than the concentration of fuels such as glucose and fat. The signals are thus catalytic. One signal molecule activates hundreds or thousands of others in the responsive cell. But there are also occasions when *small* fractional changes in the physical or chemical conditions in the blood can have dramatic effects on the behaviour of tissues. It is this which has led to one of the great misconceptions in biology, homeostasis.

THE MISCONCEPTION OF HOMEOSTASIS

Let me disturb your tranquillity for a minute and take you out into the garden. There you will find representatives of most of the major taxonomical groups – kingdoms, phyla, classes and so on. Flowers and trees, insects buzzing around the flowers, birds in the bushes, amphibians and fish in the pond, worms in the soil, fungi on a rotting tree stump, springtails, centipedes and woodlice under some of the stones, lichens and algae on the walls of the house, and bacteria you can't see in the compost heap. Here, on a tiny fraction of the Earth's surface, we can find literally tens if not hundreds of individual species, representing perhaps a dozen or more phyla from all the five kingdoms. Just marvel for a moment at the diversity and adaptation in your garden. Similarly, in a rock pool just a metre or so in diameter and a few tens of centimetres deep we can again find representatives of some six or seven phyla: bacteria, dinoflagellates, algae, hydroids and anemones, worms, starfish, shrimp, crabs and fish. Yet in a hot spring, an acid lake, a freezing antarctic pond there are but one or two species. Why?

We humans can survive and function in all sorts of different environments. We can survive without water for a few days, and without food for weeks if we have to. We can survive in ice cold or piping hot water, at least for a few minutes. Yet the cells from which our body is made, and upon which life depends, are not so flexible.

Compare a bacterium with a polar bear. Hot springs, acid lakes, alkaline pools and freezing cold ponds may have bacteria in them, but each has its own particular variety. Take one from a hot spring and put it into a freezing cold pond and it will not be able to survive or reproduce. Yet the polar bear can – well, almost at least. The secret is adaptation. But what does this really mean? What is happening inside such species that makes them able to cope with day and night, with variations in food supply and with extremes of temperature during the day-night cycle and the seasons?

In fact, examine any particular cell, whether a bacterium from a rock pool, a nerve cell from a darting shrimp or a green cell in the leaf of a plant, and you will find that it is not quite as adaptable as it might appear from the whole organism. This is because multicellular organisms have evolved to create their own interior environment. They have created their own internal ecosystem. Particularly important, and significant for the present argument, is the composition of the fluid surrounding each cell: that is, the amount of salts, vitamins and proteins, and the temperature. These are maintained remarkably constant, a fact highlighted by the nineteenth-century French physiologist Claude Bernard (1813-1878).

Bernard's ideas were developed into a full hypothesis in the first quarter of this century by an American physiologist from Harvard Medical School, Walter B. Cannon (1871-1945). He called the concept *homeostasis*, a term still widely used in medicine and throughout biology. Universities even have courses devoted to it. Yet, valuable as the concept has been, according to my contention it is fundamentally flawed as originally conceived and now needs to be replaced by a new framework which not only recognises the importance of quantal events in individual cells and tissues but also places rubicons at the heart of our view of whole-organism physiology.

What we have to explain is not the mechanisms which enable the body to maintain a *constant* internal environment, but how very *small* changes in the composition of the fluid bathing cells can cause them to cross the rubicon.

What then is homeostasis, and why do I believe that it has been misconceived?

Claude Bernard's career had humble beginnings. He came 26th out of 29 in his interne class. Yet he was to become one of the founders of modern experimental medicine. It was a French vitalist, Magendie (1783-1855), whom we shall meet later, who opened the door to Bernard's potential. Bernard was often unfairly branded a vitalist. A belief in some sort of vital force responsible for keeping animals and plants alive was common among nineteenth-century biologists. I shall be examining this important influence on scientific thinking in Chapter Eight. In fact, what Bernard believed was that physiology should be considered as a distinct science. He wanted physiology to be an autonomous science based on observation with experiment, and chemical ones at that. Following this philosophy, Bernard made four particularly important discoveries.

First, in 1846 he showed that the pancreas produced juices capable of digesting fat into fatty acid and glycerol, which could then be taken up into the body. Secondly, he identified the liver as the major internal source of sugar in the body. Thirdly, he found that the blood supply to tissues was regulated by a particular set of nerves. In other words, not all nerves are the same, even though they may appear so under the microscope. It is the group now called the vasomotor nerves which control blood supply to the tissues, through changes in blood pressure and blood-vessel size. And fourthly, he showed that the poison curare worked by attacking motor nerves but had no effect on the sensory group of nerves. Thus curare could be used as an experimental substance in animals to see whether particular functions or phenomena were controlled by the nerve group knocked out by curare.

Bernard presented his philosophy for experimental medicine in a seminal text, *Introduction à l'étude de la médecine expérimentale*, which was published in 1865, some eleven years after the Sorbonne had created a chair in General Physiology for him. He hoped to achieve four things in the book: first, to establish physics and chemistry as the scientific basis of physiology, though the latter was not reducible to them; secondly, to argue that the vital force did not explain life; thirdly, to show that vivisection was indispensable for physiological research; and fourthly to demonstrate that biology depends on determinism – that is, under identical conditions biological phenomena will be identical, even though living experimental systems are much more susceptible to individual variation than the simply random or stochastic statistical variations in experimental physics. Without Bernard's discoveries and philosophy, insulin would not have been discovered when it was. Nor would many of the biological and medical advances which today we take for granted.

Now that we know a little more about this key figure in the history of medical research I want to focus on a concept for which he is particularly famous, the 'internal environment', or *milieu intérieur*, first used in 1853 by C.P. Robin (1821-1885). 'It is the fixity of the *milieu intérieur*', Bernard wrote, 'which is the condition of free and independent life. All the vital mechanisms, however varied they may be, have only one object, that of preserving the conditions of life in the internal environment.' As J.B.S

Haldane put it many decades later, 'No more pregnant sentence was ever framed by a physiologist.'

In 1865 Bernard wrote: 'Every animal lives in two environments, the external environment in which the organism lives and the internal one in which the tissue elements live.' He realised that the internal environment was a complex fluid. But what he believed to be crucial was 'the fixity of the internal environment' as a condition of a free and independent life, and necessary for it. In other words, the cells of the body maintain the pond in which they themselves live. If the conditions within this pond are not maintained properly the whole body will not function properly either, or will even die. So our cells are not all that different from the unicellular ones we can find in an antarctic pond. But it was Cannon who latched on to this idea and extended it into his own hypothesis of homeostasis.

Walter Cannon (1871-1945) was a medical physiologist who graduated in medicine from Harvard Medical School, where he became George Higgins Professor of Physiology and taught from 1899 to 1942. He made many important observations about digestion, the hormonal regulation of metabolism, the physiological basis of hunger and thirst, temperature regulation in the body, the nervous control of blood pressure in humans, and of flight or fight responses in other animals. He is reported to have been the first to use X-rays to follow movements of the alimentary canal during digestion. This now forms the basis of one of the standard tests in modern medicine, the barium meal. Like Bernard, Cannon was particularly struck by the 'constancy' of some of the factors involved in these processes within the body: blood pressure, blood glucose, body temperature and blood acidity. He realised that the idea of a stable internal environment was not new. Two French physiologists had already developed Bernard's theme further. In 1900 Charles Richat (1850-1935) had put emphasis on 'the living being stable. It must be so in order not to be destroyed, dissolved or disintegrated by the colossal forces, often adverse, that surround it.' And fifteen years earlier Leon Fredericq (1851-1935) had written even more perceptively: 'The living being is an agency of such sort that each disturbing influence induces by itself the calling forth of compensatory activity to neutralise or repair disturbance.' Walter Cannon coined the word *homeostasis* in 1926 to describe this compensatory activity.

In 1902 Ernest H. Starling (1866-1927) and William M. Bayliss (1860-1924), working at University College in London, had isolated a substance from the pancreas which stimulated the release of juices from the gut without needing nerves. They called it secretin. More important still, they realised that they had discovered a universal principle: the ability of some cells to release substances which, when they reached a target cell, either close by or via the blood stream, were able to excite or stimulate the target cell. They called such substances 'hormones', from the Greek verb *hormao* meaning 'excite' or 'arouse'. Substances released from nerves, such as acetyl choline discovered in 1914 by Henry Dale (1875-1968), were subsequently named 'neuro-transmitters'. Plagiarising the title of a lecture published by Starling in 1923, Cannon documented the evidence for homeostasis in *The Wisdom of the Body*, first published in 1932.

The book contains chapters on the homeostasis of blood sugar, of blood proteins, of blood fat (no cholesterol mentioned here by the way), of blood calcium, of the neutrality of the blood, of the constancy of the water and salt content of the blood, and of body temperature and blood pressure. As any good scientist does when putting forward a hypothesis, Cannon provided mechanisms concerning oxygen supply, blood flow, hormones and nerve action to explain how homeostasis works. He pointed out that the nineteenth-century German physiologist Eduard Pflüger, and even Hippocrates (460-377 BC), recognised that the physiology of the body and its recovery from disease 'implies the existence of agencies which are ready to operate correctively when the normal state of the organism is upset'. How else could the cells of man survive exposure to dry heat of 115-128°C without a change in body temperature, or indeed those of an arctic mammal such as a seal or polar bear to as low as -35°C, without any sign of decrease in body temperature? How else could man or animal survive weeks of starvation if it were not for hormones accessing the body fat stores and the glucose factory in the liver, to provide energy for the organs of the body to survive and carry out their specialised functions?

To Cannon homeostasis meant 'a condition – a condition which may vary, but which is relatively constant'. He argued that 'constant conditions might be termed equilibria. But that word has come to have a fairly exact meaning as applied to physico-chemical states, in closed systems.' A 'state of equilibrium' is now used to describe a physical or chemical system in which the opposing forces or reactions are equal, exactly balanced. What does this mean? Let us take a typical reversible reaction found in the body:

$$\text{pyruvate} + \text{NADH} = \text{lactate} + \text{NAD}^+.$$

This reaction occurs in every cell in the body, and is catalysed by the enzyme lactate dehydrogenase. In fact, without this catalyst the forward and backward reactions are so slow as to be essentially non-existent. The pyruvate actually comes from a chemical pathway which starts with glucose, a pathway which is generating our old friend ATP. In muscle cells, when you run, a great deal of energy in the form of ATP is needed, so the reaction runs from left to right as you look at it, i.e. the muscle produces a great deal of lactate. This is the acid which causes the pain in severe exercise. Some lactate is also being converted back to pyruvate, but the reaction from right to left is slower. So the net result is that lactate formation wins, and the concentration of lactate goes up in the blood.

But when this lactate-containing blood gets round to the liver the reverse occurs. The direction of the reaction lactate to pyruvate wins and the liver cells have an energy reserve which enables them to convert it to glucose. As a result, the liver releases glucose back into the blood for the muscle to use again. If this reaction were at equilibrium, the rate of the reaction from left to right would exactly balance the reaction from right to left. In other words there would be neither net lactate nor pyruvate formation. Not much use to either the muscle cells or the liver.

Here we find a practical example of a universal principle of life: any chemical reaction which is capable of going forwards or backwards is never at equilibrium in a live cell. However, if we extract this reaction from either muscle or liver, even that taken from a liver on a butcher's slab, the reaction will inevitably go towards equilibrium, if we wait perhaps an hour or so. The tissue homogenate still has chemical potential, the enzyme lactate dehydrogenase is still there, but the soup is lifeless.

Thus in a chemical reaction at equilibrium the forward rate is identical with the backward rate. As I have already said, no such reactions exist in living systems, for none of them are at equilibrium. However, they may be at steady-state, where the rates of forward and backward reactions are constant. So another term is needed to describe the counterbalancing forces in the body. But it is the concept of constancy, found throughout Cannon's seminal text and in many of the chapter titles, to which I object.

Homoios is Greek for 'like' (*homos* for 'same'), and *stasis* for 'standing'. The dictionaries now tell us that *homeostasis* in biology is 'The tendency for the internal environment of an organism to remain constant', and in ecology 'for the tendency of the plant and animal populations to remain constant...'. That word *constant* crops up all the time, and it is this idea of some ideal, constant state to which the mechanisms of the body are aiming which is my fundamental objection. It is this that is the misconception!

The *Encyclopaedia Britannica* is much nearer the mark, and closer to the original perceptive thoughts of Bernard: 'Homeostasis is the self-regulating process by which biological systems tend to maintain stability while adjusting to conditions which are optimal for survival. If homeostasis is successful life continues, if not death ensues.' Many biological and clinical, oral and written presentations over the last fifty years have been generously scattered with the term homeostasis. But how many people have questioned its validity? How many can explain precisely what they mean by the term?

In clinical chemistry we use routinely the concept of *normal ranges*. This concept may be a little difficult to grasp at first; yet it is the cornerstone of our clinical working practice. In essence, the normal range of a particular substance in the blood or other body fluid is the concentration range outside which the individual is regarded as abnormal and is likely to have some pathological problem. But how do we decide what the normal range for any particular substance should be?

We measure things in units called *moles*. One mmole = one thousandth of a mole, one μmole = 1 millionth of a mole. Dissolving a spoonful of sugar containing five grammes in a cup of tea will give a solution containing some 200 mmoles per litre, forty times that in the blood, while the concentration of salt in sea water is 500 mmoles per litre, nearly four times that in the blood. The concentrations of the catalytic compounds in the blood, vitamins and hormones, are thousands or millions times lower than the concentration of common salt. Measure the blood calcium concentration accurately in a hundred people and you will get a hundred different values. But most will be clustered around 2.4 mmoles per litre of blood, the mean of the healthy population. The normal range around this is defined statistically as 2.2-2.6 mmoles per litre, so that most people who are healthy will be inside this range. You can see how narrow these ranges can be. But the *normal* range is not necessarily synonymous with the *healthy* range.

The mean cholesterol in the blood of adults in the West is similar to that of glucose and three times higher than that of calcium, 6 mmoles per litre. But we now consider this level of cholesterol to be unhealthy. The recommended total blood cholesterol level required to reduce the risk of having a heart attack in middle age is 5 mmoles per litre or less. This mistake occurred because the medical profession forgot that a high proportion of adults already have clogged arteries, i.e. atheroma, and are thus already unhealthy. The population mean is not therefore the right value to recommend the body to aim for!

Blood temperature, pressure, pH (i.e. acidity), calcium, sodium, potassium, chloride, bicarbonate, sugar, cholesterol, protein, haemoglobin, are just a few of the substances in the blood which must be maintained within certain limits or they malfunction or even death ensues. Yet very small changes can not only have dramatic results, but even provoke rubicons!

A decrease in calcium in the blood of just 20 per cent can cause the muscles to spasm in tetanic rubicons, involuntary contractions of your muscles. On the other hand, if the blood glucose drops by 50 per cent you will probably go into a faint or even a coma. And if the potassium concentration drops from its healthy value by 40 per cent even greater disaster may follow. You may have a heart attack. But don't panic! Yes, there are mechanisms for keeping the composition and state of the fluid surrounding your cells well within the healthy limits. But what goes on between them? The answer is one hell of a lot. In fact one hell of a lot of rubicons are being crossed! In all the circumstances we have looked at so far the cells and organs of the body are themselves in a feverish state – the adrenals, the pancreas, the liver and the nerves. In many of these, U-turns in the direction of metabolism have occurred, just so that the amount of the key substance in the blood can be maintained within the healthy range. Blood glucose illustrates the point well.

The chemical and hormonal changes occurring after supper and before breakfast take the body across a rubicon. When glucose is available from digested food in the gut, it is the main energy source for all tissues. The heart, muscles, liver, kidney and brain all oxidise glucose to supply their internal energy needs. This fuels the internal synthesis of ATP. But when the supply of glucose from the diet becomes limited, although the brain, blood cells and some cells in the kidney still must have glucose, the other main tissues of the body switch over to using fat for their energy. A metabolic rubicon occurs in all these tissues. The liver also crosses a metabolic rubicon, switching from storing glucose to releasing it instead. The concentration change in glucose on each side of this rubicon is small, and is deceptive. Small though it is, it still acts as a chemical switch. After a meal containing carbohydrate the reverse occurs. Most of the energy-needs of all tissues, including the liver, heart, muscles and brain are then supplied by glucose instead of fat. This reversal, this rubicon, is signalled by a consortium of hormones and other regulators acting on the various tissues. But the chemical switch initiating this major change in body metabolism is a relatively small change in blood glucose, perhaps of just 25 per cent.

Similarly, a tiny increase in blood calcium causes bone to stop releasing calcium and the parathyroid gland to switch from releasing its hormone to switching off release and depositing calcium in bone. Homeostasis, on the other hand, regards such changes as smooth, trying to take the body back to some sort of mythical, ideal equilibrium state. The misconception of homeostasis is however revealed when we look at what is going on in the individual tissues and the cells within them. They are going across rubicons.

Small changes in temperature can also induce rubicons. There are thermostat-type regulators in the body which, like the movement of the bimetallic strip in a thermostat, only switch on or off at a particular point. If your body temperature rises just a few degrees – to, say, 42°C – you will have a severe fever. But the neutrophils in your blood responsible for attacking and killing invading bacteria work better at 42°C than at 37°C. There are genes in these and many other cells which switch on or off when the temperature crosses a particular threshold. One set of proteins made by these genes are called *heat shock proteins*. They are a crucial part of the rubicon response to infection and inflammation. Without them many of the normal proteins manufactured by your cells would not fold up correctly.

The regulatory mechanisms of the body have evolved not to maintain constancy of the *milieu intérieur*, but to ensure that each tissue and each cell cross the rubicon when the conditions demand it. Do not be misled by the idea that small changes in blood components are irrelevant. This was perhaps the underlying cause of Cannon's misconception. There are plenty of ways small perturbations can be amplified to signal cells and tissues to cross the rubicon.

The regulatory mechanisms within the human body, and those in other animals, have evolved to do two things: (a) to maintain the fluid bathing cells within limits, preventing particular organs crossing a damaging rubicon or even the ultimate rubicon, cell and organism death, and (b) to control the efficiency of the body, maximising its specialised functions and defence processes. This is done within the constraints of the energy and nutrient source available, the genetic make-up and the external environment; or, if under attack, by the damage caused by pathogens. Body composition and its specialised functions are maintained by regulating the number of cells within particular organs which have crossed the necessary rubicons.

There are also feedback and feed-forward loops, down and up regulation. In a feedback loop the output, e.g. glucose, has some effect on the reactions controlling its own output. This may be positive or negative. Similarly, a substance may regulate the formation or breakdown reactions ahead of itself in a positive or negative way. These processes are termed 'graded' in Rubicon terminology. They may act as fine control after a rubicon has been crossed or they may summate to cause a rubicon to be crossed. As I argued in Chapter One, graded mechanisms of the sort visualised by Bernard, Cannon and their followers exist within these rubicons and determine if and when a rubicon is crossed. But if we are to understand fully the control mechanisms of the body, how these evolved, and what goes wrong with them in disease, we must now discard the misconceptions inherent in the homeostatic hypothesis and replace it with a dynamic hypothesis where the rubicons within each cell and tissue are defined in molecular and physical terms, together with the mechanisms responsible for taking each unit to the banks and then across. Only then will we live up to the vision of Claude Bernard when he wrote: '...the physiologist has nothing more to do with the principle of life than the chemist has with the principle of the affinity of bodies.'

Thus, to summarise, my fundamental objection to the way homeostasis was originally conceived and is still presented is the misguided idea that the regulatory mechanisms within the body are trying to maintain constancy. This is not true. The misconception arose and continues because of two essential misunderstandings. First, it seemed inconceivable that the small changes in sodium, potassium, calcium, sugar, temperature, pH and so on that occur under different conditions could possibly be doing anything in themselves. In fact they are. We now know of many mechanisms where a tiny percentage change in one substance can set off an amplification cascade ending with a hundredfold or thousandfold change in a substance at the end of the sequence. In fact the idea that small changes in a regulator can result in large changes in the target is quite old. Small changes in acidity were shown by Haldane more than fifty years ago to cause major changes in oxygen binding to haemoglobin. Secondly, in reality the body as a whole exists in a variety of states: alert or dozy, active or resting, digesting or starving, tense or relaxed, awake or sleeping, sexually aroused or lacking libido, with sugar-based or fat-based energetics, hot or shivery, well or ill. The rubicons that are crossed between these states involve massive changes in many chemicals within the body, both outside and within cells, but only tiny changes in others. However, the cells which have changed between these states have also crossed their own rubicons, as have the cells which induce the chemical changes necessary for the crossing to occur and to be maintained.

Two further questions Cannon failed to address were: (a) When did his type of homeostatic control evolve? (b) Is it in place in the newborn, or does it occur in the womb?

As happened to Darwin, followers of Cannon even tried to extend the homeostasis constancy concept to social behaviour. One particularly notable attempt was by a Harvard colleague, L.J. Henderson (1878-1942). But the development we shall return to in Chapter Five is the misconception of homeostasis applied in the Gaia Hypothesis and the environment.

Homeostasis is a sick concept. Like us, it needs to cross the Rubicon to become fit and well again!

FROM PHYSIOLOGY TO PATHOLOGY

The cholesterol myth?

Open any newspaper these days and you are likely to find some hype about cholesterol (Figure 5). It is therefore both surprising and disappointing to discover so much confusion, misinformation and myth about this substance. Fact and fiction blended together to mislead the reader, and sell newspapers!

Misconceptions include the relevance of cholesterol in food, and the nature of the factors which put someone at risk of a heart attack. In a recent Sunday newspaper under the headline 'Heart attacks are killing women too' there was a list of risk factors. It read:

1. Heredity
2. Blood pressure
3. Weight
4. *Cholesterol*
5. Smoking
6. Physical inactivity
7. Diabetes

The implication was that number one was the most important to worry about, and so on. But women are different from men, as if you didn't know. The order of risks for men is different:

1. Smoking
2. High blood *cholesterol*
3. Family history of heart attacks, i.e. heredity
4. High blood pressure
5. Lack of exercise
6. Diabetes

Weight in itself is not a risk factor. There are plenty of thin people who have heart attacks.

'Ooh, watch that sauce! It looks very high in cholesterol!' The cry goes

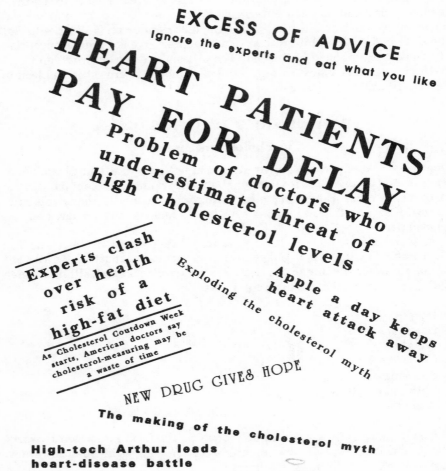

Fig. 5. The cholesterol newspaper hype.

out regularly over the dinner table. Another myth? Yes. Although there are foods which are high in cholesterol – eggs, for example – the cholesterol content is in fact irrelevant. So what is it about cholesterol that we should worry about?

Let's start to clear up some of the misconceptions by seeing what happens when you have your cholesterol measured.

A sample of blood is first taken from your arm or a finger prick, spotted onto a film or spun in a centrifuge, and then either immediately put into a cholesterol monitor or sent to the lab. It does not matter too much whether you have had breakfast or not. The values come back: total cholesterol = 9.8, HDL cholesterol = 0.7, cholesterol index = 7%. What does all this mean? First, your total cholesterol at 9.8 is well above the recommended 5.2 millimoles per litre. This is a somewhat arbitrary value, equal to 200 milligrams per hundred millilitres of blood serum, the way it is measured in the US. And your HDL, the 'healthy' cholesterol, is far too low.

Cholesterol is virtually insoluble in water; rather it dissolves in fat. So in the blood cholesterol has to be transported on a bus full of fat, whereas glucose travels round soluble in the plasma. The LDL, Low-Density Lipoprotein, takes cholesterol from where it is made, the liver, to the tissues. HDL, High-Density Lipoprotein, takes it away. Your *healthy* cholesterol in HDL is too low, as shown by an unhealthy ratio of 0.07 or 7%. It should be 20% or more. Your present level, coupled with smoking, lack of exercise, a bad family history, i.e. the fact that your parents, grandparents and several other close relatives died of a heart attack, put you in the high-risk category for a heart attack.

The doctor will do the best he can for you, give you a risk factor and life-style management advice, and possibly drugs, and send you on your way. You will be worried, for no one can tell you for certain whether you will or won't have a heart attack before you are 50, even if you follow the advice. Similarly, there are now risk factors for diabetes, rheumatoid arthritis and so on. In the genuine inherited diseases a bad gene means that, if you have it in both chromosomes, you will have the disease for sure. Cystic fibrosis is such an example of a common inherited disease. The trouble with present knowledge is that risk factors and percentages are not good enough. The person wants to know for sure whether a particular life-style will prevent the heart attack rubicon being crossed or not. So why should cholesterol be so important? Can it cause a heart attack itself?

All our cells need cholesterol. It is an essential component of the membranes surrounding all animal and plant cells, but not in bacteria apparently. Cholesterol is thus present in all our food, but the main chemical factory in our bodies, the liver, can make quite enough for our needs. The liver is manufacturing masses of cholesterol every minute of the day. The amount of cholesterol you eat has very little effect on the level in the blood. But the blood level is affected by other things you eat. Saturated fat in particular tends to make the blood cholesterol go up. This is why doctors and dietary experts often encourage people at risk to eat mackerel, truly high in unsaturates, and to cook in oil from plants not animal fat.

Cholesterol is an oily substance with the chemical formula $C_{27}H_{44}OH$. Originally called 'cholesterin' (from the Greek *cholê* 'bile', and *stereos* 'stiff' or 'solid'), it was isolated in the nineteenth century from bile and gall-stones. Like a water pipe in a hard-water area, our arteries can get clogged up. The coronary arteries in the heart are particularly susceptible to the build-up of this *plaque*. Even young adults in their twenties will already have some plaque building up. So this is the first rubicon to understand, the point at which deposition begins.

Familial hypercholesterolaemia is the technical name for the main inherited condition of high blood cholesterol. In people with this condition the plaque is very cholesterol-rich and unstable. It may crack and cause a blood clot to form on it, thereby sealing up the blood vessel completely by the time they reach their early thirties. At this point another rubicon is crossed: angina or a severe heart attack occurs. Two mini-rubicons are responsible for this: rupture of the plaque and the formation of a blood clot. If the clot and plaque are big enough the blood supply stops in that artery. If it stops for too long, the muscle cells die and part of the heart is dead for ever. If this reaches a critical mass, the whole heart stops for ever as well. The problem is that we cannot define what the precise molecular sequences are which cause an artery in the heart to reach the banks of these rubicons; nor do we know what determines when each rubicon is crossed. Yet we know quite a lot about the composition of the plaque and that the problem is centuries-old.

Atheroma, the medical name for plaque, was probably first described by Leonardo da Vinci (1452-1519), who thought that the thickening of the arteries he found at post mortem was caused by 'excessive nourishment'. Marchand in about 1860 called it 'atherosclerosis'. Plaques contain anything between 1 and 60 per cent by weight cholesterol. Not only is blood cholesterol carried around the body in fat droplets, i.e. LDL, but 90 per cent of it is in a different form from that in cell membranes. It is *esterified*. And there are cells which also build up in the plaque: phagocytes which can cross the rubicon to become foam cells packed with cholesterol, bleach-producing cells, and an increase in the *smooth*-muscle cells which line all arteries. But the crucial factor suggested by recent studies is that it is those plaques with a high cholesterol-content that crack – a rubicon – and then provoke the next rubicon, a fibrin blood clot with platelet aggregation.

Pure cholesterol is a white crystalline solid, melting at 148.5°C. However, dissolved in fat at body temperature, 37°C, it is liquid. But when examined by the pathologist plaques will be solid – like white fat on a butcher's slab. In its esterified form, cholesterol can precipitate, as in cholesterol gall-stones. A key rubicon question therefore is: Is the cholesterol in plaques solid or liquid?

There is no doubt that there is a strong correlation between 'elevated' cholesterol and heart attacks, both in people with established inherited abnormalities in cholesterol and in the general population. Lifestyles which raise blood-cholesterol, particularly in the LDL, such as eating excess fatty foods and lack of exercise, increase the risk. Regimes which reduce blood cholesterol in the population correlate with reductions in the incidence of heart attacks. This has now been shown in many countries. In Japan, where the average blood-cholesterol is much lower than in the West, the incidence of heart attacks is much lower as well. In my native Wales, where there are larger numbers of people with high blood-cholesterol and bad diets and lifestyles, we have one of the worst rates of heart disease in the world. Yet there are still disbelievers! 'My father smokes 40 fags a day. He never walks more than 20 yards without a car, and that is only to get to the pub to drink his nightly ration of 8 pints of beer. He's over 80!' There are even so-called heart specialists who are not just sceptical of the evidence but actively ignore the storm of mounting pressure to take note of cholesterol and lifestyle management. For years patients with heart trouble have been sent away from hospitals without even having their cholesterol measured. Or if it was, the heart specialist didn't know enough about cholesterol to give any proper lifestyle advice. There are even some who think it is a trick by the food industry to create new markets!

A high cholesterol is far from explaining why someone crosses the lethal rubicon of a heart attack, but it is the best we have at present. Those taking the negative Popperian approach are doing a grave disservice to mankind and the advancement of medical science. Frankly, many of the professional sceptics have contributed so little, if anything, to the advancement of true knowledge about this crucial issue that they now feel threatened. The result is a typical smoke-screen to cover their own inadequate tracks. Heart disease remains the biggest killer in the West. One in three will die of it, and many well before the age of 60. It is time for a new, positive approach from the experts! Will or won't the man or woman next to you on the station platform drop down dead? Rubicon to the rescue? We now know that you can retreat from the banks of a potentially lethal rubicon by reducing cholesterol in the plaque as a result of reducing blood cholesterol.

So lack of oxygen to the heart or brain and many of our tissues can result in irreversible rubicons being crossed, taking us on a pathway of rubicons towards cell or organ death. But oxygen is not always beneficial!

The flame that doth burn too bright

As you travel along the M4 motorway to London from Cardiff, where I live, you pass a sign to Bowood House. In this country house you will find preserved the laboratory of Joseph Priestley (1733-1804), one of the founders of modern chemistry. Priestley was the son of a Yorkshire cloth-dresser, who was encouraged by his parents to become a minister. His unorthodox views, even as a Nonconformist, and his developing interest in science from the age of 25 resulted in more and more involvement in teaching, and several moves.

The Fitzmaurices first appeared in the English county of Wiltshire in 1753, acquiring the Manor of Bramhill. Some three miles away was Bowood House which they were soon to buy. It was here, in December 1772, that William Fitzmaurice-Petty, second Earl of Shelburne and late first Marquis of Landsdowne, appointed Priestley as librarian, literary companion and tutor to his two young sons. Here Priestley, from 1773 till 1780, was given freedom to preach, write and research as he pleased. Following his three sons, he moved with his wife to the United States in 1794, where he died ten years later.

On August 1st 1774, at Bowood, Priestley tried to 'extract air from mercurius calcinatus', a substance we now call mercuric oxide. Some eleven years later he wrote: 'I presently found that ... air was expelled from it very readily ... But what surprised me more was that a candle burned in this air with a remarkably vigorous flame.' Priesley had discovered oxygen. He was, however, a believer in the unbelievable phlogiston, the magical ingredient in reactive substances invented by Stahl, whom we shall meet properly in Chapter Eight. Therefore, he actually called the gas 'dephlogisticated air'. The same gas had also been isolated some time between 1770 and 1773 by a Swedish chemist, Carl Wilhelm Scheele (1742-1786), who called it first 'vitriol air' and then 'fire air'. But Scheele did not publish his results for several years, telling only a few kindred spirits of his discovery. One was the Frenchman Antoine Laurent Lavoisier (1743-1794).

Lavoisier realised that the discovery of Scheele and Priestley could be used to sound the death knell of the phlogiston theory. Mistakenly thinking that all acids contained the gas, he renamed it 'oxygine', from the Greek *oxus* 'sharp', i.e. acid, and the root -*gen*, 'become, produce'. The spelling was changed to 'oxigène' in 1787, and then to 'oxygène' in 1835. Lavoisier was claimed by the guillotine during the Reign of Terror on Thursday 8 May 1794, but not before he, his co-discoverers and others had shown that oxygen was consumed and carbon dioxide given off when animals breathed. Yet Priestley was puzzled by an experiment he reported in 1777. A mint plant grown for a month in his dephlogisticated air was 'quite dead and black', whereas one grown in air still had living leaves. Similarly, in 1781 he reported that the pure gas was lethal to mice. Hence too much oxygen can be lethal. 'The flame can thus burn too bright.' The chemical explanation for this had to await the discovery of metabolites of oxygen in this century. These metabolites turned out to be very toxic. Fortunately we have a defence against this hazard, present in all the cells of our body. Vitamins C and E are two familiar compounds which fulfil the function. Other less well-known ones are *glutathione* and the enzymes *superoxide dismutase* and *catalase*. Without this cohort of defences against the hazards of oxygen, the cells which have evolved to make us would not have survived the oxygen holocaust which began some 2,000 million years ago.

And our bodies have learned to exploit this oxygen toxicity. So let's look at this in a little more detail.

Bugs and burns, poisons and bullets

A host of diseases and pathological rubicons are provoked by an apparently diverse group of attackers: bugs, burns, poisons and bullets. Yet as we shall see in the next two sections these are related to each other. In some instances the attack is so severe that 'rockets' or 'mortar bombs' are employed.

Colloquially in medicine, *bugs* are infective agents which cause disease. These include not only bacteria and viruses, but also protozoa, yeasts and fungi. A clear example of bacterial rubicons leading to a pathological condition is food poisoning caused by particular strains of *Salmonella typhimurium, Clostridium perfringens, Bacillus cereus, Staphylococcus aureus* and *Escherichia coli*. This is still a serious problem in the food industry and in restaurants. Even hospital caterers have been known to contaminate patients, or visiting scientists! In spite of the highly sophisticated analytical systems in modern medicine, the human gut is a much faster and more sensitive detector of these pathogens than the laboratory analyst. The analyst may need several days to confirm the presence of *Salmonella* in a sample of food. Yet within a few hours of ingestion of a contaminated meal the unsuspecting eater will have severe diarrhoea, and be pretty ill, sometimes for several days. Even if there are no live bugs in the food, you can still get food poisoning because of toxins left in the food produced by the bacteria when they were still alive. This will be a much milder form of food poisoning than when you ingest live bacteria, but very unpleasant all the same.

It has been estimated that for food to be safe it must contain less than one *Salmonella* bacterium in a handful equivalent to 25 grammes. Yet the ability to predict for sure a food-poisoning rubicon remains elusive. There are also many times in our lives when we are exposed to virulent bacteria without being ill. They can even be carried by some people in a dormant state. How then can we predict the outcome of an exposure? At present we can't. But unless we think in terms of a rubicon sequence we have no hope at all.

But what is it about *Salmonella* and other bacteria that actually makes you ill? This is where the poisons come in. Bacteria release toxins or have toxins on their surface which do the damage. We have met one example already, the toxin produced in cholera. Food-poisoning bacteria also produce toxins, which are the real culprits stimulating the severe diarrhoea and vomiting. It is these toxins which can survive in cooked food, even when all the live bacteria have been killed.

All pathogenic bacteria produce toxins, but they can work in different ways. As we saw in Chapter One, cholera toxin stimulates a signalling rubicon sequence which goes out of control. By contrast some of the toxins of *Clostridium*, *Staphylococcus* and *Salmonella* fire bullets or rockets at our cells. These bullets are protein molecules which punch holes in the outer protective membrane of the cell. Not surprisingly the cell bursts like a balloon. But it may not necessarily burst immediately. The bullets set in action a pathway in the cell, which takes time before the lethal rubicon is crossed. There are also animals which produce similar toxins. The major protein in bee stings, melittin, is a such a bullet which can punch holes in the membranes of cells, in the test-tube at least. However, exactly what happens when you get stung by a bee is not something the molecular scientists in their underground firing ranges seem to have worried much about! We will see later in the chapter that our navy has a similar mechanism for showering bullets, but this time at invaders!

Once again we see Rubicon in action, but the molecular information we have from laboratory studies fails to address and explain the real biological event.

The puffer fish produces one of the most toxic substances known, tetrodotoxin. You need a special licence in Japan to be allowed to serve this delicacy on the menu. And even then there have been disastrous mistakes. The toxin, like many snake and jelly fish toxins, blocks nerves and muscles from firing. The more potent the more potentially lethal. Yet the relationship between the biochemical properties and the relative potency of such toxins is far from clear. Why is a tiny amount of one toxin lethal, while another will only produce mild, local irritation?

We are being exposed to toxins all day, every day, in the air, in the sea, in our drinking water, and in our food. Plants produce thousands of alkaloid poisons as part of their defence against insects. Food also contains remnants of fertilisers, pesticides and pollutants. Fortunately we have a defence against these too. The liver, being such a modern chemical plant, is not only a producer of substances for transport to the rest of the body but also a toxic waste disposal unit as well. Here many toxic substances are modified chemically, and then lost through the bile or kidneys. Keep drinking those glasses of water. It really can wash the toxins out of the body!

But there may be circumstances when this disposal system gets overloaded. In the 1960s there were reports of people getting severely ill after losing a lot of weight as a result of the release of 'poisons' stored harmlessly in the fat tissue. Like cholesterol, these poisons were fat-soluble. But when a lot of this fat solvent was lost, the toxins had to be released, resulting in the crossing of critical concentration and a pathological rubicon. There is much to explore here, as there is a possible link between infections and diseases such as rheumatoid arthritis and diabetes.

We also have a defence against bullets! Stick a pin into a balloon and it will burst immediately. But stick a strip of Sellotape on the surface and then prick the balloon through it. The balloon will survive, at least for a little while. Our cells also have a protective mechanism against bullets and rockets being fired at them. As the pores form they can be inactivated or removed. This defence prevents the lethal rubicon, though it provokes others within the cell. We have proposed that the abnormal activation of these *defence* rubicons may have a role to play in provoking bleach release in the rheumatoid joint and breakdown of the sheath around nerves in the brain in multiple sclerosis. These are examples of my putting the principle of Rubicon into practice myself, and discovering something new and possibly very important.

And it is not only bugs, poisons and bullets that we have to defend ourselves against. We also have to prevent ourselves being *burned*. And I don't mean allowing your hand carelessly to touch a red-hot poker, or scalding yourself by dropping a boiling kettle. These are very painful rubicons. I am referring to what happened to the mint plant that Priestley tried to grow in oxygen. It died because of being 'burnt' in pure oxygen. In our body there are many cells capable of generating the oxygen metabolites responsible for such 'burns'. As we shall see in a moment we need them as part of our defence. But when these, and similar reactions outside cells, cross the rubicon inappropriately, a pathological rubicon may ensue.

Wherever oxygen is around, some metabolites will always be produced. Hydrogen peroxide and bleach (known chemically as hypochlorite) are perhaps the most familiar. But there is a whole family of them, including some with such unpalatable names as superoxide anion, hydroxyl radical and singlet oxygen. These are all highly reactive. They *burn* biological molecules. As a result they can damage membranes, the lipids which carry cholesterol, proteins and nucleic acids. They can also kill cells, including invading bugs.

There are many diseases where oxygen metabolite 'burns' seem to play a major role in provoking pathological tissue rubicons, including inflammation of the joints, lung, kidney, heart and brain. In dividing cells, deficiencies in the repair mechanism or protection against 'burning' of DNA result in mutations, which can lead to the formation of a cancer cell. These may remain undetectable in a small cluster, or clone, for years until something else takes them across the next rubicon and a tumour develops.

All this danger from attack seems pretty terrifying. But a major factor in the success of the mammals after nearly 4,000 million years of evolution is the sophistication of their defence system. Throughout evolution, cells and organisms have had to defend themselves against physical, chemical and biological attack. A crazy drunken orgy can cause liver failure and death. And prolonged excessive drinking leads to fibrosis and cirrhosis of the liver, with the same lethal rubicon end-result. Yet we can drink moderate amounts of alcohol because we have an active enzyme system in the liver which disposes of it.

There are even defences against physical agents such as temperature and radiation. Cold organisms in the waters of the Antarctic for example have their own antifreeze, while in a fever cells induce *heat shock* proteins to prevent mistakes in the folding of their normal proteins. Even bacteria

have found a way of defending themselves against certain sorts of attack
and starvation. Examples of their defence are the release of toxins and
antibiotics, and the presence of D- instead of L-amino-acids in their walls
preventing animal enzymes breaking them down.

To survive the oxygen holocaust, which occurred some 2,000 million
years ago when the atmosphere changed from one without oxygen to one
with it (i.e. it changed from 'reducing' to 'oxidising') as a result of the
success of the photosynthesis of microscopic plants – the blue-green algae
– cells had to develop a defence against oxygen. Thus vitamin C and the
major protein in the blood, albumin, protects the outside of cells from
'burns', vitamin E the membrane, glutathione and the enzymes superoxide
dismutase and catalase the inside of cells. But when these defences break
down or are inadequate to cope with too much oxygen metabolite production, cells and tissues close by get 'burned' and a pathological rubicon is
crossed.

Thus we have an amazing barrage of defences against oxygen *burns*,
poisons and *bullets*. Fortunately, we also have an army, navy and airforce
which defend us successfully against attack by *bugs*. When one or more of
these defences breaks down or is overcome, a pathological rubicon is
crossed. But there is another serious pathological rubicon involving the
armed forces of the body. They can mutiny!

The army, navy and airforce

Remember the little girl who tripped over her violin case (above, p. 38)?
Well, no sooner had the clot started to form than an army of cells was
signalled into action. Breaking their way through the walls of blood vessels
near the open wound, they then walked their way through the jungle of
tissue fibres to seek out and kill any invading bacteria. These are part of
the *army* of defence cells in the body. Some are found in the blood, others
within the tissue. Some white cells and tissues such as liver release protein
and other substances. This is the *navy*, which either attacks invaders
directly or supports and instructs the army to do so. The navy includes
antibodies which attach to invading cells and molecules, so that they can
be removed by refuse-disposal cells. It also includes the firing of bullets we
saw in the last section: the so-called 'complement' system consisting of
more than twenty proteins. This is activated by invading bacteria. As a
result, messengers for attracting the army into a site of infection are
generated. But the end of the 'complement' rubicon pathway is a protein
machine gun which blasts bacteria out of existence. There are also substances, normally thought of as gases, which, dissolved in the fluids
surrounding cells, provide an aerial support or bombardment.

How then does the army do its job after reaching the battle zone?

Bleach kills all known germs. So the adverts tell us. Yet Nature learned
this lesson hundreds of millions of years ago, for there are specialised cells
in our blood and in the external fluids of most animals which deliberately

produce bleach. The bombardier beetle generates hydrogen peroxide in a little pouch when aggravated or frightened. This then produces such a violent reaction that a noxious liquid is squirted at the enemy. In one beetle the reaction is so violent that the liquid is virtually boiling. It is bleach that is a major component of our army's weaponry. One such cell is the major white cell in the blood, the neutrophil. This cell is actually green, because it contains a bleach-producing factory which can kill all known germs. These cells attach to the invaders (a rubicon), engulf them (the next rubicon), and then kill them inside an execution chamber within the cell. There will be no dead bodies left, for the cells also make enzymes which digest the invaders into tiny fragments.

But in some diseases these cells turn against their own people!

Arthritis affects some eight million people in Britain alone. Some one to two million have rheumatoid arthritis. In this disease there are cells present in the joints which should not be there doing what they are doing. There is a mutiny going on! In rheumatoid arthritis the bleach-producing cells are one group of mutineers. They have been fooled into thinking that there has been a bacterial or viral invasion. Maybe there has, but it is not detectable in the same way that it is when a cut goes septic. There is no pus, for instance. The cells stay around for too long, and dump their bleach, together with a number of other components normally kept inside to degrade the 'burned' bacteria into minute fragments.

The amounts released are tiny compared with a splash of bleach around the lavatory from a bottle – a fraction of a droplet in fact. And the bleach does not get very far either – less than a millimetre from the cell which released it. Yet it still does all sorts of damage. It breaks down the lubricant of the joint. It helps to destroy the soft cartilage which cushions the bones which would otherwise grind into each other. It damages cells, and leads to pain. If we could stop all this bleach-damage, it might have a major beneficial effect on the pain and long-term damage to the joints of people with this potentially crippling disease.

Yet there are many unexplained rubicons in rheumatoid arthritis. Some patients have just one inflammatory episode, others degenerate and have severe pain for years. In some only one joint seems to be severely affected, while in others all the so-called synovial joints seem to be attacked. Some have episodic bursts of swollen joints, with excess fluid and pain. And it is not only a disease affecting old people: even children can suffer from it. A key to treatment and prevention must be to understand the molecular basis of the cell signalling, the cellular rubicons, which lead to the inflammation and the pain that follows.

The navy is also mutinying in rheumatoid arthritis. Antibodies to the patient's own proteins are produced, and the complement system is activated. Many people experience a mild swelling or inflammation of the joints some time during their lives. But only some will cross the rubicon to rheumatoid arthritis, where the joints are invaded by the army and navy, which then attack the fabric of the joint from their own bullets and flame throwers. Many patients will recover and never suffer another joint rubicon. Some, however, will cross the next rubicon, and the disease will become full-blown and chronic. The key to understanding this potentially crippling disease, which can occur in both children and adults of all ages, is to discover the signals responsible for taking these cells to the banks of each rubicon and then across.

And the mutineers are afoot in several other common diseases as well. In type I diabetes another fleet of ships, so-called cytotoxic T-cells, wiggle their way into the pancreas and attack the host cells, the insulin-producers in this case. These T-cells normally defend us against unwanted cells. They can kill tumour cells, for example. Firing accurately their own special bullets, called 'perforins', the holes punched in the pancreatic cells are lethal. The patient – child or adult – can no longer make insulin and will cross the rubicon of a diabetic coma unless an injection of insulin is given. Why do these cells attack the insulin-producing cells specifically? If we understood this rubicon the cause of diabetes would be revealed!

And what of the airforce? We have already heard a lot about oxygen. But there is another substance, only discovered in the body within the last ten years, which is also normally thought of as a gas, but which plays an important role in the heart and inflammation. During the 1970s a substance was discovered, released by cells lining certain blood vessels, which caused smooth muscle to relax. It was named Endothelial Derived Relaxing Factor, or EDRF for short. It only lasted a few seconds. This was a key observation, leading to some clever experiments to discover what it was. It turned out to be nitric oxide, NO. This chemical aeroplane is related to laughing gas, nitrous oxide, which has the chemical formula N_2O. Many cells can produce NO, including our bleach-producing cells. And it signals many other cells apart from smooth-muscle cells. A key to how it works was the discovery that it was inhibited by adding haemoglobin, the red oxygen-carrying pigment. NO binds to haem, the organic moiety in haemoglobin responsible for the red colour. NO activates a traffic-light protein within the cell. The end-result is a signalling rubicon sequence, ending in a cell doing something, e.g. a muscle-cell relaxing. Recent exciting findings suggest that NO may play a role in high blood pressure, the prediction being that manipulation of this aeroplane may prevent the dangerous rubicons in the kidney, brain and heart which can be a consequence of a prolonged, or even a brief, rise in blood pressure.

And what of viral disease? Where does this fit in to the Rubicon framework? How do the armed forces combat it?

AIDS crosses the Rubicon

'AIDS is a virus, isn't it? And what's all the fuss about? I'm not a homosexual or a drug addict, and anyway my doctor always gives me a good dose of antibiotics when I get a really bad, chesty cold. That should do the trick.' These are just a few of the misconceptions about viruses, the diseases they cause and how they can be cured which we must put aside if we are to understand the rubicons involved in cause, cure or prevention.

Let's get one thing clear from the start. Viruses are different from bacteria, and cannot be killed by antibiotics. Bacteria are cells which multiply of their own accord. They contain DNA and RNA, and the complete machinery for the maintenance and reproduction of life. Viruses, on the other hand, are not cells. They cannot multiply on their own, however much nutrient you give them. While a tube containing one bacterium suspended in a nutrient broth will have formed many millions in a day, a similar tube containing virus particles will have remained unchanged. Viruses are simply packets of nucleic acid, DNA or RNA, in a protein coat. Viruses can only multiply after infecting cells. They then take over the machinery of the host cell. One infected cell can generate thousands of virus particles.

Antibiotics kill bacteria, or prevent them multiplying. They attack specifically the machinery of bacterial cells, and are selected not to touch our own cells. If this were not so, antibiotics would have all sorts of harmful side effects. But antibiotics have no effect on the multiplication of viruses. Viruses are not cells. The reason why antibiotics are sometimes taken after a severe chest cold is to stop a major bacterial infection causing even more trouble.

Food-poisoning, a septic cut, blood-poisoning, pneumonia, cholera and TB are a few of the infections caused by bacteria. Smallpox, measles, polio, skin sores and AIDS are caused by viruses. Both viruses and bacteria can be very nasty without an adequate defence.

It has been estimated that the arrival of Columbus in the Americas wiped out some 95 per cent of the population, a drop in the Mexican population from thirty million to two million, caused primarily by measles and smallpox viruses brought over from Europe. Similarly the Black Death in the fourteenth century, caused by a bacterium, wiped out a quarter of the population, some twenty-five million people. Yet being infected by a potentially virulent virus or bacterium may not necessarily be lethal. Nor do the symptoms of the disease necessarily show up soon after the infection. Thanks to vaccination, smallpox has now been eliminated. But even when it was a scourge, you still had perhaps a fifty per cent chance of survival if you became infected without having been vaccinated.

There are at least four rubicons to be explained if we are to understand and cure the bacterial and viral diseases which still afflict us: infection, latency, potency and resistance to vaccination.

The problem with the common cold is that it keeps changing its DNA so that it beats our antibody defences primed to a previous version. It is also well established that we can carry viruses without having the full-blown symptoms of the disease which they cause. Herpes, hepatitis, cytomegalovirus and a type of human leukaemia virus are four examples. Of those infected with the latter some 95 per cent are OK, only 5 per cent will get the type of leukaemia induced by the virus. Similarly, most of us carry a form of herpes virus, but only at certain times do we get severe sores around the mouth. Some people can even carry hepatitis without the yellow colour characteristic of liver damage.

So where does that leave AIDS?

AIDS – Acquired Immune Deficiency Syndrome – is thought to be caused by a virus known as HIV, Human Immunodeficiency Virus, though there are some who believe that we have been fooled into thinking this. There are two main types, HIV I and HIV II. These infect one of the constructors of the navy: a cell known as a 'CD4 helper T cell'. When this is damaged the navy is severely under-strength. The body is unable to make antibodies effectively. The island body is thus prone to attack. In the US AIDS is becoming one of the biggest killers of heterosexuals aged between 22 and 40 , and it is rife in Africa. But HIV itself is not the killer, unlike smallpox or measles. People who die from AIDS die from a secondary infection, not from HIV itself. A simple cold which would be over in few days in a healthy person develops into full-blown pneumonia in an AIDS patient. Or athlete's foot, instead of remaining localised to a tiny part of one foot, develops into gangrene and blood-poisoning. Yet it may take 8-10 years after the initial infection with HIV for the AIDS rubicon to be crossed, and not all even then will develop AIDS. This is becoming particularly apparent in Africa, and in untreated heterosexuals who are not drug addicts.

HIV belongs to a group of viruses known as retro-viruses. They are packets of RNA, and make an enzyme which, when it was discovered, appeared to contradict one of the dogmas of molecular biology. The normally accepted dogma is that DNA makes RNA makes protein. But the enzyme reverse transcriptase in HIV makes DNA from RNA! Like the common cold virus, which is a DNA virus, HIV changes so much that a vaccine is proving very difficult to produce. In any event it seems a little bizarre to expect a damaged navy to be able to repair itself, without major outside help.

I hope I have made it clear in this section that the principle of Rubicon can give the new perspective which is urgently needed to combat the problem of AIDS and other virus diseases, as well as a host of other common afflictions. In every case rubicons are crossed, as the virus takes the host from one state to the next. There is no artificial cure for a viral disease. There are no viral equivalents of the antibiotics, so powerful at destroying bacterial infections. To combat viruses we rely entirely on our own defence system. If this breaks down we are in trouble.

Yet we have a lot to thank our army, navy and airforce for. Some thanks. When an invasion is over and successfully combated, what do we do? Instead of allowing the cells an easy retirement we execute most of them. They are destroyed. Just a few are retained as 'Reserves', ready to multiply if there is another attack from the same pathogen. This then brings us appropriately to the last topic of this chapter: an essential element of life, death.

DUST TO DUST

I know when one is dead

I know when one is dead, and when one lives;
She's dead as earth: – Lend me a looking-glass;
If that her breath will mist or stain the stone,
Why, then she lives.

King Lear, Act V, Scene III

The failure to revive a man who has dropped down on the station platform with a heart attack, the falling of a leaf in autumn, or the killing of an invading bacterium by one of your bleach-producing cells are all clear examples of death rubicons. Yet there is still a problem. The wisdom of Shakespeare, through the perceptive madness of Lear trying to decide whether his daughter Cordelia is dead, sums it up beautifully. On the face of it, it is obvious when something is dead. In biology and medicine we use the term every day, in describing the loss of an individual organism down to the loss of a single cell. But try giving a precise scientific definition of death and the trouble begins!

Yet without death life on earth would not exist. The beauties of Nature which we are fortunate to enjoy depend as much on the phenomenon of death as they do on life. No, I am not at this point moving towards a discussion of life after death, nor of the remarkable reminiscences of those who have had a 'near death', or 'return from death' experience. The aim of this section is to highlight the confusion that exists over the definition and description of death, particularly with respect to cells, and to show how Rubicon can bring some order to this chaos. But first I want to emphasise how important is the scientific study of death. Pretty obvious? Not quite so. Let me explain.

Imagine a warm spring afternoon. You are planting the first seeds of the year. They look lifeless; yet in a week or so the seed trays will be full of short, green shoots. The seeds were not dead, but dormant. The absorption of water and the warmth of the sun has caused them to cross the germination rubicon. A fly buzzes annoyingly around your head. Before you have a chance to swat it, it hits a spider's web and becomes ensnared in it. The deadly scenario is set. The fly, after struggling for a minute or so, is still. A hungry spider appears, but you know that even if you could release the fly from the sticky threads of the web before the spider begins to devour it, there can be no resurrection on this earth for the fly.

Yet all of the fly's structures appear intact. Sample a few cells from its surface or from within its body and examine them under a microscope. They look unharmed, just as they would have looked a minute or so before. Extract the chemicals from its body and analyse them with the most sophisticated biochemical analysis you can find. This will still not reveal the secret of death. No current biochemical analysis will tell you why this fly should be described as 'dead'. A similar dilemma faces modern medicine in the definition and detection of brain death.

Death is the point at which a biological unit has ceased to function. It has collapsed. An animal ceases to move, to think or breathe. A brain ceases to think, a liver stops metabolising, a heart stops beating and blood flow ceases, a kidney fails to filter the blood. Then, inside the cell, a mitochondrion ceases to make ATP, a nucleus fails to make nucleic acid, a ribosome cannot make protein. We can also define parameters which identify when a molecule is 'dead'. For example, an enzyme cannot catalyse the reaction for which it was made, an antibody cannot bind its antigen, or a receptor cannot bind its hormone.

While cessation of function is necessary to describe an organism, a cell, an organelle or a molecule as *dead*, this is not enough. What is necessary is complete and irrevocable cessation of function. A dead animal cannot rise from the dead, a dead brain can never think again, a dead cell can never do its thing again. It will never secrete, move, divide and so on. Yet a heart can start beating after a heart attack and a brain can wake out of coma when all electrical activity measured by the instruments available to modern medicine appears to be over. A paralysed leg after a stroke or spinal injury may cease to move, but it is not dead. Otherwise it would decay into a black, gangrenous mass. Cells, tissues and whole organisms, and molecules and organelles can recover from cessation of function, though they may never be the same again. Even if they have been irrevocably damaged, they are still alive. The heart or brain may have lost some of its cells, but they can still function. We must not mistake 'sleep' for death.

Cut a flower and put it into water, or it will wilt and die. Take the remainder of the rosemary you used to season the lamb for Sunday lunch. In a few days this will go brown and will also be dead. But put hormone-rooting powder on the cut end, stick it into a pot of compost and it will grow into a new bush.

A further difficulty is that, even after death, chemical processes continue. Fruit continues to ripen after being picked. Tomatoes go from green to red because of the generation of ethylene gas. There is life after death. Some hormones which stimulate live cells are actually generated by dead ones, as they decay. A compost heap, within a few months, turns into rich, black soil because of the moulds and bacteria which have degraded the dead plant tissue. Even under completely sterile conditions, dead animals and plants will decay and liquidise. This is because of the degradative enzymes in their internal incinerators, the lysosomes, which remain active for days, or even weeks, after death, breaking down nucleic acids and proteins to their individual components. Dust to dust.

Without death there can be no life, no development from an embryo, no proper development of the brain or nervous system, no proper defence against physical, chemical or biological attack, no living shapes, no seasons, and no evolution. The controlled killing of cells is a crucial part of the development and maintenance of a healthy body. The extinction of species provides the ecological and chemical space for the evolution of new ones.

Death is therefore as much a part of physiology as it is of pathology. Rubicon gives a new and better perspective on this vital feature of living systems, by describing it not as a single event but rather as a pathway of rubicons. The ultimate end may be the dissolution of a cell or whole organism into simple chemicals, but not necessarily.

Descriptions of death by the pathologist or biochemist include subjective histological terms such as necrosis and pycnosis, or complex diagrams with boxes and arrows shooting all over the page supposedly painting a picture of the chemical pathway of death. These usually include changes in our old friend ATP, movements of substance in and out of cells, degradation of small and large molecules in the cell, such as DNA, RNA and protein, and precipitates of calcium phosphate or coagulated protein in what was the cytosol or inside of an organelle. Dotted arrows purport to show where the changes go from being reversible to irreversible. Vital dyes tell us whether the membrane surrounding the cell is leaky. And so on.

Definitions of death are more often than not based on how one is detecting it, or even on what type of scientific herd you belong to. The cell biologist looks at a cell function, e.g. division or respiration. Yet bacteria can become dormant, and as a result won't form nice plaques on a culture dish, though swallowing some sea water containing such bacteria may awaken them, allowing them to grow, and precipitate a nasty gut rubicon. This can be a severe problem for those trying to detect *live* bacteria in sea water as a result of sewage pollution. Similarly loss of respiration can be reversible. For example, we can stop breathing for a short while and loss of blood flow to the heart or brain can occur, and yet we can make a full recovery. Histologists, on the other hand, much as they may protest that they look at real tissue, only examine it in the microscope when is it is dead, fixed and stained! They identify morphological changes from this staining, blue for the nucleus and red for the cytosol, nuclear condensation and chromatin fragmentation, and so on. The biochemist, on the other hand, measures ATP loss, salt uptake, protein coagulation, macromolecule degradation, loss or cessation of metabolic processes, DNA damage, permeabilisation of membranes, and damage to organelles. What a mess! If Rubicon is to come to the rescue we must first identify the executioners, those which sign the death warrant of a cell.

Cell death occurs for one of three reasons: the cell can't survive an attack, it commits suicide, or it is killed for the benefit of the host. Invading cells are killed, or our own cells fail to survive attack by a pathogen. Sick and unwanted cells – cancerous ones, for example – need to be removed; whereas cells involved in a leaf falling, spermatogenesis, the development of digits and the nervous system, the formation of the right shape in an embryo, the loss of a tadpole's tail, and the removal of the army and navy after fighting an invasion, need to be signalled.

Without death – cell death, that is – our bodies would not be alive. Death enables sick cells and damaged cells to be cleared away by scavengers and replaced by healthy ones. Millions of our cells are dying and being replaced every day. Yet some cells remain for the whole of our lives, and cannot be replaced if they die, nerve cells for example. But here too we see death in action – molecular death. Proteins and DNA are continuously being damaged by chemical and physical attack. The cellular factories and maintenance staff replace and repair these day-in, day-out so that the nerve cell remains alive and continues to function for as long as a hundred years.

Death plays a vital role in development. Without death we would have no individual limbs, palate, or fingers. We would have webbed feet. When controlled death sequences go wrong, major faults in development occur. Could this be what goes wrong in cancer, rheumatoid arthritis and other mutinous diseases? Unless we understand how death rubicon sequences occur we will not find the answer to this question.

So four important points have come out of this discussion. First, to define death in molecular and cellular terms we must look at it as a sequence of events and not simply the one obvious event, such as a man dropping down on the station platform or a leaf falling to the ground. There is a sequence of chemical rubicons both before and after these cataclysmic events. Secondly, cessation of function is necessary for death to be established but not sufficient. We must distinguish between dormancy and death. Thirdly, irreversible damage to a cell, tissue or organism does not necessarily mean that it is inevitably on the rubicon death pathway. Fourthly, death is important to the normal development, maintenance, defence and reproduction of all animals and plants.

Four rubicon death sequences

Let's look briefly at four death sequences to see Rubicon in action: the death of the heart following loss of blood supply, the killing of invading cells by the navy, the removal of the army and navy after an infection, and the death of a leaf.

The end-result of all these is that the cell, or a large number of cells, ceases to function – in the case of the heart within minutes of oxygen deprivation, with the navy within a few hours, and in the leaf perhaps days after the initial message that some cells had to die.

But between the time of the initial insult, attack or death-wish and the sounding of the death knell there are a multitude of chemical and physical changes. To rationalise these changes Rubicon looks for the thresholds which have to be crossed as a cell moves towards its final destruction.

The plaque in an artery has broken and a clot has formed. A group of cells in the heart are gasping for breath. Their inner lungs, the power-house mitochondria, stop functioning. There are several hundred in each cell. One by one they run out of oxygen and stop making ATP. The cell is now desperate for energy. It tries using its reserve supply, in the form of a chemical called creatine phosphate, but within a few minutes this has run out too. The ATP drops disastrously. As a result of this drop in ATP, there are a host of gradual and threshold chemical changes in the cell. The amounts of sodium and calcium go up, and the amount of potassium goes down. The cell stops making proteins, membranes and nucleic acids, and instead starts to degrade them. The outer membrane leaks and produces wart-like blebs on its surface. The full rubicon sequence has yet to be fully defined. However, we can guess at some of it.

The amount of calcium inside reaches a critical level and activates destruction sequences, causing precipitates to occur in the mitochondria. Thresholds in the permeability of the outer membrane occur causing leakage of small molecules. Then a second rubicon causes blebbing and a third leakage of large molecules. Finally, the inner protein skeleton inside the cell coagulates like the white of an egg when boiled. The cell is well and truly dead. But irreversible changes occurred well before this. Once large amounts of precipitate and membrane damage to a 'power station' occur it can never make ATP again, even if oxygen supply is restored. Even if the blood clot manages to dissolve or dislodge itself, rapid re-supply of oxygen can be the final insult, 'burning' already weakened cells.

A crucial feature of this sequence, often misunderstood, is the heterogeneity in the timing and number of rubicons crossed by each cell. Rubicon tells us to look closely at this heterogeneity and not to be fooled by measurements of thousands or millions of cells at a time, which average out and obscure the true rubicons being crossed. Ten minutes after a cluster of cells has been deprived of oxygen, 80 per cent of the mitochondrial power-stations will have been irreversibly damaged in some, while in others perhaps only 10 per cent. If oxygen is re-supplied at this point the latter can recover, the former will still die. Insufficient oxygen can produce a sharp line between live and dead cells in a tissue.

Enzymes are released from the damaged cells. These are used by the clinician to assess whether a heart attack has occurred. The best one now available is called *creatine kinase MB*, specific for the heart. Yet it takes several hours to detect a rise in the serum content of this enzyme. This is equivalent to perhaps a few per cent of the total enzyme in the whole heart, depending on how big the heart attack was. A key question, still unanswered and usually ignored by the medical profession, is: 'Does this represent one per cent of the enzyme from all the heart cells, or 100 per cent from one per cent of the cells?'

Similarly in liver damage the clinician asks the biochemistry lab to look for liver enzymes in the blood – *gamma GT*, for example, if he thinks you have hepatitis or are a heavy drinker. We can look for similar proteins in the blood that are released when other tisses are damaged. Yet the question I raised for the heart remains in all cases. I have to say that the clinical biochemists in my own speciality have had a very unimaginative attitude to this crucial Rubicon question. How many of the cells have been killed? Does a one per cent rise in a tissue-specific protein mean that one per cent of the cells have been shattered? Answers must be found to these questions if we are to treat the damage effectively.

A second good example of the heterogeneity of timing in a Rubicon death sequence is when one of the flotillas of the navy attacks invading bacteria or, in disease, the host's own cells. When antibodies bind to a cell they activate a rubicon sequence. First, the complement system we met earlier is set in motion. Two events ensue: one the generation of messages which tell the army to get on the march, and the second the firing of components of a mortar bomb which causes the target cell to explode. But this explosion does not happen on impact. In fact it can take many minutes, and if the cell can defend itself in time it can prevent the explosion and thus survive. The protein rockets fired at the cell insert into the membrane of the target, the first rubicon in the attack. These cluster and attract the final rocket, called *complement component C9*, to bind. This then itself inserts into the outer membrane of the cell, the next rubicon. It then aggregates, and eventually polymerises into a multi-molecular complex which looks like a large rubber ring or cylinder. An analogy is the difference between the American donut and British doughnut.

Each of these C9 rubicons is associated with a rubicon in the cell (Figure 6), involving metabolic thresholds, leakage of molecules of different sizes as a result of the damage to the membrane of the cell. Some cells will be able to remove the potentially lethal mortar bomb as it assembles, or even stop it forming at all – even if each rocket scores a direct hit. But if the

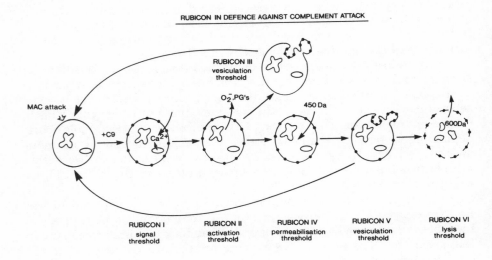

Fig. 6. A classic Rubicon sequence – the killing or defence of cells against rocket attack.

complete rubicon sequence happens fast enough, within a minute or so the cell explodes.

Yet if this battle is looked at without the binoculars which are necessary to view each cell fighting its foe, a very fuzzy picture appears. As time goes on, the sea gradually fills up with debris as the insides of cells leak out of the holes punched in them by the rockets. But this is a misleading picture. For, as the battle develops, what actually happens is that one by one the cells explode, but at different times after being hit by the first rocket. The amount of debris is therefore related directly to the number of fatalities and ships sunk, not to a gradual loss of stores in each vessel. We shall re-examine the signals involved in this sequence in the next chapter.

The lymphocytes are the principal components of the navy and consist of two main fleets, the B and T cells. The B cells make and fire one type of bullet at invaders, antibodies, and one of the T cell vessels we met earlier fires rockets which generate a mortar bomb similar to the one from complement component C9 I have just discussed. There are a number of support vessels required for the navy to do its job effectively. But as I have already pointed out, once the battle is won most of the vessels and tanks and the forces responsible for manning them are killed off. A key signal for this is an increase in the steroid cortisol, released by the adrenal gland. There are drugs – dexamethasone, for one – which are even more potent. That steroids exert control over the immune system has been known for about fifty years. What is not generally appreciated is that, as the steroid concentration rises, more and more cells are killed off, and faster. And, unlike the mortar bomb we saw just now, which scattered debris and shrapnel all over the place, even hitting innocent bystander cells, the killing of the navy and army is a much more controlled affair.

First, the steroid penetrates the cell and finds its receptor. The two, hand in hand, are transported to the nucleus, where they lock onto a particular spot in the DNA on one chromosome. This rubicon activates the next and RNA is formed, which itself leads to the formation of an internal firing squad. The chromatin then dies. It condenses and breaks up into a ladder of fragments. The cell can now no longer make RNA, and stops making protein. It lies still and puts out the white flag. On the outside of the cell receptors are expressed which await the refuse collectors which will eventually incinerate the cell corpse. There are no limping vessels or cadavers left strewn about this battlefield!

In a leaf signalled to fall in the autumn there is a similar controlled killing of a particular target set of cells. These form the zone where the leaf will eventually drop off. And at least six rubicons can be identified which lead to the complete demise of the plant leaf. The first causes maximum function of leaf photosynthesis and guard cell activity O_2 and CO_2 exchange to decline in performance. The second results in organised removal of leaf contents, and is followed by the formation of a layer of dead cells, the abscission layer. The leaf then falls and the refuse rubicons begin. The leaf is attacked by moulds and bacteria. The final rubicon has been crossed when complete loss of all cellular material has occurred.

In these four rubicon death sequences there were in fact three different types of cell death.

Three types of cell death

The three types of cell death are called *lysis*, *necrosis* and *apoptosis*. The mortar bombs cause lysis. Lack of oxygenation in the heart causes necrosis, and the killing of the armed forces and the autumn leaf involves apoptosis. These types of death occur throughout the animal and plant kingdoms. Bacterial death is less easily defined in these terms, though lysis certainly can occur.

Necrosis results in nuclear condensation. The chromosomes cease to function and protein coagulates like egg white. Permeability barriers in the outer and inner membrane break down, but the cell does not actually explode as it does if lysis is the final death rubicon. Lysis is a molecular catastrophe. The plasma membrane breaks down, releasing small and big molecules rapidly. Apoptosis, on the other hand, is even more controlled than necrosis. It enables cells to be removed without leaving rubble, or the activation of bleach-producers. The term 'apoptosis' was first coined some ten years ago by Professor Cossack in Edinburgh to describe programmed cell death, from the Greek for leaves falling from a tree, though in modern Greek it means loss of hair follicles! Going bald is a good example of apoptosis in action, though the brain underneath the surface may remain alive and as wise as ever! Apoptosis may be a suicide, or it may be triggered by an external messenger. Whichever, it has to be signalled.

Signalling cell death

Signalled cell death is responsible for tissue and organ shape, for control of the size and composition of the body's army and navy, for leaf-falling in autumn, for the digits in animal hands and for determining whether birds have webbed feet or not. In a duck cell-death is restricted and therefore it has webbed feet. While chickens have four digits as a result of controlled cell-death during development, without which they and we would have webbed hands and feet. Quite an unnerving prospect. In the nervous system cells are killed in a controlled manner during development.

Most children in spring will be familiar with the outcome of another example of apoptosis. Next time you see some tadpoles, put them in a jar of water and watch what happens to their tails day by day. They get shorter and shorter as the animals move along the rubicon sequence to become young frogs. For this to happen the hormone released from the tadpole's thyroid gland has to kill the cells in the tail in a highly controlled and organised way. Getting rid of cells in the wrong place at the wrong time, or those that have missed the boat, is also a key function of apoptosis.

Cancer cells may be killed by bleach-producers, lysed by mortar bombs from T-lymphocytes, or killed by apoptosis. I will deal with some of the signalling mechanisms involved in these types of cell-death in the next chapter. But what happens to the debris and the lifeless apoptotic cells? Fortunately for us, we have a very efficient refuse-collection service.

The refuse collectors

There are cells in the blood and lining the inner surfaces of our tissues which have a voracious appetite. They are the phagocytes ('cell-devourers'). When they come across a dead or sick cell, or a bit of rubbish left lying around, receptors on the 'refuse cart' surface latch on to it. The particle is then taken up into the incinerator inside the phagocyte, and is degraded back to small molecules, so that these can be reprocessed. So dust to dust.

Apoptotic cells make special receptors which the refuse collectors, the macrophages, recognise, enabling them to engulf the dead cell without generating the bleach they might otherwise have done if they thought it was an invader.

So after all these rubicons of life and death, can we find a structure, a topology, a five-dimensional array, to impose some order on these thresholds? That is the role of taxonomy.

RUBICON – A TAXONOMY

Taxonomy, from the Greek *taxis*, 'arrangement' and *onoma*, 'name', is a word usually employed by biologists when referring to the classification of organisms into groups from kingdoms to individual species, and even sub-species. But I want to use it to try to produce a classification of Rubicon.

Linnaeus, one of the pioneers of biological taxonomy, believed in three kingdoms: animals, plants and *stones*. Now we have five: monera (bacteria and blue-green algae), protists (algae, yeasts, protozoa), fungi, plants and animals. These are then sub-divided into smaller and smaller groups, until the individual species is reached. There has been much debate about the criteria by which we put a species into a particular biological group. Classification is not the same as description. The former uses the latter to place an apple on the right branch of the right tree.

Phylogenetic classification places organisms into Kingdoms, Phyla, Classes, Orders, Families, Genera and Species, with super- and sub-divisions where necessary. Some believe in the true cladism ('branching') of Hennig (1913-1976), and argue that the ultimate aim is to develop a tree-like classification representing as closely as possible the evolutionary descent of organisms. Thus species in the same genus have formed from a common ancestor and so on. Others, arguing that much of the evidence for such a procedure is subjective, or the result of convergent evolution, prefer to ignore deliberately evolutionary relationships and join the infamous transformed cladists. The taxonomy of Rubicon has a quite different objective.

The taxonomy of Rubicon is a river, not a tree. Rivers flow in another dimension and in the opposite direction from a tree. A tree has a thick trunk, which divides out into smaller and smaller branches. By contrast a river starts as a small stream, each branch point joined by other streams which lead to the main waterway, until the river finally reaches the open sea or a lake. Likewise we can classify biological rubicons, not phylogenetically or on the basis of fundamental cell type, but rather by working back from the mouth of the river, where it becomes the whole phenomenon, from ecosystem to individual molecules.

How then do we the fit an orgasm, a runner, the smell of honeysuckle, the sound of an orchestra, an idea, and the flash of a firefly – all examples of thresholds – into the Rubicon taxonomy? An orgasm is concerned with reproduction, or is it? Ultimately yes, but in humans at least it plays another vital role, communication and maintenance of the pair bond between male and female. Likewise the flash of a firefly is a form of communication, used to attract a mate. Smell, sound and an idea also come within the Rubicon phylum: Communication and Senses. What about the Rubicon class? An orgasm requires movement, both transmission of an electrical signal down a nerve fibre and contraction of smooth muscle to allow the penis to fill with blood and hold an erection. The sperm are also moving because they have flagella. Secretion from cells is also required, transmitters from the terminals of nerves, fluid into the vagina as a lubricant allowing the ejaculation of sperm to take place.

Similarly for the runner, nerves will be firing, releasing transmitters at the nerve-muscle junction, and movement of muscles will depend on the number of individual fibres contracting. An increased rate of heart beat will also be needed, stimulated by a release of adrenaline from the adrenal gland. The firefly flash requires the release of a neurohormone to trigger the luminous cells. Smell, hearing and sound again all require the activation of particular nerves. As we have already seen, these cells can be considered in three sections: the cell body, the axon and the nerve terminal. The cell bodies of most of our nerves, particularly those in the brain, have so-called dendritic processes each of which can receive a chemical signal from an adjacent nerve terminal. These generate a tiny electrical signal in the cell body of the nerve. When these add up to a big enough combined signal, an action potential is generated which can travel down the axon to nerve terminal. There are inhibitory nerves near the cell body which can prevent this threshold from being achieved.

So, starting from the mouth of the river, we decide on the type of river we are dealing with, i.e. whether we are dealing with a phenomenon concerned with the maintenance and reproduction of existing species (Rubicon *Kingdom*: Physiology), or with a sick system (Pathology), or with the interaction of groups of organisms with each other and the environment (Ecosystem), or with something concerned with the evolution of a phenomenon (Evolution). The Rubicon *Phyla* embrace the essential features of living systems: maintenance, reproduction, development, death and so on. Reproduction plays a part in all the Rubicon Kingdoms, as does death. Millions of the cells in our body are being replaced every day, though some, like nerves, never divide.

A cancer does not represent just one pathological rubicon. There are at least four rubicons we need to identify if the cause and natural history of cancer is to be understood fully. The first is the transformation of a normal cell into a cancer cell. Within a tissue it is either killed by the body's defence or it remains lurking, a deadly 'sleeper'. The next is an awakening of the dormant cell, which then divides and forms a small clone. Such clones are still too small to detect, even with the sensitive X-ray, MRI or biochemical methods available to modern medicine. The third is the signalling of this clone into a rapid division phase, allowing a tumour to form. The fourth is the sloughing off of one or more of the tumour cells. This triggers another rubicon sequence leading to secondary tumours, sometimes all over the place, at sites where the sloughed off-cells have attached.

Similarly ecosystems reproduce themselves on an acute time-scale and on a time-scale of hundreds of millions of years. Death, on the other hand, often conceived as the final frontier, the ultimate rubicon, has a vital role to play in the development and maintenance of a healthy body and ecosystem.

The Rubicon classes embrace the specific phenomena or functions of living systems. Once again we can see that each class can lead right through to a Rubicon Kingdom. All organisms and cells can move in some way or other. Animals can run. Plants have seeds and can open and close their flowers, leaves or other organs. Fungi have spores and grow over surfaces. Just look into a sample of pond water to see the movement of unicellular organisms. But even cells in a multicellular organism move – a heart beats and the cilia on the cells of the gut wiggle. Phagocytes are attracted into the site of an infection. They move like an amoeba. The sting cells of a hydroid, part of the life cycle of a small jelly-fish, form at the base of the stem and then move up the stem to locate in the tentacles where they can anaesthetise and ensnare their prey.

This then is my suggestion for a taxonomy of Rubicon.

The Rubicon Kingdoms
    Physiology
    Pathology
    Ecology
    Evolution
The Rubicon Phyla
    Development
    Survival and maintenance
    Reproduction
    Adaptation to and of the environment
    Sensing and communication

Defence
Death
The Rubicon Classes
Movement
Sensing
Release
Uptake
Metabolism
Transformation
Growth
Aggregation
Division
Collapse
The Rubicon Orders = Fundamental cell type
Prokaryta
Archaea
Eukaryta
The Rubicon Families = Cell type
Flagellate
Amoeboid
Germ line (ecto-, endo- or meso-derm)
Tissue type (muscle, liver, nerve or xylem or phloem in plants)
The Rubicon Genera = Organelle or sub-cellular structure
Nucleus
Mitochondrion
Endoplasmic reticulum
Golgi apparatus
Lysosome
Secretory vesicle
Peroxisome
Endosome
Nematocyst
Plasma membrane
Enzyme or protein complex
Chromosome
Microtubule
Microfilament
Chloroplast
Tonoplast
The Rubicon Species = Individual molecular species
Nucleic acid
Protein
Lipid
Carbohydrate
Metabolite
Electrolyte

Some events can be arrived at by following this classification with just one taxon involved at each level, while others require a symbiosis of rubicons for the pathway to reach its conclusion. A molecular or cellular rubicon may involve just one cell or even one molecule. Yet to define many physiological or pathological events a matrix of cell and molecular rubicons is required. What at first site looks like a single event turns out to be a sequence of events.

As we follow the tributaries of Rubicon towards its mouth we find thresholds at every taxonomic level, but only when we look down on the complete path of the river will we understand why it is alive or why it has stopped flowing at all.

There are now two key questions we must examine. First, how does a cell cross the rubicon? And secondly, how can we view the rubicon to discover this?

3

How to Cross the Rubicon

ALL OF A QUIVER

It is your daughter's birthday and you are expecting a horde of ravenous children for tea. What else is there for it but to make jam sandwiches and jelly? The home-made blackberry jam is one of your best yet. Obviously buying a jam thermometer was a good idea. The pectin content is high enough for it to have set, unlike the last lot, which was hopelessly runny. So to the jelly. But what is jelly made of and why does it set?

The substance in tissues which binds the cells together is collagen. Collagen is a protein, and there are at least five types, depending on the tissue. It is manufactured by cells called fibroblasts which are all over the body. Collagen, like all proteins, consists of a chain of amino-acids, but is unusual in being particularly rich in two, glycine and proline. In tissues, collagen is found as a triple helix of three such chains interwoven with each other, a triple corkscrew. As a result it is insoluble in water. But treat animal hides, skin, bones or any tissue with alkali or acid and then boil it, and the collagen breaks up and dissolves. The resulting protein is called gelatin, and is widely used in cooking to 'jellify' sweets, soups, aspics and soufflés. In 1880 gelatin was introduced as the medium for dispersing the silver, in the form of halide, in photographic plates, and remains the standard today.

You can buy gelatin in granulated form, as a powder form or as a jelly. To convert these into the jelly for the children's tea party all you have to do is dissolve it in hot water with sugar and fruit-flavouring and then allow it to cool. So long as you get the proportion of water to gelatin right you will end up with a beautiful quiverer or wobbler. So with cells.

Take a giant nerve fibre – for example from a squid – cut off the end and squeeze out the contents. In spite of the fact that it is 70 per cent water it will be a jelly, or *gel* as we say. Add calcium to it and it becomes a free-flowing liquid, or *sol*. Just as the jelly cubes dissolved in hot water, so selected regions inside the cell become a free-flowing liquid, but at the temperature of the body, 37°C, well below the near-boiling water needed to dissolve the gelatin. When the calcium is removed, the region of the cell *jellifies* again. Everyone is familiar with the central structural role calcium plays in bones and teeth. But gel-sol transitions are an example of another biological role for calcium, central to Rubicon. We will examine this universal property of cells in a minute.

For the moment, back in the kitchen we see how the jelly is an example of how a rubicon can be crossed in a cell. When cells secrete or move there can be a gel to sol conversion inside the cell which allows globules, vesicles and even molecules to move rapidly to their destination, thereby allowing the event to occur. But while still in the gel state the particles or molecules are held and prevented from reaching the banks of the rubicon.

The protein responsible for this quivering inside cells is not collagen or its derivative gelatin, but another protein called actin. This forms the skeleton inside cells, just as collagen does outside. Unlike a blood clot outside cells, made of another protein, fibrin, which cannot be dissolved, actin can dissolve and jellify over and over again. But jellies and gooey substances are not always proteins. Carbohydrates are sugars, and the big ones made up of a long string of sugar molecules can also undergo gel-sol conversions. Starch in flour prevents a sauce being runny. Agar, extracted from the cell walls of seaweed helps to make ice-cream soft without being runny. Pectin, polygalacturonic acid, is found in fruit, and helps jam to solidify. These jellifying substances are essential to the work we do in the lab every day.

To grow bacteria on a solid substrate we pour a liquid containing the bacteria on to a plate of agar and leave it overnight. The next day there will be dozens, even hundreds, of colonies of bacteria, each from a single parent. To separate DNA or proteins we put them at one end of a gel and put a voltage across it. DNA is negatively charged, as are many proteins. So they move towards the positive pole. Because each molecular type of DNA or protein has a different charge on it they separate from each other within an hour or so. But without a gel everything would flow all over the place. Gels inside cells enable the living unit to polarise chemicals and structures, keeping them in the right place.

The jelly and jam sandwiches have crossed the Rubicon, and there are many other rubicons to be crossed in the party games you have planned. Your daughter has been given a bubble-maker, and the drawing-room is full of bubbles popping and fusing with each other. Likewise in the cells. Vesicles containing hormone or neuro-transmitter, so small that millions could fit onto the head of a pin, will soon be moving to the edges of the children's nerve cells as they rush about. Here the vesicles hit the outer membrane and fuse, releasing their contents outside. Another rubicon has been crossed.

But no children's party would be the same without balloons! One rascal of a boy has found a pin, and puts any balloon he can reach through its death rubicon. They pop with a bang. But, as we saw in the preceding chapter, you can prevent the balloon popping by sticking a piece of Sellotape on to the balloon before inserting the pin. Unfortunately the balloon is not a cell and can only delay the pin bursting it. Eventually it will burst, although usually it deflates slowly, rather than popping as it does without the Sellotape.

A key feature of both this protection mechanism and the gel-sol transition, as well as the vesicle movement and fusion, is that they all have to be signalled. The signal which starts the process leading to dissolution of the gelatin for your jelly was turning on the gas to boil the water. But what turns on the gas inside the cell? It is by examining what does this, so that the traffic-lights turn from red to green, that we discover the true trigger for sending a cell across the rubicon. Furthermore, there will be molecular mechanisms which prime the cell – that is, turn it from red to red-amber – and we also need mechanisms which put the traffic-lights there in the first place. These will be the development signals, enabling the trigger signal to switch the cell to green for GO!

What then does determine if and when you have an orgasm? What tells a tree to shed a leaf or a flower to exhibit its splendid bloom? What message does the brain send to our muscles to instruct them to start running, whether fast or slowly, and then stop? What causes us to go to sleep or to wake up and have an idea? What makes us have a headache or to suffer premenstrual tension? All these events have to be signalled. First, a message reaches the outside of the cell. This then generates a messenger inside the cells, which starts the internal rubicon-sequence.

Let's therefore look at this fundamental property of all living cells, which is destroyed when the cell is broken and yet has been essential for the evolution of life.

SIGNALLING A RUBICON

A century of signalling rubicons

In the last chapter I mentioned the two physiologists from London, William Madock Bayliss (1860-1924) and Ernest Henry Starling (1866-1927), who discovered hormones. In 1902 they injected the extract of the jejunal mucosa from the gut into the pancreatic vein of a dog. They succeeded in stimulating the secretion of digestive juices from the pancreas. They had proved for the first time that there were chemical stimuli produced by one cell type in the body capable of arousing another. They called their first substance *secretin*. But, realising that this must be but one of many similar types of signal in the body, Starling, in 1905, decided that a generic name was needed and called such substances *hormones*.

In fact they were looking for such a substance, since it was already known that removal of particular glands – the thyroid, adrenals and the pancreas – from animals produced symptoms similar to certain human diseases. These glands must be producing something. In 1856 A.Vulpian (1826-1887), a French physiologist who played a leading role in encouraging Pasteur to use his anti-rabic serum, had extracted the adrenal gland of a sheep. On leaving the extract exposed to the air he noticed that it turned pink, something he described as 'tout à fait remarquable'. He thought it was likely to be released into the blood, but it was to be another forty years before the actions of the real active ingredient of the adrenals, adrenalin(e), were discovered. In 1894 Oliver and Schäfer found that the adrenal extract caused arteries to contract, and increased the rate and strength of the heart beat. John Abel (1857-1938), in 1897, called the active substance that he and Crawford had succeeded in precipitating from adrenal extracts 'epinephrin'. The true active principle was eventually purified in 1901, and shown to have the right signalling activity, first by Jokichi Takamine (1854-1922), who called it 'adrenalin', and soon after by Aldrich. (There is some confusion as to the origin of the modern spellings, 'adrenaline' and 'epinephrine'.) As always with a chemical substance, the structure of adrenaline had to be confirmed by making it in the laboratory. This was achieved by Stolz in 1904 and Dakin in 1905. But it was the oxidation product of adrenaline, now called 'adrenochrome', which turned out to be the pink substance that Vulpian had observed some forty-five years earlier.

These experiments on secretin and adrenalin led to an explosion of discoveries, by which many signalling molecules of considerable and immediate medical benefit were isolated and characterised. Insulin was isolated from the pancreas by Banting and Best in 1921, saving the lives of many diabetics. In 1895 Baumann identified iodine as a major element in the thyroid gland. In fact one quarter of the iodine in the body is found here, because it is part of the hormone made by the gland, thyroxine. By 1914, extracts of thyroid had been used to treat patients deficient in the hormone, alleviating the lethargy and tiredness of thyroid-deficient patients. Graves' disease, named after the Irish physician Robert James Graves (1796-1853) who was one of the first to give a full description of it, is caused by excessive thyroid hormone-production from a goitre.

The thyroid provides an interesting example of Rubicon in action. Up to 90 per cent of radioactive iodine injected into the blood ends up in the thyroid. The gland produces, in fact, two hormones, thyroxine and tri-iodothyronine. Thyroxine, or T_4 for short, was discovered in 1915. But it was not until 1952 that T_3 was discovered. Both are derivatives of the amino-acid tyrosine. T_4 has four iodines attached to it, while T_3 has only three. T_4 can be converted into T_3 in various parts of the body. T_3 can be as much as 500-1,000 times more potent than T_4 at stimulating basal metabolism. If you are thyroid-deficient you cross the lethargy rubicon and feel cold, but people with over-active thyroids are hot and over-active. Hormones and neuro-transmitters can be proteins, or they can be small molecules derived like T_4 from amino-acids or components of fat. All small molecule hormones are stored within the cells that make them in the same form as they are released, except for the thyroid. T_4 is stored in the thyroid gland linked to a large protein called thyroglobulin. When it is to be released the T_4 has to be chopped off so that it is free. Why? It seems a little cumbersome. The reason is that T_4 is not very soluble in water. If it were to be stored inside granules, like adrenalin, when it was secreted in the blood the solubility rubicon would take ages to be crossed. The blood would be full of particles of undissolved T_4. Evolution has solved the problem by storing it in a form which is accessible to rapid solubilisation, and is carried in the blood on another, soluble, protein.

There are plenty of other hormones. And nerves also release stimuli which cause the adjoining cell to fire. These are the 'neurotransmitters', or in invertebrates, where they often travel much longer distances, 'neurohormones'. Prostaglandins and eicosonoids are sometimes known as 'paracrines', as they seem to work locally. Some of these are particularly important in the vaginal tract, in triggering the uterus to contract for birth to occur, and around a local infection.

The neutrotransmitter acetyl choline, first isolated by Dale in 1934, is released at our nerve-muscle junctions and triggers the muscle to contract. Dozens of natural cell-stimuli have been now been isolated. Some, like acetyl choline, hit cells only a few millionths of a metre away, while others have to travel several metres round the body in the blood before they hit their target. Some 'hormones' are the primary external switch telling the cell target to cross the rubicon, i.e. from red to green, while others *prime* the cell so that it can cross the rubicon in response to a primary stimulus, i.e. a priming agent takes the cell to red-amber. Two particularly important groups of rubicon primers are the growth factors and cytokines. The latter include substances such as interferon, which hype up many cells in the body to enable one to combat an infection. The liver protein factory and the bleach-producing cells are just two examples. Many growth factors are active all the time, enabling cells to mature so that they are ready to cross the rubicon when hit by a primary stimulus. Growth factors help to put the traffic-lights in place. And there are rhythms and oscillations which are types of cycling rubicons, which must also be explained. The menstrual cycle and the daily fasting-feeding cycle are just two examples from the human body. The gut and brain suffering from jet lag is a familiar example of a problem encountered when we disturb such rhythms. Invertebrates and plants also exhibit rhythms, and even molecular events inside cells can involve waves and oscillations, essential to the control of the cell event.

In development there also seems to be an *internal* switching system. This is controlled from the DNA by a family of genes called *homeobox* genes. If these are defective, a whole segment of the body may be missing, defective or in the wrong place. So rubicons, the fifth dimension, need to be controlled in four dimensions.

Chemical stimuli are not restricted to animals; nor are they all in soluble form. Plants have plenty of hormones controlling their development and behaviour. Ethylene, the ripening hormone in tomatoes, is of course a gas, as are insect pheromones, showing that some rubicon stimuli can act over quite large distances. And they are made not only by live cells. The chemical process of taking a dead cell back to its constituent molecules can generate hormones. This may be particularly significant in plants and animals during development. In bacteria the chemical stimuli are usually directly related to nutrient supply. If starved, some genes get switched off, while when exposed to a nutrient like lactose the genes responsible for metabolising it must be switched on.

The initial signal does not have to be a chemical. There are many physical and biological stimuli: light, electrical impulses, touch, particles, bacteria and viruses, to name but a few.

But there was a real puzzle. How did these external and internal agents actually cause the cell to get from red to green, or from red to red-amber? It was made even more puzzling when the biochemists failed to reproduce in the test-tube effects of hormones easily demonstrated by injecting them into the blood. Injection of insulin reduces blood sugar, and adrenalin stimulates the heart. Deficiencies in hormone glands can be alleviated by such injections. Diabetic children can thus survive their inability to make their own insulin, and patients in whom the thyroid has had to be removed can lead an active life. Many effects of these hormones can be demonstrated on isolated tissues. For example, adrenalin or glucagen stimulate a perfused liver to produce glucose, and insulin stimulates it to store glucose. But try to get effects on broken cells and the trouble begins. Try as they might the early biochemists could not get hormones or neurotransmitters to cause a tissue homogenate to cross the Rubicon. There had to be a signal-transduction system, which would only work if the cell remained intact.

The key to unlock this system was the receptor which a hormone or neurotransmitter first locks on to. Steroid and thyroid hormones can cross the outer membrane of cells and they then find their respective receptor inside. The complex of the two then transports to the nucleus, where it locks onto the DNA and sets the rubicon sequence in motion. Genes are first switched on, and the proteins which these code for then alter the composition of the cell so that it behaves differently. By contrast, in the case of all other hormones, neuro-transmitters, paracrines, cytokines and growth factors, exemplified by insulin and adrenalin, the receptors are on the outer surface of the cell, placed there as a result of the action of growth and other developmental factors. Once the hormone key is in the receptor lock what happens next? Surely, if a hormone cannot penetrate the cell, there must be some sort of messenger generated when the key is turned in the lock?

This is the *intra*-cellular signal, the study of which is one of the most exciting growth areas in modern biology. There are mini-rubicons all the way from the key unlocking the receptor, through generation and movement of the intra-cellular signal, to the cell-rubicon itself, whether this be movement, secretion, transformation, division or death. And like the discovery of the hormones and transmitters themselves, the story of intracellular signalling begins over a hundred years ago. To discover it, let us return to Nature.

One hundred years of calcium

A glance into any rock pool will reveal many animals and plants in which calcium plays a key part in their skeletal structures. The shells of the whelks, limpets and barnacles, the bones of the fish and the hard coat of the pink *Corallina* seaweed so familiar on the slopes of the pool are just a few examples. The White Cliffs of Dover bear witness to the importance of calcium in fossil deposits. The calcareous remains of blue-green alga have been found in rock some 1,800-2,000 million years old, well before multi-cellular organisms evolved and close to the time of the oxygen holocaust. So calcium was involved in life from very early on.

Early in June 1808 Humphry Davy (1778-1829) (Plate 4(a)) carried out a pioneering experiment at the Royal Institution in Albermarle Street, London, in which he connected a large battery made by himself across a moist mixture of lime and red oxide of mercury. We have come across this substance before, as it was the one used by Joseph Priestley when he discovered oxygen. Unlike Priestley, who was unaware of Scheele's experiments leading to the discovery of the same gas (above p. 66), Davy needed an idea from the experiments of two other Swedish scientists to get his to work. The idea came from Jöns Jacob Berzelius (1779-1848), one of the founders of modern chemistry, and Magnus Martin Pontin (1781-1858). Like Berzelius, Pontin was a doctor, appointed court physician to the College of Medicine in Stockholm, to replace Berzelius when he was made Professor of Medicine and Pharmacy at the School of Surgery. They shared living quarters. The two lived together and both carried out experiments in the kitchen, which Berzelius had converted into a laboratory! Yet great discoveries could still be achieved under such circumstances. Berzelius had already discovered cerium in 1803 and, like Davy, went on to discover and isolate several other elements, including selenium, thorium, silicon, zirconium and titanium. Chemistry is indebted to him for the determination of many atomic weights and the development of modern chemical symbols.

Although Berzelius published most of his 250 or so papers in Swedish, Davy was aware of his pioneering work. Davy thus added a globule of mercury at the negative electrode immersed in the moistened lime. After a while a mercury amalgam formed. On removal of the mercury by distillation, a tiny amount of a greyish-white metal with the lustre of silver was produced. No wonder so many early chemists died of mercury poisoning! In fact the tube broke when hot and the metal burned avidly with an intense white light when exposed to air. Davy called it *calcium*, from the Latin for lime.

Davy reported his discovery, together with that of the other alkaline earths including magnesium, strontium and barium, to the Royal Society on 30 June 1808. The year before he had used a similar technique to discover sodium and potassium. Davy believed that electricity would be of great value in discovering 'the true elements'. This was because he had the vision to realise that what we call salts – a general term used in science for many metal compounds in addition to common table salt – were composed of negative and positive parts. What better way to test this hypothesis than to separate them by using the voltage produced by a battery?

The important point is that the biological roles of calcium are intimately linked to its electrical charge. In a calcium salt in solution, calcium is present not as the uncharged metal but as a positively charged ion. It is the ability of this ion, with its two positive charges, to latch on strongly to, i.e. 'complex' with, anions that holds the key to its unique biological chemistry. Calcium latches on to phosphate in bone and teeth, to carbonate in shells, and to sulphate in the balancing organs of jelly-fish. Calcium can also bind to DNA; positive unites with negative. Calcium ions can carry electrical current across the membranes of cells. This is particularly significant in every beating heart cell. But it is the ability of calcium ions to bind to certain proteins which holds the key to its role as a signal inside cells.

The first clue to this began at the turn of the century in University College Hospital Medical School, London, with the experiments of Sydney Ringer (1835-1910) (Plate 4(b)). But scientists don't always get things right first time. During the 1890s Ringer was the first to investigate systematically the requirements for salt in the normal function and survival of animal cells. And I don't just mean sodium chloride, table salt. True, the main salt in our blood is sodium chloride, about a quarter the strength it is in sea water, but potassium, magnesium and calcium are also major metals with salts required for biological function. As we saw in the last chapter quite a small decrease in blood calcium can trigger tetany in muscle or, if too high, start the rubicon sequence towards a calcium stone. Ringer made up various mixtures of salts and looked at their effects on the contraction of an isolated frog heart, the development of fertilised eggs and tadpoles, and the adhesion of cells. In 1882 he had apparently shown that calcium was not required for the beating of a frog heart. But he had made a mistake. His technician had made up the solutions in London tap water. As anyone who has washed his hands in it knows, a scum forms because of the calcium in this hard water. The concentration of calcium in hard water approaches that of the blood stream. Next year Ringer wrote, somewhat embarrassingly: 'After the publication of a paper in the *Journal of Physiology*, vol. III, no. 5, I discovered that the saline I had used had not been prepared with distilled water but with pipe water supplied by the New River Water Company. As it contains minute traces of various inorganic substances, I at once tested the action of saline solution made with distilled water and found that I did not get the effects described in the paper referred to. It is obvious therefore that the effects I had obtained are due to some of the inorganic constituents of the pipe water.' He found that the critical missing constituent in his solution (saline) made up in distilled water was calcium.

Ringer's experiments were followed by those of Locke, Loeb, Mines,

Loewi and many other physiologists in the early years of this century, who confirmed that calcium outside cells was essential for maintaining the structure and normal function of all animal and plant cells, and even sometimes bacterial cells. In 1894 Locke and Overton showed independently that the transmission of impulses from nerves to muscles requires external calcium. Others showed that the removal of calcium from the solution bathing cells and tissues resulted in drastic changes in cell and tissue structure, including tissues falling apart, and decreased the growth rate of some cells. Loewi and others found that calcium also seemed to be involved in the action of cell stimuli and drugs, including the effects of the recently isolated adrenalin and of the drug digitalis on the heart. Not bad for 1917!

A German plant physiologist had realised that the same was true in plants. In a classic paper of 1892 published in *Flora*, D. Loew wrote that 'all animals from amoeba to man, and all plants, except for some lower algae and fungi, require calcium'. In fact even the latter do, but they need only tiny amounts.

But what is the calcium doing? Is it working outside the cells or inside? Is it needed to maintain structure? When does it have an electrical role? What is so special about calcium that evolution has selected it as a rubicon switch, and not sodium, potassium, magnesium, zinc and so on? To answer these questions we must measure calcium inside cells. We must find out whether, when a cell crosses the rubicon, there is a *change* in calcium inside the cell before the rubicon is crossed. If the calcium changes after, rather than before, the rubicon, the calcium change can only be a consequence, and not a cause, of the cell event.

Remarkably, as long ago as 1928 Herbert Pollack, a Cornell student of Robert Chambers (1881-1957), a pioneer of microinjection of cells whom we shall meet properly in Chapter Seven, injected into an amoeba the red dye sodium alizarin sulphonate, known to precipitate with calcium. The amoeba rounded up, movement ceased temporarily and 'a close examination of the cytoplasm shows fine red granules scattered throughout the cell'. When the amoeba tried to move again by putting forward a membranous foot, known as a 'pseudopod', 'a shower of red crystals was seen to appear in this area and the pseudopod formation was immediately stopped'. Pollack predicted that the precipitate had lowered the internal calcium, so that movement stopped, and the cell had a calcium reserve. This enables the cell to replenish the calcium in the cell matrix. When the calcium ions are fully recovered the cell can carry on as normal. Whatever the validity of this experiment, it is truly remarkable that Pollack should have realised that calcium could act as an internal trigger for amoeboid movement and that the cell had a calcium reserve, nearly fifty years before the Nobel prize was awarded to Earl Sutherland for the discovery of the first so-called intra-cellular messenger, cyclic AMP.

But how could this calcium be working? And how general was this? Indeed was calcium a universal internal chemical switch inside cells? It was an American zoologist and physiologist, Lewis Victor Heilbrunn (1892-1959) (Plate 5(a)), who had this vision and was to become one of the great protagonists of 'calcium as a universal regulator'. Heilbrunn realised that calcium did not simply have a structural function outside cells in the calcium precipitates of phosphate and carbonate in bones and teeth, and shells, and as a glue sticking cells together, but that it also had a vital function inside cells, as a chemical signal telling them when and what to do. In the first edition of his classic textbook of Physiology of 1937 Heilbrunn wrote in a chapter entitled 'Environmental conditions – chemical factors': 'The calcium ion has an unusual importance in biological phenomena, and the literature concerning its effect is extremely voluminous.' A few pages later he wrote, with equal insight: 'No other ion exerts such interesting effects on protoplasmic viscosity as the calcium ion.' This protoplasm is the cell 'jelly' we examined at the start of this chapter.

Like many pioneers of cell biology in the United States, Heilbrunn began his experimental work at the marine station at Woods Hole, Massachusetts. Marine animals have played a key part in the signalling story as they provide the physiologist with model cells, easily penetrable by their micro-electrodes and micro-pipettes. In view of his close association with this famous laboratory, of which he became a trustee in 1931, it is surprising that a review of work published for this lab in the 1940s made no mention of Heilbrunn's pioneering work. He was an inspiration to his students, an enthusiast and a seeker after truth. As his obituary says, 'His untimely death in an automobile accident on 24th October (1959) snuffed out a creative spirit science can ill afford to lose, but his influence will continue for generations to come.'

Heilbrunn's radical contribution to the calcium story was the idea that calcium movement inside cells was the trigger for a whole host of cellular events. The essential ingredient of his 'calcium release theory' was that a primary stimulus, such as a nerve impulse, caused calcium to be secreted inside the cell from a 'store' near the surface of the cell. Yet it is difficult to grasp today the lack of enthusiasm for Heilbrunn's hypothesis. Now every year many thousands of scientific papers are published about calcium, where it is dogma that calcium is a universal chemical switch inside cells. But in the 1930s and 1940s it was biochemistry, metabolism and molecules that were receiving the greatest attention from biologists. Why get excited about the movement of tiny amounts of ions across the membranes of cells? Indeed Heilbrunn, thought to be too obsessive about calcium, was regarded rather as 'a calcium maniac'. Accumulate evidence as he might, the proof outsiders wanted was lacking.

Then, in 1947, a student, Floyd Wiercinski, had a breakthrough. Painstakingly making first quartz micro-pipettes, for fear of contamination from Pyrex-type glass, Wiercinski micro-injected tiny amounts of calcium chloride into the muscle cell of a frog leg. The response was dramatic, an immediate shortening of the muscle by some 40 per cent or more. As Wiercinski remembered much later, 'It was fantastic to watch. We injected the calcium, and the fibre instantly pulled into a mass.' Yet to his joy other salts, such as sodium, magnesium and potassium did not. Nor did water alone. Only calcium chloride 'even, in rather high dilution' triggered the fibre to contract. They commented: 'The results lend support to the calcium release theory of stimulation and they are opposed to Szent-Györgyi's belief that the potassium ion is primarily responsible for the contraction of muscle.' The experiments at last met with some interest. The proof was there! Or was it? Then came the seemingly fatal rebuttal.

Archibald Vivian Hill (1886-1977) was a distinguished British physiologist who became Nobel Laureate for Physiology or Medicine in 1922 for discoveries about heat production by muscle. He put the boot in. After initially supporting the work, Hill then did a U-turn, calculating that the rate of diffusion of calcium from the outer edges of the cell to the contractile machinery deep within the cell would be too slow to account for the fast contraction in a real muscle. As Dr Marian LeFevre, another of Heilbrunn's students, remarked later, 'In those days, whatever A.V. Hill said was instant law.'

But Hill was wrong. In 1951 Marsh discovered a tubular system in muscle cells which was soon shown by others to be the inner calcium store Heilbrunn needed. When the electrical signal in the membrane moves down the fibre at breakneck speed, this causes release of the calcium store inside the cell very close to the contractile apparatus. When the electrical signal has passed, and the muscle has contracted, the calcium is pumped back into the inner store using energy from ATP, ready for the next signal to rubicon. So Hill's estimate of slow diffusion from calcium at the surface was irrelevant. Ironically, had Heilbrunn but known it, the miraculous inner membranous system had been observed many years before.

Emilio Verati, working in the lab of Camillo Golgi, had noticed in muscle cells viewed under the light microscope an elaborate network of fibres surrounding the contractile units inside the cell. Not being able to provide a function for them, his observations were submerged in the studies of his boss and the network of membranes in the cell which now bears his name, the Golgi apparatus. Not until 1955 did the electron microscope, in the hands of Stanley Bennet and Keith Porter, also a committed Woods Hole man, reveal the ultrastructure of this inner room of the cell house. Now we know that every cell has such a compartment, and they all contain calcium which can be released to cause a cell to cross the Rubicon.

Important as the removal of this stumbling block was to Heilbrunn's hypothesis, there were two other reasons why his vision was not realised in his lifetime. First, Pollack's experiments gave no clue as to how incredibly low the concentration of free calcium in a healthy cell would actually turn out to be. Secondly, where did the energy come from? There was no way that there was enough energy in such small amounts of calcium to provide for a muscle to contract. There was no mechanism by which calcium could trigger contraction. The proteins, actin and myosin, in muscle cells which slide over each other to cause the movement of the cell were only being isolated in the 1940s. The idea of chemical switches was not understood then. The special proteins, which selectively bind calcium to transmit the calcium signal into a cell event, were not discovered until the 1960s. Even as late as this there was still much scepticism about the calcium story. But Heilbrunn did his case no good at all by emphasising the importance of the 'mysterious protoplasm'. There is a warning here for Rubicon enthusiasts. The lack of a reductionist mechanism should not have allowed the scientists of the day to reject Heilbrunn's principle, which was based on sound experiment and observation.

Heilbrunn realised that many calcium salts, both inorganic and organic, often formed precipitates. He also knew from the experiments of Ringer and the others that calcium was required to maintain cell adhesion in tissues, to maintain the relative impermeability of the outer membrane of cells to ions, solutes and large molecules such as proteins, and to maintain surface charge and electrical excitability. Removal, or lack, of calcium 'is usually highly injurious to living systems'. Remarkably, as early as 1937 Heilbrunn and another student, Karl Wilbur, predicted that calcium was the trigger for nuclear breakdown following fertilisation or parthenogenetic stimulation of an egg from the ragworm *Nereis*. Equally amazing, in view of the current interest in – nay, obsession with – stores of calcium inside cells, were Heilbrunn's experiments in the 1930s with eggs of the common sea-urchin in the US, *Arbacia*. Heilbrunn was intrigued by the apparent similarity between the blood-clotting reaction and the 'surface precipitation reaction' he observed in many cells, particularly when exposed to calcium.

Collect a few millilitres of blood in a glass tube, tilt it to and fro, and within a few minutes a clot will have formed. A simple scheme to explain this was put forward by Morawitz in 1903, a key protein in the reaction being thrombin. It was this, Heilbrunn knew, that required calcium. For many years it had been known that removal of blood calcium by citrate, first isolated from lemon juice by Scheele in 1784, would stop the clot forming. If you add citrate to fresh blood it will not clot unless you add back calcium. Calcium salts are the only naturally occurring ones that will do this. When you go to the doctor for a blood sample to be taken, the tube into which the blood is collected will contain a chemical to bind the calcium if the lab needs unclotted blood for a cell count, as it usually does. Furthermore Kühne, in 1864, had shown that muscle plasma, like blood plasma, could be clotted by thrombin.

But from all this fascinating history there is an important principle to be learnt about calcium as a signal. To understand this I have to give you a little more detail about how a blood clot forms – a rubicon outside cells.

Let us remind ourselves of a real natural situation where a blood clot forms, when the little girl fell over at the start of Chapter Two. She grazed her knee but the cut soon stopped bleeding. However, it was not calcium in the blood that signalled the clot to occur; nor do we believe that small changes in calcium in the blood affect the rate or extent of the clot. Calcium is an absolute requirement for the rubicon to be crossed, but it is not the trigger taking the blood across. The trigger is the protein called thrombin. Thrombin itself is not present in normal blood but is formed by clipping its precursor, prothrombin, as a result of damaged tissue. This sets in motion a rubicon cascade outside cells, involving clipping bits off several blood proteins, including prothrombin and involving one called 'Christmas factor'. The result is a local cluster of molecules from the protein fibrin. This is the main protein in the clot, and is formed by clipping off a bit from its precursor fibrinogen, which is found in blood. It is this clipping reaction which is provoked by thrombin. The fibrin molecules mesh together, like the gelatin in the jelly we made at the beginning of the chapter, and form a solid clot. What is not so clear is the critical amount of fibrin necessary for the clot rubicon to be crossed. Is it two, twenty, or twenty million? More of numbers later.

So the principle is that, if a molecule is to be the signal for a rubicon to be crossed it must undergo a substantial change in quantity at the target site. It is *changes* in calcium inside the cell that enable it to act as a trigger. How better to test this than to inject some into the cell? This is precisely what Heilbrunn did with Floyd Wiercinski in 1947. But how big do these changes have to be to make a leg move, or for an arm to lift something? It was when this was discovered that the key to the signalling role of calcium was unlocked. It turned out that there was an enormous gradient of calcium across the membrane of all living cells.

But hold on a minute! I said just now, when describing the experiments of Wiercinski and Heilbrunn, that *tiny* amounts of injected calcium did the trick. Let me explain.

I mentioned earlier that the amount of free calcium in the blood is about the same as that in hard water. But inside the cell things are very different. The water is as soft as the softest water you can imagine. Virtually all the calcium inside the cell is stored within cupboards, ready to be used when asked for. Inside the cell there are at least three cupboards for storing calcium. The result is that there is a ten-thousandfold gradient across the outer membrane of the cell. Imagine dropping a small coin off the top of a mountain 10,000 metres high. Because of air resistance the coin will reach a set velocity, probably a hundred miles an hour or so. But now imagine dropping it the same distance down a tube which has no air in it, in other words in a vacuum, in which there will be no air resistance. This time the speed of the coin will be much faster. When it hits something, even such a small object will have quite an effect. So with calcium.

Take an electrical example. The voltage of the mains in houses is about 200 volts. If it were 10,000 volts it would be lethal. Yet when a plastic comb run through your hair generates static electricity the voltage can be very high. As with calcium, the absolute amount of electrical charge on the comb is tiny; yet it is powerful enough to cause dry hair to stand on end.

A small absolute movement of calcium, as the result of a small increase in the permeability of the outer membrane of the cell or release from the internal cupboard, will cause a rapid, large fractional increase inside the cell, even though the absolute increase will be small. If you had a box full of apples on one side and one virtually empty on the other, what would be the effect of moving, say, one per cent from the full one to the empty one? If you started with a 100-apple box, only one would move. But if you started with a 10,000-apple box, a hundred would move – enough to fill one of the small boxes. The free calcium in the cell can increase 100 times and yet the increase in the total calcium of the cell will be less that 0.5 per cent. This is impossible for sodium and potassium. Even 50 per cent increases or decreases in these would have disastrous consequences for the cell.

The first clue that such a large gradient of calcium existed across the outer membrane of cells came once again from experiments with a marine animal. Hodgkin and Keynes at Plymouth used the giant nerve fibre of the squid *Loligo*, collectable in sufficient numbers only at particular times of the year. They found that calcium moved much more slowly through the cell than sodium or potassium. Therefore they predicted that there must be stores of calcium collecting it as it tried to diffuse through the cell. They were then able to estimate an upper limit for the free calcium in the cell. This was less than ten thousandths the concentration of potassium in the cell. We shall see, when we 'View the Rubicon' in Chapter Seven, that there are now methods for measuring this calcium accurately, and for watching it change in a single cell. This was first achieved using the chemical reaction that produces light in a luminous jelly-fish, and showed that the free calcium in a cell is even lower than Hodgkin and Keynes first thought. It is in fact about a millionth that of potassium!

So a change in free calcium acts as a chemical switch inside all muscle cells telling them to contract. It tells secretory cells to secrete – for example, to release transmitters from nerve terminals, insulin into the blood from one type of cell in the pancreas, or digestive enzymes into the gut. Calcium is the signal which tells the protozoan *Paramecium* we found in the pond in the last chapter to reverse its beating cilia when it bumps into something. It is the trigger telling a luminous jelly-fish to flash or a shrimp to secrete a luminous cloud. And calcium is also important in cell defence. It is a trigger for bleach production (Figure 7; Plates 5(b) and 11) and for transforming antibody-generating cells. It signals a defence of cells against attack by pore-forming proteins. An increase in intracellular calcium activates metabolism in many cells, including glucose production in the liver, fatty acid released from white fat and internal glucose production in exercising muscle.

Calcium is a universal signal, instructing cells to cross the Rubicon. It is used by all animal cells, some plant cells, and occasionally in bacteria. But calcium is not the only way cells can switch their traffic-lights to green. Furthermore, as Heilbrunn realised, too much calcium inside cells is not only harmful but can be lethal. So we must distinguish when calcium is friend or foe.

There are plenty of mini-rubicons in the calcium story. The internal

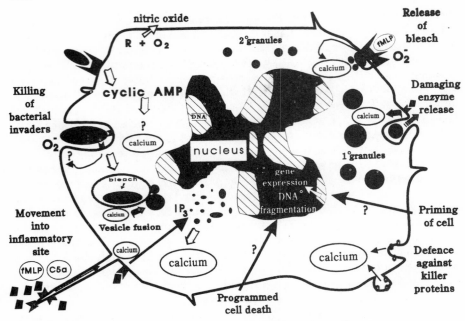

Fig. 7. Calcium-signalling rubicons in a bleach-producing cell.

store release is quantal, and localised. In some cells waves of calcium and oscillations are set up (Plate 5(b)). There are channels of communication between cells in a tissue like the liver. The instruction to release the calcium switch can thus be transmitted from cell to cell. These channels of communication are called gap junctions. But if the calcium close to this communication channel gets too high it switches it off.

Literally hundreds of scientists over the past century have contributed significantly to establishing calcium as a universal regulator instructing cells to cross the Rubicon. This is one reason why no one has yet been awarded the Nobel prize for calcium, though several prizes have been awarded for other aspects of the traffic-lights system. Heilbrunn would no doubt be excited to learn how important calcium inside cells has become in cell biology. Work continues in earnest. Heilbrunn has a special place in the century of calcium that has passed since Ringer's original experiments removing calcium from outside cells.

The words of Otto Loewi, a calcium pioneer, in 1959, strike a chord in all us calcium freaks: 'Ja, calcium, das ist alles.' But calcium is not *everything*. There are other signals, and mini-rubicons making them work.

The gang of three

There are two other classes of small molecular signal used inside cells. The first is made from our old friend ATP, or compounds related to ATP, the second from chemicals in the membranes of cells. Like calcium, they are all present in tiny, catalytic amounts – about the same as calcium, in fact.

The one formed from ATP is called cyclic AMP, and is found in cells at about 1,000-10,000 times lower amounts than ATP. So not too much energy is needed to make it. As I mentioned in Chapter One, it was discovered in 1956 by Earl Wilbur Sutherland (1915-1974) as a heat-stable factor from liver capable of stimulating breakdown of the sugar store in animal cells. This is called glycogen and is similar to starch in plant cells. Sutherland received the Nobel prize for Physiology or Medicine in 1971 for this discovery, for cyclic AMP turned out, like calcium, to be another universal signal. It is even used by bacteria to combat starvation. And there is another related compound called cyclic GMP, made thi time from GTP. This signal is important in controlling the contraction of the smooth muscle cells which line our blood vessels, and in signalling a rubicon in the cells of the eye when light hits them.

The other class of intracellular chemical switches comes from fats, in the membrane of cells. Its discovery can be traced back to the 1950s. But some of the key experiments which identified the first true signal were initiated by Michael Berridge and Bob Michel in the mid-late 1970s, and led to the identification of a compound called IP3 around 1983. This was the missing link in the calcium story.

The problem was how calcium could be released from an internal cupboard without there being a primary messenger opening the door. There had to be something generated at the inner surface by a hormone, which then moved to the calcium cupboard, releasing it into the open spaces of the cell. IP3 was this messenger, though we now know that there are several other ways to open the calcium cupboard. IP3 is formed from a fat in the membrane which consists of two parts: IP3 which is soluble in water, and the fatty bit, called diacyl glycerol, or DAG for short. DAG also can act as internal signal. So the splitting of the DAG-IP3 into its two halves generates two messages which move off to find their respective addresses. The key experiment carried out by Berridge and colleagues in 1983 was to show that addition of IP3 to the calcium cupboard did indeed cause it to open and release its calcium.

The principle of the traffic-light system inside a cell, therefore, is that in order to switch it from red to green a messenger is generated inside the cell. This messenger then finds its target and the next rubicon is crossed. The rubicon sequence is completed when the instructions received from the messenger have been read, understood and acted upon. The rubicon of movement, release, change of state, replication or death is crossed.

'Two's company, three's a crowd' may also be the case. These messengers sometimes work together, in harmony. But at other times, when all three get involved, they can antagonise each other. The strongest wins. As a result the crossing of a rubicon may be prevented.

Until the mid 1980s the gang of three was thought to contain all the primary messengers setting rubicon cascades in motion. But when the way growth factors work began to be studied in detail their effects on gene expression in the nucleus could not be explained by the release of a simple chemical signal such as IP3, cyclic AMP or calcium. It turned out that in this case the messenger was a protein. The protein was switched on and given its instructions directly at the inner surface of the cell. The chemical process involves sticking a phosphate on to the protein – crucial to taking the cell across the Rubicon.

THE WAY ACROSS

How signals work

In 1956 two biochemists, Fischer and Krebs, working in the United States, published a paper showing that phosphate could be attached to proteins inside cells. For this discovery they were recently awarded the Nobel prize for Physiology or Medicine. We now know that the phosphate is attached to one of three amino-acids: serine, threonine or tyrosine. Their discovery heralded a new era in intracellular signalling. The modification of proteins is the way the cell moves off when the traffic-lights switch to green, whether triggered by calcium, cyclic AMP or DAG. In the last thirty-five years some 130 modifications to proteins have been discovered. How phosphate is added to a protein is the one most thoroughly studied. The importance of putting phosphate onto proteins can be seen by examining the molecular basis of diarrhoea.

Between 1976 and 1982 more than a thousand people in Japan had to be treated for gastroenteritis after eating boiled mussels, scallops and clams which were contaminated. As we saw with cholera in Chapter One and food-poisoning in the last chapter, this pathological gut rubicon does not necessarily need the live organism. The toxin is the dangerous agent. If the food contains enough of it, and it is not destroyed during the cooking, the unsuspecting eater will suffer a nasty rubicon passage.

The toxin okadaic acid was first isolated as a polyether fatty acid from the marine sponges *Halichondria okadaii* and *Halichondria melanodacia* (the former gives it its name). The importance of this compound was established when it, or related substances, were found to be the active ingredient produced by the culprits of shellfish food-poisoning. The Japanese outbreaks, and the many of those seen in countries as far apart as Mexico, Scandinavia and Spain, were caused by a single-celled marine organism called a dinoflagellate. This is a planktonic animal. One type is the cause of luminescence in the sea on a summer's night. These are safe, but many others produce nasty toxins. The dangerous ones in the present story are from the genus *Dinophysis*. The shellfish are filter-feeders. They suck in sea water, remove goodies and spew out the waste from a siphon. Unfortunately they also retain the dinoflagellates.

Cholera toxin induces the formation of cyclic AMP in gut cells, which then catalyses the adding of phosphate to key proteins in the cells. Okadaic acid, on the other hand, blocks the enzyme which normally removes this phosphate after eating is over. The result is that the proteins in the gut cells responsible for controlling fluid in the gut remain hyperactive. Pain and diarrhoea ensue. But we still don't know how to translate the reductionist information which has identified the targets in the gut cells into a painful and messy rubicon.

There are many other, more pleasant, examples where controlled protein modification of this sort is the next step in a rubicon sequence after generation of the initial internal signal. These include smooth muscle contraction in the arteries, cell division, growth and differentiation, and priming of the immune system, to name but a few.

Let's move on to the banks of the last rubicon in the sequence — the crucial one in fact: the crossing where the event actually happens. Here a matrix of chemicals generates the end-response.

A chemical consummation

Wales is separated from England by the river Severn, which forms an estuary with one of the biggest tidal falls in the world. Once or twice a year a tidal rubicon occurs whereby a wall of water forms called a *bore*, which moves up river at two or three times the speed of the tidal current, a delight for water sports enthusiasts. At low tide examination of the exposed rocks reveals small holes. Tap the rock at night and these holes reveal a spectacular starlight display as the piddocks inside squirt out a luminous secretion, presumably to detract predators. These molluscs (Plate 6) live all their lives in the hole they make for themselves. *Pholas dactylus*, to give the common piddock its scientific name, can be found all along the south coast of the United Kingdom, from Plymouth to Beachy Head, and on the coast of France. It also occurs in the Mediterranean. Though apparently rarer than it was, it used to be found as a delicacy in fish markets. Its demise in certain areas may have been misinterpreted, for most piddocks are in rock never exposed at low water. This water is often turbid with particles, and no use for scuba diving.

The Roman investigator Pliny the Elder (AD 23-79) described the luminous piddock in his *Natural History* (IX.87.184). The *Natural History* became a classic in the monasteries of the Middle Ages and was translated into English in 1601 by Philemon Holland. It is divided into 37 'books' and deals with man, mammals, fishes and other marine species, birds, insects, plants, medicine and drugs, as well as cosmology, geography, ethnology, minerals, and art and architecture. To us much of it is 'unscientific'. Nevertheless it is a remarkable work, produced centuries before natural history and biology became a true science. The common piddock first described here was to play a key role in unravelling the chemical consummation responsible for flashes and glows in luminous animals some 1,800 years later.

This chemical consummation was first unravelled by Raphael Dubois, a French physiologist working at Lyons. Dubois carried out some elegant experiments first on a luminous click beetle, *Pyrophorus*, and then on *Pholas*, which he published in 1885 and 1887. He took one luminous gland and ground it up in cold water, observing a glow which disappeared within a few seconds or minutes. Then he ground another gland, or the other one of the pair in *Pholas*, in hot water. After a brief flash, darkness. But when he added this latter extract, now cooled, to the cold water extract in the dark he saw a glow. He therefore predicted that there must be two components required to produce light. Of the one extracted first in hot water he wrote: 'Elle est soluble dans l'eau, peu soluble dans l'alcool, soluble dans la benzine, dans l'essence de pétrole et l'éther.' He called this *luciférine*. The other was 'un albuminoid actif, comme ceux que l'on désigne sous le nom de ferments solubles, diastases, zymases, etc'. In other words, what we now call an enzyme. He called this *luciférase*.

This generic nomenclature has remained ever since. The vital principle that Dubois established was that *all living light is chemical light*. But each group of animals has its own chemical reaction. We now know that all luciferases, the catalysts for bioluminescent reactions, are proteins. Each species has a unique luciferase, though there are close similarities between related species. Each group of luminous organisms has a different luciferin. In other words, take the luciferin from the luminous beetles or a luminous jelly-fish and they won't work with the luciferase from the piddock. No light. Yet there are quite unrelated animals which use the same luciferin. The midshipman fish on the West coast of the USA is only luminous if it eats luminous crustaceans called ostracods. These supply the luciferin the fish needs to make light. This chemistry and that in the luminous jelly-fish is found in seven distinct phyla, the commonest chemistry responsible for living light in the sea. Quite a problem for Darwinian evolutionists to explain, as Darwin himself pointed out. Dubois had identified a chemical consummation causing a rubicon. The cells in the piddock signal the release, i.e. secretion, of the luciferin and luciferase from separate cells. They mix, and a visible glow is achieved to frighten a would-be predator.

Newton Harvey (Plate 7(b)) continued to extend Dubois's luciferin-luciferase concept in this century, and published some remarkable works of scholarship describing the history of the study of luminescence. But some didn't appear to conform. Osamu Shimomura realised that this was the case for extracts of luminous jelly-fish. He showed that the luciferin and luciferase are bound tightly together inside the cell. So what causes a jelly-fish or its relative the hydroid to flash? Calcium! Calcium enters the cell when the jelly-fish or hydroid is touched. When it hits the proteinaceous lantern complex it stimulates it to flash. Thousands of lamps consummate in synchrony so that there is enough light to see.

But there is still something missing. The piddock's luminous consummation will not occur in a vacuum, yet the jelly-fish's one will.

This had, in fact, been demonstrated some two centuries earlier by Robert Boyle (1626-1691) (Plate 7(a)). Boyle had developed an air pump, and could use it to evacuate a sealed jar. He put glowing wood, now known to be caused by the honey tuft fungus *Armillaria mellea*, into his bell-jar and evacuated it. This light went out. Re-emit the air and the light returned. Boyle observed the same thing with glowing flesh, which we now know to be caused by an infection of luminous bacteria. This was the first demonstration of oxygen requirement in bioluminescent reactions, some one hundred years before Priestley and Scheele discovered it. Boyle published a lovely paper in 1672, comparing and contrasting the properties of glowing wood with burning coal. In 1888 Eilhardt Wiedemann highlighted the fundamental difference between phenomena generating light because they are very hot and 'cold light' where the energy for light emission comes from the excitation of electrons. Although Wiedemann's paper was published six years before the discovery of the electron by J.J. Thompson, he used the word *luminescenz* to distinguish light from luminous animals and other non-incandescent sources from incandescence produced by very hot objects.

All living light requires oxygen. The reason why extracts of luminous jelly-fish can still flash is that oxygen is also tightly bound to the luciferin-luciferase complex. Unlike the haemoglobin in your blood cells, which would release all its oxygen in a vacuum, in the jelly-fish chemical lantern the oxygen is so tightly held it remains stuck – only to be released in a glorious consummation when triggered by calcium.

But all biological events require energy, in addition to the signal. So with living light. In 1947 William McElroy had been extracting ATP from various cells. The importance of ATP was already recognised in Europe, but in the USA it was young enthusiasts like McElroy who were keen to show their elders the true nature of energy supply inside cells. So when he became interested in the luminous fireflies, common in some parts of the US in the summer, McElroy naturally thought that the energy source must be ATP. It was already a puzzle that when you grind up a firefly, or its British relative the glow-worm, the extract is poorly luminous. McElroy had the inspiration to add the ATP he had carefully purified from rabbit muscle to the firefly extract. High drama. Masses of yellow light was seen.

But ironically ATP is not the true energy source. In fact one can calculate, using Einstein's equation, that ATP has less than a fifth of the energy required to make the light of the firefly. As we have already seen it is oxidation, 'burning without heat', that is the real source of energy for bioluminescence. The possibility still exists that control of ATP supply inside the cells of the firefly or glow-worm could be responsible for triggering the rubicon of the firefly flash or glow-worm glow. All components – luciferin, luciferase, oxygen and ATP – must be present for the consummation to be completed. It is a remarkable fact that in spite of nearly fifty years of test-tube investigations into the biochemistry of the firefly reaction we still don't know for sure how it flashes. This is as much a reflection on the attitude of the researchers as on the difficulty of the problem itself!

So in luminous organisms the components are kept in separate compartments, sometimes even in separate cells. To cross a luminous rubicon the components have to mix. In luminous dinoflagellates in a warm summer's sea the luciferin is kept away from the luciferase, being released by an acid signal when the cell is touched. But this mixing principle is not restricted to luminescence. Signals, whether outside or inside the cell, and the components of the event have to reach their own targets.

Out of water

Precipitation is a rubicon essential for formation of the hard structures of animals, and some plants. If this rubicon had not evolved we would not be here, or be able to enjoy many of the wondrous elegant shapes of Nature (Figure 1).

Calcium phosphate and carbonate come out of water to form bones, teeth and the shells of sea-urchins, clams, limpets and winkles. A little ball of solid calcium sulphate forms the balance mechanism enabling jelly-fish to sense whether they are the right way up. And calcium precipitates can occur both inside and outside cells in several diseases: stones of calcium oxalate in the kidneys, or minute calcium phosphate stones in mitochondria of cells swamped by calcium. And of course there are gallstones, full of cholesterol and other insoluble substances precipitating from bile.

One compound of silicon, silicon dioxide – sand – has been of immense importance to man. But silicon is not used by our body, except when showering it with talc (magnesium silicate)! However, silicate precipitates form in vast numbers in many small animals and plants, including the beautifully-shaped foraminiferans, radiolaria and diatoms. And there are other elements which occasionally precipitate: iron oxide in magnetic bacteria, lead and zinc sulphides, manganese dioxide.

To form a precipitate a 'nucleus' of protein is required. It is interesting that the calcium in our blood is high enough to precipitate the phosphate also present. Fortunately, however, it can remain super-saturated, until the conditions are changed to allow the precipitate to form.

Phase change

So far we have seen two examples of phase changes causing a cell to cross the rubicon: jellification and precipitation. But there is a third.

Take a bottle of meths and pour it into a jug half full of water. The two liquids mix together quite happily. Now, instead of the meths, pour in a bottle of cooking oil. Of course, these don't mix. They form two phases, the oil floating on top of the water. This also happens inside a cell when fat droplets form, or when bits of membrane are shed either into the heart of a cell or to the outside. Remember, the membrane of a cell is made of liquid fat with proteins floating in it. Sometimes these proteins are moved to one area of the membrane. They form a cap, or cluster. Such a group of proteins is far more powerful than each on its own. Only as a cluster can they take the cell across a threshold.

Channels

Not only are there proteins floating in membranes, but some actually go right through it. As a result they can transport molecules from one side to the other. There are pumps throwing sodium and calcium out of the cell, and carriers to take sugars and amino-acids into the cell from outside. But some of these transporters can cross the rubicon. These are the ion channels which are either open or closed. Like tiny selective lock gates, they open and only let particular traffic through: one for calcium, another for sodium, and so on. But what signals them to open?

One type of channel is opened by an electrical signal, another by a chemical signal. At the end of a nerve, when the electrical impulse arrives it causes channels to open which let calcium into the cell. Enough gets in to trigger the release of the transmitter. When this transmitter meets its receptors on the other side – for example, on a muscle cell – it opens another set of channels, in this case for sodium. If the number of channels open is great enough, and fast enough, they combine to generate an action potential which is then able to travel down the muscle cell and signal it to contract. This involves yet another set of channels. For the calcium is let out of the inner cupboard in a controlled manner, by the opening of channels on its surface.

There are several hormones and neuro-transmitters capable of opening channels. And one of the gang of three inside the cell will also do this. IP3 has a receptor on the calcium cupboard which opens the door, so that only calcium comes out. There are even channels inside cells which are opened by calcium itself, providing a self-amplification mechanism for Rubicon. Once again the clustering of channels and the receptors which open them provide a molecular mechanism for inducing the rubicon signal at a particular moment, in the right region of the cell.

Reaching the target

Hormones are released into the blood. When a critical concentration is achieved at the target site, sometimes half way round the body sometimes very close by, one or more of the target cells will fire. The target for a neurotransmitter is within a few millionths of a metre of the nerve ending which released it. Yet if the rate of arrival at the target is too slow the next nerve or muscle will not fire. For the nerve ending itself to fire, an electrical signal, the action potential, had to get there after being initiated at the other end of the nerve. So also inside cells. Signals released at one place in the cell have to move and find their target.

A beautiful example of this was demonstrated in 1978 by a group of American biologists, led by Lionel Jaffe, using an image-intensifier to watch the movement of the signal in the cell.

They first took a single egg from the Medaka fish and injected it with the light-emitting protein we met just now, extracted from a luminous jelly-fish. They then allowed a sperm to wiggle its way to the egg. When it united, they saw to their great excitement, a wave of light moving down the egg. These eggs are quite big, a millimetre or so across. The light wave, reflecting a calcium wave equivalent to more than a hundred-fold increase at the peak of the wave, took about two minutes to traverse the egg. As the wave passed, it was followed rapidly by events associated with the fertilisation reaction, including an explosive secretion from granules close to the inner surface inside the egg.

Oscillations in signals inside cells can also occur, to maintain the cell activated. Otherwise the signal would be lost outside the cell, and the cell would slip back across the rubicon and stop firing. In the liver, for example, oscillations in calcium seem to play an important role in keeping the signal going so that the cell continues to make glucose.

Thus the timing of a rubicon sequence is critically dependent on how long it takes for each signal to reach its target. Calcium takes time to move across a cell, even a small one. Sometimes the signal has to be moved from one compartment of the cell to another. For example, calcium and the proteins which put phosphate groups onto target proteins have to get into the nucleus if they are to signal gene expression or cell division.

Signalling death

Programmed cell death can be signalled by hormones, or in development and in ageing by an internal clock. For the tadpole tail it is thyroid hormone, for cells of the immune system steroids, in plants indole acetic and abscissic acids. Here the key to starting the rubicon death-sequence is the generation of a signal in the nucleus. Sometimes this may be calcium again, but there is still much to understand about such rubicon sequences.

But for cells killed by mortar bombs it is the arrival of sufficient *toxin* that signals the death sequence. These include pore-forming proteins from our own lymphocytes and from the system in the blood called complement I have discussed already, as well as certain bacterial toxins and some viral proteins. But there is a pathway of molecular rubicons enabling cells to defend themselves against this attack (Figure 6). First, there is a barbed-wire barricade on the outer surface of cells to ensnare attackers. But if the attacking proteins succeed in getting through this barrier there is a second line of defence within the cell which then gets brought into action. The first rubicon inside the cell is a rise in calcium, as a result of the protein rockets breaking through the outer defences. This, at first anyway, is both friend and foe. It activates inappropriately the traffic-lights in that cell. So it may start secreting bleach, for example, which will damage the surrounding environs – a particular problem in the rheumatoid joint.

But the calcium also instructs the inner defence staff to get moving. The dangerous mortar bomb components which have penetrated into the membrane must be inactivated quickly and then removed, either by engulfing them or by shedding them off. Unfortunately, as with all centralised facilities, the organisation doesn't work fast enough, and the next two damaging rubicons ensue. A second, more damaging penetration of the cell membrane occurs, and things start to leak out of the hole that has been formed. But still the defence staff work, in earnest. There is still time before the bomb explodes. Too late. Bang!! There was another bomb on the other side of the cell ticking away. The cell failed to remove it, so the ultimate rubicon was crossed.

All the rubicons, between the initial attack and the final disaster, require movement of molecules within the membrane and the inner compartments of the cell to a defined target.

The killing of cells by bleach also involves making holes in the outer membrane of cells. The bleach burns proteins, sugars and fats on the cell surface. As a result, the cell becomes leaky and may explode. It is not clear whether the cell also has a defence against this. It certainly has a firefighting department. In the membrane there are chemicals which can quench the bleach. It would be surprising therefore if there weren't also staff to remove burnt proteins. In the nucleus there is a DNA hospital. For oxygen damage can occur here as well, as a result of an internal fire without smoke. Like the bleach outside the cell, the oxygen derivatives burn holes in the DNA. It starts to fragment, and when it replicates mistakes are made. The sibling cells may thus turn into a cancer. But the DNA surgeons can remove the bit of burnt DNA and replace it so that a full recovery can be achieved. But they need time. If the cell doesn't stop for a moment or two the DNA doctors just can't get their chemical scalpels into the wound!

The take-over of a cell by a virus can also set in motion a rubicon death-sequence. First the virus attaches to a receptor on the outer surface. This enables it to inject its DNA, or RNA if it is HIV, into the cell. A takeover rubicon is then crossed. The virus stops the cell from being able to do its own thing, and takes over the nucleic-acid – and protein – manufacturing plants for its own purposes. Once hundreds, or even thousands, of new viruses have formed inside the cell, the virus says: 'Thanks a lot', and dumps the lot outside, for it to float off and infect other unsuspecting cells. Unfortunately this final rubicon usually breaks the cell asunder.

Yet there are also viruses which can remain lurking inside the cell. I have already mentioned the ability of herpes, the cause of sores around the mouth, to remain dormant inside cells. The awakening, the rubicon, from latency appears to be triggered by certain growth factors, and requires the switching on of specific genes in sensory nerves. There is still much to learn about the signalling of death and latency in viruses.

And there are organelle rubicons. Vesicles move and fuse with the outer membrane to secrete hormone or neurotransmitter. The membrane coat surrounding the nucleus has to disappear just before a cell is about to divide. Also before cell division the Golgi apparatus, part of the machinery for protein-processing and export, has to fragment into many, many pieces. This enables each sibling cell to have its fair share. The calcium cupboard inside the cell either dumps its calcium, or it doesn't. It behaves in a rubicon manner too. And there are other intriguing possibilities. Does the power-house of the cell, the mitochondrion, rubicon? We need to find out whether the ATP needed to fuel cell rubicons is also made in a quantal manner. When the amount of ATP fuel being made doubles, has the cell recruited twice as many mitochondria? Rubicon predicts yes. This would certainly help to resolve some of the remaining controversies in the Mitchell hypothesis we met in Chapter One.

The rubicon sequence inside a cell can thus be broken down into four mini-rubicons:

1. The generation of the first intracellular signal.
2. The intracellular signal reaching its target, including penetration of the required organelle.
3. The concerted action of a molecular complex.
4. An organelle crossing a threshold.

At each stage molecular and organelle rubicons are necessary for a particular sequence to be followed. The primary signal hits the cell in sufficient quantity in the right time-interval to initiate the first rubicon. Throw a defined amount of transmitter at a muscle fibre and it will contract. Take a second muscle fibre and expose it to the same amount of stimulus, but now allow it to diffuse slowly to the muscle. This time the muscle will not necessarily contract. Timing is as important to rubicon as is the amount of signal. So in the cell, the intracellular signal, e.g. calcium, has to move and reach its target. There it binds to proteins, and when the appropriate level of binding has occurred the next rubicon is crossed. An organelle starts to move, a fibre contracts, the jelly of the cytoplasm turns into a free-flowing liquid, a vesicle fuses with another or the outer membrane of the cell to release its contents.

There are still many examples of Rubicon where we don't know the precise mechanism, but, as Heilbrunn pointed out, 'It is far better to acquaint students with the uncertainties of knowledge in such a frontier subject as general physiology, and to make them sceptical of new experiments. If there were more teaching of this sort our laymen and physicians might not be so gullible in accepting false discoveries.'

Let us therefore conclude this chapter by examining a feature of living systems which is often overlooked: the smallness of living units. It is this which not only holds the key to crossing the Rubicon, but also often obscures its very existence, because onlookers cannot believe that such small changes could do anything.

SMALL IS BEAUTIFUL

There are about one hundred million, million cells in the human body, and yet only a few thousand or fewer in a tiny worm or hydroid. How many cells does it take to make an organism? How many molecules are required to make a cell? How many calcium ions are needed to switch a cell from red to green?

In 1973 E.F. Schumacher published his now famous book *Small is Beautiful: A Study of Economics as if People Mattered*. We musn't get too anthropomorphic, but the point of this section is to re-emphasise that individual, tiny cells matter. Tissues are made up of cells, each with its own individuality, each at a different stage of development, and having been exposed to different environments: oxygen, nutrients, stimuli, pathogens and the like. But I have cited Schumacher's title for two other reasons.

First, because of the following question with which he concludes Part I: 'Are there not indeed enough "signs of the times" to indicate that a new start is needed?' Secondly, in section V of Part I he deals with 'The question of size'. I don't want to push the analogy with economics too far, but it does raise the central question for Rubicon, 'What scale is appropriate?' What, for instance, is the appropriate size of a cell or organelle? Does it matter?

I believe it does.

In the pancreas one islet of Langerhans is 0.2-0.4mm in diameter and contains about 4,000 cells. Seventy per cent of these are insulin-secreting B cells. The rest are cells secreting other hormones – A cells producing glucagon and D cells secreting somatostatin and pancreatic polypeptide. The B cells illustrate Rubicon nicely, as the amount of insulin released is proportional not only to the number of B cells switched on but also to the number of islets switched on. The cells in each islet can work in synchrony to release insulin together. This is fundamental to an understanding of the reduced capacity of the body to handle sugar in diabetics, highlighted by the clinical test – glucose tolerance.

Insulin is a key hormone instructing muscle and fat cells to take up glucose. When insulin is deficient the glucose in the blood stays high for longer than in a healthy person. In type II diabetics, unlike type I, the B cells are still intact. It has been proposed that in type II diabetes a reduced ability to secrete insulin after eating sugar may have its origin in poor nutrition in the womb, i.e. initiation of the rubicon sequence began in the foetus, the final sickness rubicon being crossed decades after birth. The key question for Rubicon is: Is a changed release or action of insulin in response to glucose in a diabetic the result of a changed amount of insulin within the pancreas or a defect in the traffic-lights system resulting in a different number of cells being switched on, either in the pancreas or elsewhere?

The size of cells is just right for signals to reach their targets at the right time. But, more significant, the laws of conventional thermodynamics break down because of the smallness of it all. Physical biochemists have long accepted that they must use non-equilibrium thermodynamics. But what they have rarely grasped is that they still regard biochemical systems as a giant soup. If one is to use mathematics to analyse a biological process, it is essential that the unit being analysed be identified. Hawking's marriage of thermodynamics and quantum theory may be a universal theory, but when applied to a real phenomenon we look at one black hole at a time, not at a blend of all the black holes in the Universe which are at different stages of development. So with a cell and its intracellular structures! A liver cell has 1,000-2,000 mitochondria, but biochemists never consider them as individuals. They must. Rubicon demands it. So let's look at a few numbers to get it into perspective. How many cells? How many granules? How many molecules? This will throw up some surprises, I hope!

But first I must explain one technicality in chemistry, the concept of the mole – or mol for short. John Dalton (1766-1844) was the son of a Quaker weaver in Cumberland. Of his many contributions to science it is the law which determines the amounts of chemical which react with each other that he is particularly associated with. He devised a system of chemical symbols, the development of which we still use today. By careful measurement he was able to determine the relative weights of atoms, and he discovered that when chemicals combine in a reaction the proportions that react do so always in a simple ratio based on these weights. Thus the concept of atomic and molecular weight was born. In recognition of his work we describe the weights of molecules in Daltons, Da for short. A protein such as the light catalyst in the firefly has a weight of 62,000 Da.

Consider, then, the simple reaction of oxygen and hydrogen reacting to form water. Using chemical symbols to represent these, the reaction is described thus, as you will know:

$$2H_2 + O_2 \rightarrow 2H_2O$$

The molecular weight of hydrogen is 2, and of oxygen 32, so from Dalton's theory we know for sure that four grammes of hydrogen will always react with 32 grammes of oxygen to form 36 grammes of water. If you relate this to the equation above, it will perhaps be obvious that the molecular weight of any substance in grammes will always contain the same number of molecules, whatever the substance. In 1811 Amedeo Avogadro (1776-1856), a professor of higher physics at the University of Turin proposed this law, first for gases, though it wasn't accepted generally until 1858, thanks to the Italian chemist Stanislao Cannizzaro (1826-1910). The number of atoms in a gramme-atom or molecules in a gramme-mole turned out to be huge: 600,000 million, million, million, written 6.023×10^{23}. It is now known as the Avogadro constant.

A glass of water containing 100 millilitres of liquid therefore contains about 3×10^{24} molecules. But the volume of a cell such as one of our bleach-producers is minuscule compared to a glass of water: in fact, about a million, million times less, written as 10^{-13} or 100 fempto-litres. This cell therefore contains only about 3 billion water molecules. But more significant is the number of calcium atoms needed to switch on the bleach production. You will have to take my word for the calculation, but it turns out that the release of just 10,000 or so calciums into the cell can induce the cell to produce perhaps 10 billion bleach molecules – an amplification of at least 100,000. Here we see the economy of Nature in action. Small is beautiful. A small number of molecules is needed to generate the chemical switch which will lead to an event several orders bigger than the switch itself. A similar calculation can be made about glucose release from the liver triggered by the chemical switch cyclic AMP in the cell.

The problem of dimensions

Is there enough time? Is there enough?

Some events take just a few thousandths of a second while other rubicons take months or years. And that isn't even thinking about ecology or evolution. A neutrophil is but seven millionths of a metre across. But a nerve in our body or muscle can have cells a metre or more in length. Try and get that into a microfuge tube. At school we used pipettes which enabled us to suck up tens of millilitres. But in the lab now we handle one microlitre or less. You can hardly see that. Try sucking that much up by mouth! But what do all these millis and micros mean?

For convenience, science uses units which go up and down in thousands. One thousand grammes is a kilo, one million a mega. But because of the smallness of the amounts in biological systems we have to go down, not up. There is little logic to the names, just smaller, smaller and smaller. A thousandth of something is milli-, a millionth micro-, a thousand millionths nano-, a million millionths pico-, a thousand million millionths fempto- and a million million millionths atto-. And that's it. That is as small as the conventional scientific units can go. However, when I began working with bioluminescence I realised pretty early on that, because I was measuring reactions generating just a few hundred photons at a time, I was below the attomol limit. So what about a new unit?

As you travel into Wales you will find the signposts in two languages, English and Welsh, or the other way around if you are in North Wales. We Welsh are rightly proud of the language. It is surely no coincidence that the two most musical languages in Europe, Italian and Welsh, have produced such fine singers. The Welsh are fed up with having English words contaminating their language as new terms develop. So what about putting a Welsh word into the English language. The Welsh for little is *tipyn*, so I suggested some years ago that a thousand million million millionths should be known affectionately as a tipomol. But hold on a minute – how many molecules in a tipomol? When you work it out it comes to 603. The next one down would of course be an impossomol! You can't find one impossomol but you could find ten.

But the smallness of these numbers has another consequence, crucial to Rubicon. We need to change our thermodynamics to describe the energetics of molecular reactions in the cell. Let me illustrate what I mean by reminding you of the crisis in the power-house, the mitochondrion, resolved by Mitchell.

Mitchell worked out an equation to show how much energy could be generated by an electrical and chemical gradient across the membrane of the mitochondria. It was enough to generate the inner fuel needed inside the cell, ATP. So far so good. This gradient involved the hydrogen ion, the ion responsible for acidity. To prove that mitochondria can make the environment acid you have to put billions of mitochondria into a test-tube for them to generate enough to measure. Conventional thermodynamics only works when the numbers are large like this. But in the cell each mitochondrion is an independent unit. When you calculate how many hydrogen ions, or calcium ions, are moving, or present free at any one time inside one mito it is only a handful. Perhaps only ten or twenty. There is a buffer to keep topping up the free hydrogen inside as it gets pumped out. But Rubicon insists that, if we are to understand how such units work in the cell, the smallness is vital to enable each to cross the rubicon. In a cell some mitos will be working flat-out while some will be idle. You can only decipher this by watching each one independently, and by using equations which consider a population in a test-tube as a mixture of independent, distinct thermodynamic units.

And the numbers on the cell surface are also small. A cell may have only a hundred, or as many as a million, receptors on its outer surface. Rubicon asks the question: 'How many have to be occupied to turn on the chemical switch?' In a bleach-producer you may need tens or even hundreds to be occupied before the cell switches on its bleach-production. The occupancy may also affect the timing. Those with large numbers occupied will switch on the chemical signal inside the cell fastest.

Similarly, at the junction between a nerve and a muscle cell Nature has seen to it that only a few thousand molecules of the transmitter are released very rapidly in a pulse, so that the rate of occupancy at the muscle end-plate is fast enough to switch on the electrics of the muscle cell. The electrical potential then moves down the cell, releasing calcium rapidly from the inner cupboard to trigger the contraction rubicon. What matters to the organism is whether the rubicon of a moving electrical signal is generated or not. Without it the muscle will not contract.

There are some other interesting aspects of numbers of molecules inside cells. If you add up all the As in the DNA in one cell you find that there are about 200 million. The concentration of ATP inside a cell is around five millimoles per litre. So in a bleach-producer there are also only about 200 million at any one time. So, although the bleach-producers can no longer divide, other cells can. These need to make a hell of a lot of As and quickly if they are to cross the rubicon and become two cells

It is my intention to use these numbers to generate a rubicon equation. Don't panic – that is the next book!

What matters for Rubicon is how the initial molecular and organelle rubicons lead to a threshold higher up in the rubicon taxa. The excitability of one oxyluciferin molecule doesn't make a firefly flash, but the switching on of one gene or the opening of one channel in the plasma membrane can be sufficient to start a sequence ending in a cell rubicon. As with cells, it is the timing, the synchrony, the position within the cell and the magnitude of a molecular or organelle rubicon that will determine if and when a biological rubicon is crossed. This is what we are really after, the explanation of real physiological events.

Life is a network of micro-environments from the unique solvent characteristics of the active centre of a particular enzyme up to the special physical, chemical and biological features which characterise a habitat in an ecosystem. We can therefore identify six levels of micro-environment:

1. The electrostatic field within a protein cleft.
2. The physical and chemical characteristics within an individual organelle.
3. The electrical potential and concentrations of ions and organics close to the surface of a biological membrane.
4. The chemistry of the *milieu intérior*, i.e. the fluid bathing the outside of cells.
5. The physical, chemical and biological parameters controlling life within an ecosystem.
6. Macro-forces affecting life on a global level.

These micro-environments are susceptible to their own rubicons. When is a catalyst a true catalyst interacting with the reactants, and when does a protein simply provide a special solvent in which the reactants are concentrated and interact?

Several mechanisms have evolved for amplifying small physical and chemical changes. These include so-called wasteful cycles, flux and accumulation, bacterial tumbling and cell wiggling, and catalytic cascades such as those initiated by calcium or cyclic AMP. In a typical catalytic cascade one molecule generates 100 which generate 10,000 and so on. An increase in temperature of a few degrees switches on genes which make the so-called heat-shock proteins. Some of these are needed to help other proteins get into the right shape, made more difficult at the higher temperature. Amplification is necessary for a rubicon to be crossed but it is not sufficient. For a physical or chemical event to occur a critical mass must arise in the right place at the right time.

So now we move from the very small to the very big, from rubicons which take milliseconds or seconds to cross to ones which take millions of years and have involved the largest land animals who have ever lived. The one unifying force in biology, and a topic which has stirred up more rubicons in the scientists who study it, the church and the general public than perhaps any other area of biology – evolution!

4

Four Thousand Million Years of Rubicons

A dozen or so miles from Big Ben can be found the house of Charles Darwin, the man who proved the Bible was wrong! Or did he? I will address this myth later, but for now I want to highlight how Rubicon can give us a clearer perspective on the biological process which is associated so much with Darwin's name – *evolution*. First, let me tell you about an incredible feat of genetic engineering which highlights an important characteristic of evolutionary rubicons.

THE MARSUPIAL POTATO

Marsupials are primitive mammals limited to Australasia, New Guinea and neighbouring countries, South and Central America, though some are found in North America. The particular feature found in most of them and for which they are best known is the pouch in which the prematurely-born foetus completes its development. The genes responsible for this process in kangaroos have recently been isolated. They have been transferred to a potato plant, which then produces beautiful little new potatoes from the many little pouches distributed over the surface of each large parent potato. Once the baby potato has been removed from its pouch a new one re-seeds itself in its place. The wonders of genetic engineering! Why could Nature not have evolved marsupial potatoes on the Earth by natural processes?

I'm only joking, of course, but I am also trying to make a serious point. The diversity of forms and actions which can be found in life on the Earth today is awesome. There are universalities in Nature, but the marsupial's pouch illustrates the fact that certain structures and processes can be unique to a particular group or species. Only their ancestors have crossed this evolutionary rubicon. It is remarkable that there are no animals which contain chlorophyll, and no plants which can move. There are no triffids to be found anywhere. Thus, although the forces of evolution can generate a remarkable diversity of species, once certain rubicons have been crossed the evolutionary path is set. The reptiles may be the ancestors of man and the other mammals – we had a common ancestor – but we do not expect modern reptiles to evolve into a new mammalian form in ten or a hundred million years time.

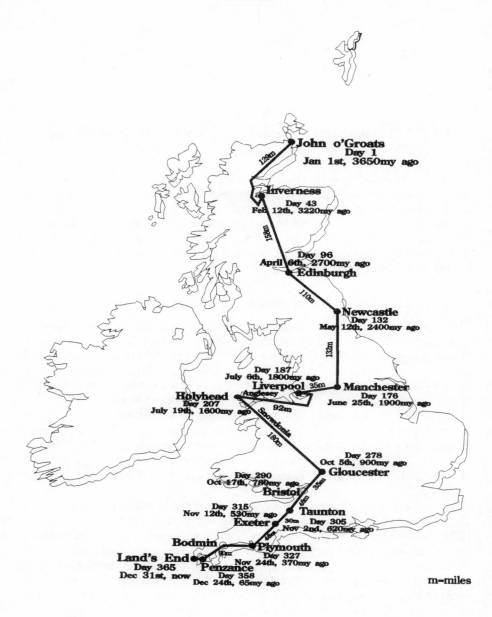

Fig. 8. From John o'Groats to Land's End: an evolutionary year (10 million years (my) a day).

Let me take you on an imaginary journey from one end of Great Britain to the other. It is going to last one year, but in reality it took 3,650 million years – ten million years of evolution for each day of the trip. The most direct route from John o'Groats to Land's End is some 870 miles, but the route I have chosen will be slightly longer, 1,092 miles to be exact (Figure 8) – or some three miles a day. This will enable us to detour to Ynys Môn, the Isle of Anglesey, where some of the oldest sedimentary rocks in the world can be found.

We are going to experience many surprising things, including several geographical and climatic rubicons. There will be major changes in temperature and climate, including tropical heat and ice ages, severe radiation from the sun before the ozone layer has built up and exposure to the Earth's inherent radioactivity, which has decayed considerably over 4,000 million years. The composition of the sea and atmosphere will change as time goes on. And the geography of the land will alter dramatically. Earthquakes, land upheavals and subsidences will mould the mountains. Glaciers will mould the valleys and there will be movement of the five tectonic plates. Two hundred million years ago there were six continents all huddled together round the equator. The movement of land via plate tectonics will convert this single land mass into the six continents, separated by thousands of miles in some cases, exposing the organisms stranded on them to quite different climates. There will be some major catastrophes, such as meteors from space hitting the earth, devastating much of the planet. Ice will freeze major parts of the land surface. More than 99 per cent of the organisms which have evolved are now extinct. So we will witness a lot of death, as well as new life. Some of these biological changes occur so rapidly and involve such a wide range of species that you will consider them to be 'mass extinctions'.

Keep a look out for other rubicons, the rubicons in the physical and chemical state of the atmosphere and the sea, as well as in the geography of the land mass. Some of these will have been caused by the biosphere, others will cause the biosphere to cross its own rubicons. It is these evolutionary rubicons on which I want now to focus.

FROM JOHN O'GROATS TO LAND'S END

We are standing in the middle of the most northerly town on the mainland of Britain, John o'Groats. Like many walkers before us, we are about to start on the journey from one end of our island to the other. We are on our way to Land's End. But unlike most walkers we are togged up in a space-suit. A little cumbersome maybe, but without it we would be dead, because the time is 3,650 million years ago. The earth is solid and the sea liquid, but the earth is still quite hot, with lots of volcanic activity. More significant to the human body is that the natural radioactivity is some four times more than it is today. And also there is no ozone layer, so the ultraviolet and other radiation from the sun is intense. But not quite as bad as it might be, because the sun's radiation is only a quarter of what it is today.

What's more the atmosphere is distinctly hostile. There is no oxygen. We have arrived just after the 'big belch', the leakage of gases as a result of thermal activity from within the earth's core which converted the weak atmosphere of just a little argon and other noble gases, water vapour, cyanide and formaldehyde to one containing methane, nitrogen, hydrogen, ammonia and water, in that order of prevalence, with a little hydrogen sulphide, carbon dioxide and carbon monoxide. In 1953 Harold C. Urey of the University of Chicago showed that, by bombarding such an atmosphere with lightning discharges for a week, the amino-acids alanine and glycine and other biological molecules could be generated. So as we leave John o'Groats the sea is nothing like as salty as it is today, and freshwater pools are full of the ingredients to enable life to form.

It is 129 miles to Inverness, mid-February on the banks of Loch Tay, too soon for the ospreys whistling over the rivers, grabbing fish. No birds, no fish, no Nessie even. We are still 900 miles, 3,000 million years, before the age of the dinosaurs. But on the way through northern Scotland we notice that the first rubicon of life has been crossed. We begin to find the first cells. Soon they are forming siliceous algal mats and fossilising as stroma-tolites. The atmosphere is changing rapidly. The hydrogen, being such a light gas, has mostly escaped into space, as have the other light gases, methane and ammonia. Two gases predominate: carbon dioxide, having leaked from inside the molten core and keeping the earth warm via the greenhouse effect, and nitrogen. The carbon dioxide is beginning to dis-solve in the oceans and rivers to form bicarbonate, leaching calcium and other minerals from the rocks. The oxygen content of the atmosphere is less than one per cent of that of today and the carbon dioxide perhaps sixty times as much, so we still need our space-suits!

The oldest true fossils are the cyanophytes – ancestors of the blue-green algae – the oldest coccoid ones found some 3,100-3,200 million years ago. The success of the pre-Cambrian cyanophytes was due to their ability to survive in low oxygen. The appearance of the first photosynthesis system enabled these primitive unicellular, prokaryotic 'plants' to use the energy from sunlight to reduce the atmospheric carbon dioxide to sugars and other nutrients, using hydrogen or organic substrates as reductants. This occurs in modern blue-green algae, or cyanobacteria, and sulphur photobacteria. Let's be on our way.

Day 150, the end of May, and just over 450 miles travelled. We are half way between Newcastle and Manchester. Here, some 1,800 million years ago, a molecular rubicon is crossed which is to alter for ever the evolution-ary potential of the biosphere. Photosynthesis system II appears in some of the blue-green algae. This enables them to use the energy from sunlight to split water into oxygen and reducing hydrogen equivalents through our old friend NADP. This means that, with photosystems I and II, these microbes can both reduce carbon dioxide to sugar and oxidise water to molecular oxygen. Both mean that sunlight makes ATP.

As a result, by the time we reach Manchester 1,900 million years ago, the atmosphere has changed dramatically. You might even risk taking off your space-suit for a while. The atmosphere has a composition similar to that of today. The carbon dioxide has been reduced by fixation into carbonate deposits through photosynthesis and chemical precipitation, and the oxygen has risen to some ten per cent of the modern level. But this causes a catastrophic rubicon. The first major holocaust.

To most primitive bacteria and algae oxygen is lethal, splitting DNA asunder, destroying proteins and the fats in the membranes by oxidising them. Until now life had survived for nearly 2,000 million years and was about to commit suicide. The waters are strewn with the scum of 'burnt' bacteria. But for the next remarkable series of biochemical rubicons, life might have destroyed itself. Fortunately, you find some bacteria which have survived. The reason? They have developed mechanisms for protecting themselves against oxygen damage: vitamin C, glutathione, superoxide dismutase to name but a few, and the first oxygen-binding pigments. Later, multicellular organisms will exploit these pigments to carry oxygen in the blood and to fit the generators into the power-houses inside the cell. Just outside Manchester, towards the end of June, you find the first calcareous blue-green algae. Another holocaust is on its way, this time 'precipitated' by calcium. The sea is littered with specks of chalk, the remnants of cells killed because they cannot protect themselves from calcium. All this happened just before you reached Liverpool, some 1,800 million years ago.

It is mid-July. Let's pop across to Anglesey and find some orchids and puffins. It is a bit too early for that yet, I'm afraid. But still a remarkable rubicon has been crossed. You find your first eukaryotic cell, and by Holyhead, 1,600 million years ago, it has been able to divide by mitosis and meiosis, i.e. chromosome separation. This means that the pairs of chromosomes in the primitive eukaryotic cells can divide to make four and then be partitioned into four cells, the gametes, each with a single copy of the DNA. Real sex can begin!

Wales has a distinguished place in the history of geology. Adam Sedgwick named the Cambrian period after the Roman name for Wales. But it is too early for Cambrian trilobites – 1,000 million years too soon. Still the passage through the Welsh mountains of Snowdonia to Gloucester is exhilarating. The diversity of unicellular eukaryotes is increasing million-year by million year. By the time you reach Bristol in mid-October, evolutionary spring rather than autumn is in the air. Eukaryotes can move by flagellate or amoeboid movement, and they can do many other things modern cells can do. They can secrete, divide, respond to light, metabolise, and die. But the Cambrian era has yet to dawn. There are still no multicellular organisms. No plants and no animals. What heralds the end of the pre-Cambrian era is the ability of some cells to transform, to differentiate. The metazoans, which you find in the embers of the pre-

Cambrian rocks near Taunton in late October, 600 million years ago, contain the first multicellular animals. These are not just conglomerates of cells, but clusters of cells with different shapes and functions, originating from one cell through mitosis followed by transformation.

Only two months, and less than two hundred miles, to go. The pace of life really begins to hot up now. At last, we have found the first fish and the first animals with a spine, i.e. chordates, though as yet uncalcified, near Taunton, 600 million years ago. It is early November, and between Taunton and Exeter the diversification of animals and plants is staggering. First land plants, then jawed fish, amphibians, trilobites, and proper trees and ferns. In late November just outside the late Peter Mitchell's Institute in Bodmin, Cornwall we come across a mass extinction, immediately followed by reptile diversity. The chalk cliffs of Dover are forming fast, though still submerged under the sea. The first vertebrates, as well as formans, bivalves and molluscs can be found.

But things are getting dangerous again. Mid-December, 235 million years ago, and you come across some animals which are going to evolve into some pretty terrifying species. The age of the 'terrible lizards', the dinosaurs, is about to begin. It will last some 170 million years. But during this time we also meet the first mammals, archeopteryx and then the first birds. And there is a great diversification of molluscs, corals and other invertebrates. This is also the era of the ammonite, a shelled mollusc and ancestor of the modern squid (Plate 10(b)).

We have arrived at our last major town, Penzance, made famous by Gilbert and Sullivan in *The Pirates of Penzance*, and the birthplace of Humphry Davy. It is Christmas Day, 70 million years ago. But we must go on if we are to reach the rocks of Land's End by New Year's Day. A couple of days out from Penzance we leave the Mesozoic and enter the modern era, the Cenozoic. The dinosaurs have disappeared completely and there is a wonderful diversity of flowering plants, trees, mammals and other animals. Horses are beginning to look familiar. Is that a primate over there swimming in that lake and climbing into a tree?

It is 9.30 p.m. on New Year's Eve, a couple of miles short of Land's End. Just time for a quick pint at The First and Last, the last pub in England. What luck, there is a human behind the bar, a first meeting with our ancestors. Looks a bit scruffy though.

Australopithecus was an upright hominid living 3-4 million years ago, with a brain cavity equivalent to that of a chimpanzee or gorilla. He was followed by *Homo habilis* and *Homo erectus*, with a brain cavity twice that of *Australopithecus*. It is very cold. Another damned Ice Age. The total volume of ice on the Earth today is about 25 million cubic kilometres, including some 100,000 glaciers. At the height of the Ice Ages there was three times as much, resulting in a lowering of sea level of 130 metres (425 feet). If the present ice were to melt, many of the world's major cities would disappear – London, New York, Tokyo.

Homo sapiens crossed his first rubicon some 0.5-1 million years ago. We meet him in the car park at Land's End asking for a toilet. Man has become aware of himself. The first utterings of language and questioning have arisen. The age of discovery has begun!

During this long journey we have seen the chemistry and biology of the Earth evolve together, each affecting and interacting with one another, a rubicon in one provoking a rubicon in the other. The origin of life, the first cell, the first oxygen-producer leading to the biggest atmospheric pollution ever, the first eukaryotic cells, the first calcium and silicate precipitates, the first cellular events, the first animals and plants, followed by an explosion of life and death. Yet until we got to the car park at Land's End there was hardly an organism which was identical with anything found today. Every organism we met between John o'Groats and Land's End has either become extinct or changed – evolved into a new species. How then should we view this change – gradual and smooth, gradual and bumpy, or small step by big step? Rubicon argues that we should view evolution as a series of gradual changes leading to the banks of each Rubicon. After crossing, a new organism, a new cell type, or a new molecular species, has been born or become extinct.

The appearance, development and extinction of species is evolution. But to Darwin the word evolution had quite a different meaning from the one it has today! But which Darwin? The originator of the modern concept of evolution was Charles's grandfather Erasmus (1731-1802), physician and one of the great polymaths of the eighteenth century.

WHAT IS EVOLUTION?

Biology crosses the Rubicon

Charles Darwin (Plate 8(a)) spent five years on the *Beagle*, between 1831 and 1836. But it was not until his return that his ideas began to crystallise. His rubicon for speciation came in March 1837, when he read John Gould's analysis of the mocking-birds from the Galapagos Islands. While there himself he had ignored the anecdotes about the giant tortoises being recognisable from each island by their different shells, and the finches which seemed so similar from island to island yet each were a separate species. John Gould (1804-1881) was a celebrated English ornithologist. It was his analysis that opened Darwin's eyes to the reality of the Galapagos.

From then on, Darwin was determined to disprove the fixity of species, and to prove their transmutation. He crossed a second rubicon a year later. On 28 September 1838 he read 'for amusement' Malthus's *Essay on the Principle of Population* (1798), which argued that unchecked growth of the human population would lead to famine – the struggle for existence. Darwin realised the significance of this as a force for selecting best-adapted individuals, but he rarely used the word 'evolution', prefering the phrase 'descent with modification'. Why?

Evolution is one of the few unifying forces in biology, in fact for the whole of science. But evolution is a fact, not a theory. Evolutionary theories are there to explain *how* evolution occurred not *that* it occurred. If we are to understand what exactly this fact is, we must look at the history of the development of the concept of evolution.

It is a history full of confusion and heated debate – of science and polemics, of speculation and imaginative experimentation or observation. No other concept can have polarised to such an extent the layman and the scientist, or scientists themselves. Even the ideas of Copernicus and Galileo, heretical as they were to a non-scientific public and religious community in the sixteenth and seventeenth centuries, were soon agreed by the scientists and by the end of the seventeenth century were accepted by many layfolk. Yet after more than two centuries of heated debate the arguments about evolution continue.

There are two obvious sources of the confusion: first, the word 'evolution' has a different meaning in science today from the early seventeenth century when it was first used; and secondly, there is confusion between what evolution is and the theories propounded to explain how it occurred.

Imagine that it is early spring and you are walking past a small pond where your children find some frog spawn. They put some into a jam-jar they have brought with them. Back home in a few days the jar will be full of tiny tadpoles swimming about. During the next week or two these new life forms will change beyond recognition. They will have legs, their tails will have disappeared, and they will begin to assume the green colour of a frog instead of the black of the tadpole. If you are lucky, you will soon have an adult frog capable of swimming and hopping from stone to stone in your garden pond, which will lay its own eggs next year. This is but one example of one of the most remarkable features of life, the development of animals from new-born to mature adult – metamorphosis. The same phenomenon can be observed by watching a seed germinate and grow into a flowering plant or tree. It was this type of development within what we now call a single species that the word evolution was first used to describe.

The word, from the Latin *volvere*, 'to roll', and *e*, 'out', first appeared in 1670 in *The Philosophical Transactions of the Royal Society* to describe the 'natural evolution and growth' of parts of an insect. Erasmus Darwin (1731-1802), Charles's grandfather, described the 'gradual evolution of the young animal or plant from its egg or seed' in his poem *The Botanic Garden*. To Albrecht von Haller (1707-1777) and Charles Bonnet (1720-1793) evolution was the unrolling or unfolding of hidden life forms within each individual. This idea was closely allied to the concept of epigenesis introduced by William Harvey (1578-1657), a pioneer in the study of the blood and of medicine as a science. In his *De Generatione Animalium* Harvey argued that material from the germ gains form gradually as a result of epigenesis or preformation. Development was an unfolding of a pre-existent form. Thus the shape and behaviour, and the chemistry, of an individual species undergo dramatic changes as it develops. But what about the diversity between the species themselves?

Once people started examining fossils, it was obvious that there were thousands of animals and plants which had existed at one time on the earth or in the oceans but were no longer extant. This appeared to conflict with Chapter 2 of Genesis – a flood causing mass destruction. Where was the Jules Verne hidden world, if Noah had taken representatives of every species onto his Ark? Benoît de Maillet (1656-1738), the Swedish taxonomist Carl von Linné (Linnaeus) (1707-1778), and the French naturalist and philosopher George-Louis Leclerc, comte de Buffon (1707-1788), had all come to the conclusion that new life forms must have come into being since the Earth was formed. But it was a Swiss naturalist, Charles Bonnet (1720-1793), who proposed a key role for catastrophe in evolution.

Bonnet discovered parthenogenesis, the development of an animal without fertilisation of an egg by sperm. Going blind, he turned his agile mind to philosophy. In 1769 he published his seminal work, *La Palingénésie philosophique* (*The Philosophical Revival*), in which he hypothesised that the Earth suffers periodic catastrophes. These destroy most life forms. The survivors then multiply and step up to the next *evolutionary* slot. This was the first use of '*evolution*' in its modern sense. Erasmus Darwin and Lamarck, however, were the real founders of evolutionary theory. But Lamarck and both the Darwins used the word evolution sparingly or not at all, because to them it was still synonymous with differentiation from embryo to adult.

The French philosopher Montesquieu had proposed, in 1721, the idea that one species could change into another, *transmute*, or evolve in modern parlance. The French equivalent to transmutation was *transformisme*. There is some controversy among scholars as to whether Lamarck (Plate 8(b)) actually used the word, or whether the term took a generation or more to gain acceptance. What is beyond doubt is that both Erasmus Darwin and Lamarck did hypothesise that species could change. Both also believed in spontaneous generation and were sure that this was still occurring.

Some thirty years before the Victorian age in Britain the question being asked by the first disciples of the new science of biology was: Is there any real evidence for species transmutating? It went against all religious belief. If it was so, argued Charles Lyell (1797-1875), where were the links in the fossil record? It was Lyell who was one of the first to use 'evolution' in the modern sense – i.e. organic transmutation – in 1832 in a discussion of Lamarck's ideas. If there was evidence for 'evolution', how did the transmutation occur? How were the variations maintained from generation to generation?

It was here that Charles Darwin stepped in with *natural selection*. But in the first edition of *The Origin of Species*, published in 1859, only four of the fourteen chapters were concerned extensively with 'origins' and natural selection, the hypothesis that he and Alfred Russel Wallace (1823-1913) (Plate 8(c)) had proposed to explain how changes, one by one, could lead from one species to another. For every small change that makes the animal or plant 'fit' (the old sense of the word – 'well adapted' or 'suited') into the environment better, the more prevalent the change becomes as life moves from one generation to the next. In *The Origin,* Darwin used the fossil evidence and the development of agricultural and domestic animals to support his theory. He also addressed what he saw as the major problems of the hypothesis. However, he rarely used the words 'evolution' and 'transmutation'. They are absent from both the Index and the Glossary of Principal Scientific Terms of the sixth edition of 1876. The great promoter of the term *evolution* in the modern sense was the 'Social Darwinist' Herbert Spencer (1820-1903), who distinguished progressive development of species, i.e. transmutation, from embryological development.

The fossil record showed that the organisms on the Earth now are different from those in early times. There could be one of three explanations:

1. Common species responsible for the fossil record died out, allowing modern ones, already present but too few to be found in the fossil record, to become more common.
2. Spontaneous generation, but from what?
3. Gradual transmutation.

No. 2 was just credible for microbes. But elephants?

In October 1844 the Edinburgh publisher Robert Chambers (1802-1871) issued anonymously a highly speculative treatise on what we call evolution. Although *The Vestiges of the Natural History of Creation* annoyed Darwin and his followers intensely because of its lack of scientific rigour, it did help to put transmutation in the forefront of the debate in mid-nineteenth century biology. This was vital if Darwin was to overcome the over-emphasis on the 'principle of uniformitarianism'. This held that the same processes were responsible for both past and present events. It had been proposed by James Hutton in 1788 and championed by Charles Lyell in his *Principles of Geology* (1830-3), the seminal geological text of the nineteenth century. As a result Lyell, though a strong supporter and a friend of Darwin, remained sceptical about the main message of *The Origin*. But geology was to be vital in the argument for the 'fact' of evolution and for natural selection.

Hiccups in nomenclature

Geology is the science of the Earth, and includes palaeontology, the study of fossils. The trouble is that both disciplines deal with incredible spans of time. Furthermore, though many fossils are clearly related to modern-day major taxa today – phyla, classes, orders and so on – many of the species in the fossil record are quite unlike any extant organisms, i.e. those still in existence. Thus new distinctive names had to be invented, such as dinosaurs, 'terrible lizards', which weren't actually lizards at all.

As we have already seen, the oldest sedimentary rocks – those formed as a result of debris settling, both chemical and biological – have been dated as 3,800 million years old. The first cells must have come into existence not long after. Fortunately, when the geologist examines sedimentary rocks, he finds not simply a random array of rock forms full of fossils, but rather a layered structure, each layer containing a definable rock type and a different variety of fossil. It was pioneering geologists such as Lyell, Murchison and Sedgwick in the nineteenth century who were among the first to exploit this regularity. As a result, order was imposed on the fossil record. A set of -oics, -enes and -ites was defined, the first two representing geological spans of time based on the rock layers, and the last enabling extinct species to be named in a way which would not allow them to be confused with modern species.

Thus we have *stromatolites, belemnites, ammonites, graptolites* and *trilobites*. Stromatolites are fossilised mats of ancient blue-green algae, or cyanobacteria, in rock as old as 2,800 million years. The pre-Cambrian fossil record (i.e. 3,000-600 million years ago) is full of them. Many have modern-day equivalents. Belemnites and ammonites, on the other hand, were much more recent and are extinct ancestors of the octopus and squid respectively. Both fossils have distinct and easily recognised shapes and are found in large numbers in the Cretaceous period and other Mesozoic periods, i.e. 235-65 million years ago. However the range for ammonites goes from the Ordivician to the Cretaceous (i.e. 515-65 million years ago), whereas belemnites lived from the Carboniferous to the Eocene (i.e. 345-35 million years ago). The portion of the belemnite left as a fossil is the 'guard' and shaped like a rifle bullet, whereas the ammonite had a shell in the form of a spiral. Trilobites (Plate 10(a)) were arthropods, ancestors of the modern insects and crustacea such as the crab, and particularly common in the Cambrian period 600-515 million years ago. They lived from the mid-Cambrian until the Permian (i.e. 550-235 million years ago). Graptolites, on the other hand, were cup- or tube-shaped colonies of a marine organism related to modern coelenterates, the jelly-fish and corals. They were common in the mid-Cambrian to Carboniferous periods (550-290 million years ago).

I must admit I find these geological time spans and terms a little difficult to remember. But it is important. Figure 9 is an aide-memoire.

EVOLUTION – A THEORY IN CONFUSION OR CRISIS?

Natural selection works

Natural selection is the theory proposed by Charles Darwin and Wallace to explain how evolution occurs – the survival of the best-adapted forms followed by their inheritance by the next generation. Imagine you have just bought a beach game consisting of a box of a hundred rubber balls of different sizes, with a 'goal' consisting of another box with a hole in the top. The hole is quite small but all the balls will go through it, though for some it is a very tight fit. You throw the first set. Your aim is not perfect, so the

my ago	Aeon	Era	Period	Epoch	lasted (my)
15.000					1
14999					10.000
5000					500
4500	Hadean	pre-Cambrian			600
3900	Archean	pre-Cambrian			100
3800	Archean	pre-Cambrian			700
3100	Archean	pre-Cambrian			600
2500	Proterozoic	pre-Cambrian			600
1900	Proterozoic	pre-Cambrian			400
1500	Proterozoic	pre-Cambrian			500
1000	Proterozoic	pre-Cambrian			200
800	Proterozoic	pre-Cambrian	Sturtian		130
670	Proterozoic	pre-Cambrian	Vendian		80
590	Phanerozoic	Paleozoic	Cambrian		85
505	Phanerozoic	Paleozoic	Ordovician		67
438	Phanerozoic	Paleozoic	Silurian		30
408	Phanerozoic	Paleozoic	Devonian		48
360	Phanerozoic	Paleozoic	Carboniferous		74
286	Phanerozoic	Paleozoic	Permian		38
248	Phanerozoic	Mesozoic	Triassic		35
213	Phanerozoic	Mesozoic	Jurassic		69
144	Phanerozoic	Mesozoic	Cretaceous		79
65	Phanerozoic	Cenozoic	Tertiary	Paleocene	11
54	Phanerozoic	Cenozoic	Tertiary	Eocene	17
37	Phanerozoic	Cenozoic	Tertiary	Oligocene	13
24	Phanerozoic	Cenozoic	Tertiary	Miocene	19
5	Phanerozoic	Cenozoic	Tertiary	Pliocene	3
2	Phanerozoic	Cenozoic	Quaternary	Pleistocene	2
0.01- now	Phanerozoic	Cenozoic	Quaternary	Holocene	who knows?

smallest balls have a better chance of slipping into the 'goal'. Many of the large balls don't hit the goal at the right angle and so bounce away. You repeat this exercise several times, using only the balls which have successfully got through the hole, and you find that quite soon you have selected only the smallest balls. This is essentially how natural selection works. Certain small

Origin rubicon	Extinction rubicon at end of period	Continuous change
origin of the Universe		
origin of the Milky Way		
formation of our solar system		formation of planet masses
formation of the Earth		cooling of the earth's surface
earth's crust forms		atmosphere builds up
origin of life - the first cells		
oldest stromatolite fossils (b-g algae)		
oxygen producing microbes		rise in atmospheric oxygen
oldest calcified blue-green algae	oxygen holocaust	ozone layer builds up
the first eukaryotic cell, mitosis	calcium holocaust	
origin of real sex - meiosis		
higher algae and protozoa		decrease in stromatolites
multicellular animals - trilobites, corals, jelly-fish		
most major animal and plants		big expansion in invertebrates and algae
reef-building corals, first vertebrates	mass extinction	invertebrate expansion- bivalves and echinoderms
plants and invertebrates invade land		
bony and cartilaginous fishes (e.g. sharks), ammonoids, insects, amphibians, conifers	mass extinction	trilobites, corals and then fish spread and diversify, peak of jawless and jawed fish
reptiles		forests, ferns, insects spread
new types of bony fish	mass extinction, end of trilobites	reptiles proliferate, insects diversify, amphibians decline, swamp forests grow
dinosaurs, mammals, moths & wasps	mass extinction	gymnosperm & marine invertebrate expansion
birds, frogs, new type of bony fish - teleosts, lizards, and land mass all together as Pangaea		dinosaur and ammonite expansion, gymnosperm plants dominant
modern sharks, snakes, flowering plants, major drop in sea level	mass extinction (K-T), dinosaurs	mammals, insects (butterflies, bees & flies), plants diversify; continents drift
ants, modern insects, primates, continents separated		spread of mammals, birds and plants
modern animal families, horse, rats		flowering plants bloom, primates spread
pollinating insects		expansion of modern groups and insectivores, and diversification of apes
elephants		proliferation of fishes
mammoths, *Australopithecus*		dominance of birds and mammals
origin of man - *Homo sapiens*	mammoth, saber-tooths, big mammals	cooling and climate fluctuations
Caesar crosses the Rubicon; ??	dodo, species made extinct by man	man's disruption of the ecology

Fig. 9. Geological time. my = million years.

differences between individuals make them better suited to a particular environment. Those which increase the chance of producing offspring, and which are inheritable, will be passed on to the next generation. As with the box of balls, the population will eventually contain the best 'fit'. Differences which make the individual less suitable will be lost by natural selection.

After his return from the *Beagle* in 1836 Charles found himself a wife, Emma Wedgwood (Plate 8(a)). In 1839 they married and settled in a small house in Gower Street in the centre of London. Three years later they moved out into the country, to the Kentish village of Downe, about 12 miles from the centre of London. The village was originally known as Down, and Darwin's house was Down House. In the mid-nineteenth century the villagers decided to add an 'e' to avoid confusion with County Down in Ireland. Down House, however, retained the original spelling, and was saved for the nation by the Royal College of Surgeons. Here, as a scholar and experimenter, Darwin worked for over forty years, studying barnacles, worms and orchids, and trying to germinate seeds from pigeon crops and seeds soaked for days or months in sea-water. Darwin published nineteen books. Many try to support his pet theory, a mechanism for evolution – natural selection.

Darwin was an observer with a keen eye, an accurate describer from global events down to the minute dissected parts of a barnacle or orchid. He was also a wise philosopher and theorist. How else could he handle the plethora of criticisms of natural selection? But most important, and often ignored, he was a brilliant and imaginative experimenter. He bought in varieties of pigeons to test natural selection using domesticated animals; he grew orchids to test his theories on fertilisation by insects. He and his son Francis (Frank) tied up the leaves of insectivorous plants, to see what role movement in plants had to their survival. He even worked out how much earth could be moved by earthworms, calculating that there were 53,767 per acre at Down House. Darwin based much of his faith that natural selection was correct on the overt evidence of man's selection of domestic animals and plants, and spent a great deal of time experimenting with various species of pigeon. The trouble is that many animals and plants generated in this way are genetically unstable. Look at a Mallard on a park pond. Try to grow a Cox's pippin from an apple pip. You can't. The horticulturalist has to use grafts.

In the early 1950s a zoologist, Bernard Kettlewell, carried out a series of elegant experiments at Oxford with a common species of moth, which for the first time demonstrated natural selection in action over a very short time-scale in evolutionary terms. In the last century the peppered moth was light-coloured over its entire range; this helped to camouflage it against predatory birds when it settled on a pale rock or leaf. The industrial revolution, however, left many of the trees and rocks upon which the moth liked to settle blackened with industrial soot. The pale moth was no longer well hidden against its background. But natural selection took over. By the 1950s it was recognised that in industrial environments a dark form of the moth was predominant. To demonstrate that this had occurred by natural selection Kettlewell decided to show by experiment that the selection of the two forms did occur in the appropriate environment. He released some 1,600 moths, a mixture of dark and light forms, some into unpolluted forest and the rest into the darkened woods of Birmingham, in the heart of the British industrial midland. He succeeded in recapturing some 10-20 per cent of them. In the unpolluted forests twice as many of the recaptured moths were light compared with dark, whereas in the Birmingham woods the recaptured dark form outnumbered the light form by two to one. The Dutch zoologist and ethologist Niko Tinbergen (1907-1988), Nobel Laureate for Physiology or Medicine in 1974 for his pioneering work on animal behaviour, was able to film birds eating the moths, confirming the selectivity of the light over the dark in the light environment, and vice versa.

Another modern-day example is the antibiotic selectivity we exploit in genetic engineering. We use it every day. In the genetic engineer's laboratory, only bacteria containing the gene we want to clone will grow, because we have put it into the bacteria coupled with a gene which destroys penicillin. Any bacteria failing to take up this DNA combination will be killed. This is the reason why the over-use of antibiotics has had potentially dangerous consequences. It leads to selection of antibiotic resistant strains. These can now be found in most hospitals.

Up and Downe

Many of Darwin's books sold rapidly and went through several impressions and editions. Yet, in spite of his success as a scientist and his fame, Darwin's life was full of ups and downs, and tragedy. Throughout his time at Downe, Darwin had trouble with his health, particularly his gut. How much of this was due to stress is not known. But it must have been difficult to remain passive amid the constant onslaughts of laymen, clerics and scientists.

Darwin's ideas about natural selection were already under attack before *The Origin*. There have been many attacks over the past century and half, and they persist even today. And I don't mean just from the creationists. There have been serious scientific arguments not against the principle of evolution but against the concept of natural selection by gradual change. Darwin himself knew there were problems. In the first edition of 1859 and the sixth edition published in 1876 he devotes the whole of Chapter VI to 'Difficulties of the theory'. And he wasn't referring to the objections of others. These he dealt with elsewhere, particularly in Chapter VII, 'Miscellaneous objections to the theory of natural selection'. Rather they were his *own* concerns with *his own* theory of natural selection by small change: the lack of innumerable transitional forms; the lack of chaos in nature instead of distinct species; the difference in importance of organs – some like the eye vital for survival, others like the giraffe's fly-swatting tail a luxury – the origin of 'instincts'; and the origin of evolutionary novelty. These were all things that worried him.

Darwin realised that there were anomalies in nature where it was impossible to see how small change had lead to a new biological event. Two particularly interesting examples he presented were the 'luminous insects' and fish with electric organs. In a section entitled 'Special difficulties' he wrote: 'Although we must be extremely cautious in concluding that any organ could not have been produced by successive, small, transitional gradations, yet undoubtedly serious cases of difficulty occur ... The electric organs of fishes offer another case of special difficulty; for it is impossible to conceive by what steps these wondrous organs have been produced ... The luminous organs which occur in a few insects ... offer ... a difficulty almost exactly parallel with that of the electric organ.'

But the most significant problem was that there were no mechanisms known for generating the small changes, and no mechanisms known by which they could be inherited. The artificial evidence from man's interference with Nature to produce domestic animals and crops did not convince the sceptics. How could small changes in one species lead to the evolution of another? How could small changes even occur? Though DNA was isolated in 1868, its role was not established until the 1940s, and there was no science of genetics for Darwin to use. Darwin rejected Lamarck's theory of the inheritance of acquired characteristics. A giraffe did not have a long neck because, by stretching up to the higher branches, it elongated it and this feature was then acquired by its offspring. Rather the primaeval giraffe population had a range of neck lengths determined by what they inherited. Those with the longest necks could get more food; so, year by year, more of the long-necked animals survived to produce offspring.

August Weismann (1834-1914), a German biologist and one of the founders of the science of genetics, proposed the 'germ plasm' theory, pre-DNA, to replace the inheritance of acquired characteristics. Getting the idea from a study of the sex cells of jelly-fish, he proposed – in a book published in German in 1886 and in English in 1893 – that what is 'essential' for an individual species is passed on by the 'germ plasm' with the sex cells. Characteristics of the organism apart from its reproduction are in the soma. This idea remains in place today – germ cells and soma – the former passing on individual characteristics through the DNA in its chromosomes.

But even before Weismann Darwin was aware of the problem of the lack of a mechanism for transmitting small changes through the egg or sperm needed to explain how natural selection worked. He therefore developed an idea of his own. In *The Variations of Animals and Plants under Domestication*, volume II (1875) he entitled a chapter 'Provisional Hypothesis of Pangenesis'. On page 350 he quotes Whewell: 'Hypotheses may often be of service to science, when they involve a certain portion of incompleteness, and even of error.' Then he says: 'Under this point of view I venture to advance the hypothesis of Pangenesis, which implies that every separate part of the whole organisation reproduces itself. So that ovules, spermatozoa, and pollen grains – the fertilised egg or seed, as buds – include and consist of a multitude of germs thrown off each separate part or unit.' He was getting perilously close to Lamarckianism here. But for something to be inherited, and thus be susceptible to the forces of natural selection, it had to be in the germ line. Darwin proposed the movement of globules (gemmules) from the tissues to the germ line. He carried out many unsuccessful experiments looking for the gemmules of pangenesis which he hoped would carry the changed phenotype to the germ cells. Unfortunately, far from increasing the credibility of natural selection, pangenesis actually undermined it. Few believed it.

By the end of his life, to his great disappointment, natural selection was not so much being challenged as being ignored. Even Huxley in his lectures stressed the crucial importance of Darwin in establishing the principle of evolution, but played down, or forgot to mention, what Darwin really cared about – natural selection. But Darwin knew that the origin of the idea of evolution lay not with him, but with his grandfather and Lamarck. Lamarck had also been attacked by leading scientists of his day, including his compatriot Georges Cuvier (1769-1837) and Charles Lyell. Yet, incredible as it may seem today, by 1900 Darwin's theories were also in considerable disrepute. Lamarckianism was resurgent. Darwinism was in eclipse.

One particularly infamous Lamarckian study in the early years of this century concerned the midwife toad. Toads are of course found on land, but usually return to water to breed. Like frogs, they produce swimming larvae – tadpoles. Anyone who has tried to pick up a wet toad will know how slippery toads are. In fact, in order to cling on to the female during mating the males of most species have processes or pads on their hands to help them grip her. The midwife toad, however, lives permanently on land, the male having adapted to carry the eggs around its back legs. This toad therefore does not need such a grip. But Paul Kammerer (1880-1926), an Austrian biologist, claimed that he could induce thick pigmented pads in the males of midwife toads by keeping them in water for several generations. He also claimed that different acquired characteristics could be inherited in the organs of other animals, such as the siphons of sea-squirts. William Bateson and other contemporaries were extremely sceptical, and demanded the evidence. Someone else must see his specimens. When, in 1926, G.K. Noble and Hans Przibram examined a preserved toad they found that the pads had been artificially coloured with Indian ink. It is not unknown for museum and laboratory specimens to be 'doctored' to show of their best. But this was the proof the scientific world needed. Kammerer was a fake. He committed suicide a few months later.

Lamarck had the vision to see the truth of evolution. Darwin turned the world to it. By the 1880s Huxley was still Darwin's bulldog. As he so pointedly argued, Darwin had turned the attention of the world of science and the world as a whole to evolution. Yet Darwin died a disappointed man. Many accepted that evolution was a fact, and that transmutation of species had occurred and did occur. But practically no one remained a convert to Darwin's brain-child, 'natural selection', not even Huxley. Wallace and Spencer were notable exceptions. Darwin's champions constantly reminded their audiences about the enormous debt science owed to Darwin, particularly to *The Origin*, but few if any argued for the mechanism of natural selection. Was ever a man so misunderstood?

Neo-Darwinism

In 1866 an unknown monk, Gregor Mendel (1822-1884), living in an Augustinian monastery at Brunn (later Brno), had published the results of hybridisation experiments with peas. Born Johann Mendel, the son of a peasant, he entered the monastery in 1843 and was ordained in 1847. He 'felt compelled to enter a station in life which would free him from the bitter struggle for existence'. It was ironic that he never met Darwin. In the monastery he found an intellectual community, which included a maths teacher, Fr. Aurelius Thaler (1796-1843), a pioneer in botany. Realising Mendel's bent for science, the abbot sent him to study physics under Doppler (1801-1853). On his return Mendel set about trying to demonstrate the law which explained the origin and development of hybrids, using peas and hawkweeds. In 1868 he was elected abbot. Some doubt has been cast on the accuracy of his analyses. There have been accusations that the gardener fiddled the results. The data are too precise. They fit the hypothesis too well! But the conclusions are accepted and were what was needed. Yet their rediscovery in 1900 did not have the impact on Darwinism that we might have expected. Instead of being used to re-establish natural selection by gradual change, Mendel's results, and those of others such as Bateson and deVries, were used to argue that species arise in one step or at most a few steps, rather than by gradual change.

The 'modern synthesis', named after Julian Huxley's book of neo-Darwinism (1942), began in the 1930s as a result of the experiments and analyses of six scientists: Theodosius Dobzhansky (1900-1975) with the humble fruit fly, *Drosophila*, Sewell Wright (1889-1988), Ernst Mahr (b. 1904), J.B.S. Haldane (1892-1964), George Simpson (1902-1984) and Ronald Fisher (1890-1962), a British geneticist and statistician.

In 1930 Fisher published his *Genetic Theory of Natural Selection*, a key treatise in establishing neo-Darwinism. In it he illustrated the power of natural selection. In simple terms, a mutation giving an animal a selective advantage of one per cent would be to all intents and purposes undetectable in each generation. Yet Fisher calculated that within a hundred generations or so this slight advantage would make it the major gene in the population.

But there are still problems. Michael Denton in *Evolution: A Theory in Crisis* (1985) has highlighted several. Why is there such a paucity of 'missing links'? Is Archeopteryx really a precursor of the birds, and the coelacanth a living fossil? What caused the disappearence of the dinosaurs and other mass extinctions – 'the big five' (see below, p. 142)? Richard Milton in *Facts of Life* (1992) highlights the lack of hard scientific evidence for natural selection. And there are severe problems in marrying two contrasting views of evolution in action – evolutionary sequences seen through fossils or molecules. Milton's book was heralded in a Sunday newspaper with the headline 'Scientist threatens to make Darwin extinct'. This statement is plain rubbish. Evolution is a fact, and so is natural selection. The key question is: What is the precise role of natural selection in the evolutionary process? Let us see if Rubicon has anything to offer. I hope to convince you that we do need something else in addition to the principle of natural selection, if we are to understand fully the stages responsible for evolution from molecules up to whole ecosystems.

FOUR THOUSAND MILLION YEARS OF PROBLEMS

Earth or ocean?

At 9 a.m. on 26 October 4004 BC a remarkable event occurred: the creation of the Earth. So Archbishop Ussher calculated in 1664 by counting back generations listed in the Old Testament. Now, that would have been quite a rubicon if it were true! Scientists believe they have developed a better way of estimating the age of the Earth. Buffon (1707-1788) was one of the first to attempt it. He thought that by measuring the melting and cooling rate of iron balls one might be able to guess the time the Earth had taken to cool to its present temperature. The answer he got was longer than Ussher's: 75,000 years. Still far too short to be believable. Why? Because measurements of erosion and sediment rates, and from the passage of salts down the rivers into the sea, told geologists of the nineteenth century that it must have taken millions of years at least to form the mountains, valleys, gorges, lakes and seas which make up the topography of the earth.

In 1854 Herman von Helmholtz considered the luminosity of the Sun and estimated twenty million years as the age of the Earth. This contradicted Immanuel Kant's estimate that the Sun would burn out in only a thousand years. Yet it was still too short for the evolutionists. But it was Lord Kelvin, formally William Thompson (1824-1907), who really put a spanner in the works.

Kelvin was one of the leading physicists of the nineteenth century, who played a major role in establishing the laws of thermodynamics and their application to natural phenomena and technology. Kelvin expanded Buffon's and Helmholtz's calculations and reached a figure of 20-40 million years for the age of the Earth, probably nearer 20. This was still far short of the age Darwin and the nineteenth-century geologists needed to explain the chemical and biological evolution of the Earth. They pointed to dramatic geological features such as the Grand Canyon, arguing that this alone must have taken 25 million years to form. Sadly Darwin died (in 1882), fourteen years before the discovery which was to solve the problem once and for all. For in 1896 a French physicist Henri Becquerel (1852-1908) detected a radiation emanating from uranium salts. He had discovered radioactivity.

What was needed to date the Earth accurately was a 'clock', which has ticked on incessantly inside minerals and rocks ever since they first formed either from molten lava or by sedimentation. You also need a way of telling the time of this clock and how long it has been ticking. Ernest Rutherford (1871-1937) not only discovered many key features of radioactivity, but also realised in 1905 that you could use it as such a clock. Radioactive elements act as a geological clock, having been entrapped following solidification. Radioactive decay is the dream of the alchemist come true, for when a radioactive element decays it is converted to a new element. Thus radioactive uranium decays to lead and radioactive potassium to argon or calcium. There is a universal feature of all radioactive decays. The time for half the element to decay is constant, for ever. Thus if you take a block of pure uranium half of it will have decayed to lead in 4,900 million years. Half of the remainder will decay to lead in the next 4,900 million years, and so on – till none is left. In order to date rocks we need a radioactive element whose product as well as itself are both easy to find and measure in all rocks. We select an element with a decay matching the particular geological time-span we want to study.

Most of the carbon in Nature, including ourselves, is carbon-12. But a tiny amount is radioactive, carbon-14. It decays with a half-life of 5,570 years, but is formed continuously from nitrogen in the atmosphere by the interaction with neutrons created from bombardment by cosmic rays. Its half-life makes it suitable for dating fossil bones and artefacts 500-50,000 years old. The body contains a small cup of potassium (about 150g). Most of this is non-radioactive potassium-39. But one ten thousandth of it is potassium-40, which is radioactive. It has a half-life of 1,300 million years. By contrast, that of rubidium-87 is some 50,000 million years. These then are some of the radioactive elements providing radioactive clocks covering the age of the Universe (Figure 9). By measuring the amount of radioactive element still left in a piece of rock, together with its known stable product, you can then use the half time to calculate how long it has taken to reach this state. The assumption has to be made that no losses of product have occurred during the time between the formation of the rock and the measurement. This can be a problem when looking at elements such as argon which are gases and may not remain trapped. Similarly sedimentary rocks cannot be used to date rock strata by this means, as they have undergone exchange of material. Sedimentary rocks are therefore dated by using minerals, i.e. igneous rocks, surrounding them. Using this principle, Frederick Soddy (1877-1956) and Rutherford calculated in 1913 that the Earth must be billions of years old, at least. Nowadays mass spectrometry, developed first in the 1920s and 1930s, enables extremely accurate measurements to be made of radioactive elements and their products. The Earth is 4,600 million years old.

It took 10^{-42} of a second to form the universe, some 15,000 million years ago. At this point the temperature was 100,000,000 degrees Kelvin ($0°K = -273.15°C$). Within a million years the Universe had cooled a little, to about 3,000 °K, enabling the first element, hydrogen, to form from the union of one electron and one proton. Our galaxy, the Milky Way, formed within the next few million years. Yet it was to be more than 10,000 million years, twice the lifetime of the Earth, before the Earth condensed and the crust could form.

Once the crust cooled to below 100°C the oceans could form. More than two thirds of the Earth are covered by sea. Life began about 3,800 million years ago. Whether this was in the sea or in fresh water on the land, and whether there were multiple centres of life, is still not known. What is certain is that by 3,500 million years ago, the first rubicon of life had been crossed.

Systematics in confusion or chaos?

To be able to study animals and plants we need some order – a classification that brings like-species into groups. This is taxonomy. Yet biologists still cannot agree on the way this should be done. Linnaeus, the father of taxonomy, used sexual characteristics. This is useful but not sufficient to deal with the complexities of life-forms in the five kingdoms: bacteria, plants, fungi, protists and animals.

In 1950 the German entomologist Willi Hennig (1913-1976) published *Grundzüge einer Theorie der Phylogenetischen Systematik*, which was a revolution in systematics. It led to the form of classification known as 'cladistics', which has provoked much heated debate. A clade is a group of organisms with common characteristics. But should these characteristics be grouped descriptively or should the groups be related to an evolutionary pathway, putting the closest evolutionary ancestors next to each other in the classification, and so on? Ideally an evolutionary grouping would be the true basis of any classification. But how can we be sure that we have the evolutionary relationships right? There are many pitfalls waiting for the evolutionary taxonomist.

The importance to Rubicon of this 'chaos' in systematics is that it highlights a fundamental feature of our concept of evolution: the separation of species. Obviously a mouse is a different species from an elephant, and they cannot mate with each other. But what if you implanted DNA from a mouse into an elephant? The point is that we still don't understand fully the molecular basis of what is perhaps the most common-sense property of life – the individuality of species. The DNA of distinct species just won't mix. Rubicon argues that we must discover the pathway of rubicons which lead to the final bank, across the other side of which is the separation of two species. Let us therefore look at an example of this fundamental problem on the Earth today.

The species problem

Every summer Britain is invaded by DNA. Dozens of species of birds fly in to find a partner for the single-copy DNAs in their germ cells. One is the lesser black-backed gull (*Larus fuscus*). This gull is similar to the herring gull (*Zarus argentatus*), made famous by Niko Tinbergen through his behavioural studies, and in particular for the function of the bright red spot on the lower bill, a target for the chick's hungry beak. The herring gull is distinguished from its cousin the lesser black-backed, by having a bright yellow instead of a dull greenish-yellow bill, pink legs and light grey instead of dark grey wings. In Britain and Europe these gulls do not interbreed; they are distinct species. But things are very different elsewhere.

Travel east to Russia and the herring gull gets less and less prevalent. The lesser black-backed becomes increasingly different from the European species, and by the Bering Straits it is very like the herring gull. Go west from the UK and the converse is true. The lesser black-backed disappears, but the herring gull, found right across the US, gets more and more like the lesser black-backed the further west you go. In eastern Siberia the form of the gull is almost a half-way house. In contrast to what happens in Europe, all these different races interbreed. The ultimate evolutionary rubicon is the division of two relatives into separate species, each with common characteristics and capable of breeding only with its own species – the herring gull and lesser black-backed gull. Sub-species include individuals which sometimes interbreed but may produce sterile male offspring. Other animals and plants show this trait. Any orchid spotter knows the difficulty of identifying not only sub-species but also local varieties.

But what is a species in molecular terms? We still don't know. In spite of his title, *The Origin of Species*, this was the one thing in evolution that Darwin failed to explain – how natural selection by small changes leads to the rubicon sequence of speciation.

The intermediate forms of gull and orchid hybrids might be looked on as 'missing links' if palaeontologists in a hundred million years time are lucky enough to find their fossil remains. The lack of missing links is another 4,000-million-year-old problem for evolutionists.

The missing links problem

In 1912 a British lawyer and amateur antiquarian, Charles Dawson (1864-1916), claimed that he had found the fossilised remains of a cranium and jawbone in a gravel pit on Piltdown common, near Lewes in Sussex. Named *Eoanthropus* ('dawn man') *dawsoni*, the find was thought to be so significant that controversy raged for forty years. It wasn't simply the man-like features of the fossils that aroused the excitement, but the close proximity of other animal fossils dating from the Pleistocene period. But in 1926 the gravel was found to be much less ancient than had at first been thought. The professionals had to face the fact that Piltdown man might be a fake.

After a careful study, initiated in 1953 at Oxford and the British Museum (Natural History), it was established that the skull fragments, the jaw and the teeth were the cleverly disguised remnants of a modern man and a female orangutan. The material had been filed, chemically treated and then placed in the gravel. The faking had been skilfully done!

But genuine 'missing links' have been found. Archaeopteryx and the coelacanth are established examples. Or are they? Detailed evolutionary sequences for a single group of animals or plants have also been described from the fossil record. But are they complete enough? Archaeopteryx is not a fake. It was thought to have evolved from a dinosaur known as a coelosaur, and to be a missing link between dinosaurs and birds. But coelosaurs have no collar bones. Archaeopteryx has. Furthermore, birds have wings composed of the second, third and fourth fingers of a hand, while Archaeopteryx's wing is from the first, second and third fingers. So is it really a 'missing link'?

Coelacanths first appeared 350 million years ago. They were thought to have been extinct for some 60 million years. But this myth was destroyed by a fisherman who caught a live specimen in the Indian Ocean off the coast of East Africa in 1938. In fact these fish were well known to the inhabitants of the Comoro Islands, who ate them when dried and salted. The discovery created great excitement, for the group of fishes that the coelacanth belonged to were thought not only to be extinct but to be relatives of amphibians and thus of all land vertebrates. At last science had a living fossil to dissect and could discover the soft structures lost during fossilisation. But alas, when the soft parts inside a coelacanth were examined carefully by expert anatomists, they had a problem. These soft tissues were not those necessary for it to be an ancient ancestor of the Amphibia.

One of the best established 'evolutionary sequences' is supposed to be that of the horse. Yet it has glaring gaps in it, illustrating once again the fact that no 'missing links' – that is, intermediary forms analogous to the herring gull and lesser black-backed gull or the orchids – have ever been discovered.

We are lucky that we have any fossil record to look at. Even so there are big gaps. These gaps can be equivalent to 100,000 years, or even more. As a result, there are many examples of animal lineages seen in the fossil record remaining relatively similar for millions of years, but then suddenly changing dramatically in shape or form, without there being any detectable transitional forms. The number of organisms that have been left with us as fossils is but a tiny fraction of those that actually existed. The chance of finding transitional forms is therefore very small, a needle in a haystack.

But in 1972 Niels Eldredge and Stephen J. Gould gave a different perspective to the problem. They proposed that the discontinuities in the fossil record really were a reflection of how evolution had progressed – evolution involved long periods of relative stasis punctuated by periods of very rapid change. Small, localised populations provide the richest environment for rapid evolutionary change. Having crossed the rubicon, each new distinct species, only able to reproduce with itself, spreads geographically and becomes abundant enough to be found in the fossil record. This was the theory of *punctuated equilibrium*. It includes the traditional neo-Darwinist process of gradual change. The possibility that the discontinuities could have been caused by macro-mutations is separate from the theory, and not necessary for it to be true.

As we saw in Chapter Two, death plays a crucial part in the life of our body. So with evolution. Without extinction there would have been no evolution. But there have apparently been some pretty dramatic death rubicons in evolution.

Holocaust

And the Lord said unto Noah, Come thou and all thy house into the ark; ... For yet seven days, and I will cause it to rain upon the Earth forty days and forty nights; and every living substance that I have made will I destroy from off the face of the Earth.

And Noah went in, and his sons, and his wife, and his sons' wives with him, into the ark, because of the waters of the flood. Of clean beasts, and of beasts that are not clean, and of fowls, and of every thing that creepeth upon the Earth. There went in two and two unto Noah into the ark ... (Genesis 7: 1, 4, 7, 8 and 9).

Noah's Ark may have saved representatives of most species on the Earth from the Biblical flood, but the geological evidence tells us something different. First, there have been several occasions in the past 3,000 million years, not just one, when a catastrophe has wiped out a large numbers of species. Secondly, though some species survived these holocausts, many new species appeared for which there is no evidence in the preceding geological record.

There are now some 5-10 million species of animals and plants, several million of which are insects. Yet only a few tens of millions of years ago none of these species existed. It has been estimated that 99 per cent of all the species that have ever existed are now extinct. Examination of the fossil record reveals seven particularly spectacular rubicons over the past 2,000 million years (Figure 9). Between 600 and 65 million years ago there were five great extinctions, 'the big five' as they are often called. I suggest that there was another one about 1,800 million years ago caused by calcium accumulation in the sea, as a result of erosion of minerals and dissolution by bicarbonate as the carbon dioxide rose in the atmosphere releasing free calcium into the rivers, which lead to the sea. As we saw in Chapter Three, cells have to maintain a very low free calcium inside to prevent precipitation of calcium salts, disruption of the chromosomes, killing of the mitochondria's ability to make ATP, and activation of degrading enzymes which break down proteins, DNA and RNA, and membranes. Those species which evolved pumps to keep the calcium low inside their cells, or had found a way of precipitating calcium salts outside their cells, survived the calcium holocaust. The massive fossil deposits of calcareous algae in the USA bear witness to this success in molecular evolution. But the first holocaust on the Earth was even more dramatic, even though the variety of species which may have been lost was less than in the extinctions which followed.

The early atmosphere consisted of methane, ammonia, carbon dioxide and perhaps a little hydrogen, though this soon escaped into space. There was no oxygen. We all need oxygen to survive, as do most organisms now living. But this was not always so. As we saw in Chapter Two, oxygen can be very toxic. It is very reactive, 'burning' and bleaching proteins, DNA, RNA, membranes and many small molecules, particularly the coloured ones. Many bacteria, living for example in mud where there is virtually no oxygen, are very sensitive to oxygen. Even growing them in air will kill them. We, and the other species living in the oxygen-containing atmosphere for the past 1,800 million years, are able to do so because of the chemicals inside all cells which protect them from the potentially lethal bleach. In bacteria which can grow in air you will find similar protection mechanisms against the toxicity of oxygen. But 2,000 million years ago cells had no such protection. When the oxygen accumulated in the atmosphere, as a result of photosynthesis II, many cells crossed the lethal rubicon. Oxygen wiped out most microbes. Only a few survived – those which had the semblance of a protection mechanism, or which were not exposed to the lethal rubicon levels until they had evolved one.

But what of the 'big five'? What happened then? The 'big five' are the mass extinctions which occurred at the end of five Phanerozoic periods – the Ordivician (438 million years ago), the Devonian (360 million years ago), the Permian (248 million years ago), the Triassic (213 million years ago) and the Cretaceous (65 million years ago). The last of these – the K-T extinction – is the most famous and best-studied mass extinction. T stands for Tertiary and K for Cretaceous, to distinguish it from Cambrian and Carboniferous. It is most famous because it was here that the dinosaurs crossed their ultimate rubicon. They were wiped out. The biggest creatures that have ever existed on land just disappeared, in the space of a few million years. But they were by no means alone. Virtually all animal and plant groups lost species and genera at the Cretaceous/Tertiary boundary. Nearly 40 per cent of all marine genera became extinct, including reptiles, fish, sponges, snails, shell-fish, ammonites and sea urchins. A mass destruction also occurred in the surface foraminiferans. Though there were only a few species of these elegant, single-celled animals, the sediments of the Cretaceous are dominated by their silicious and calcified skeletons. The White Cliffs of Dover bear witness to this. If all the carbon dioxide fixed in such terrestrial deposits were to be released, it has been estimated that the Earth's atmosphere would be 98 per cent carbon dioxide at a pressure sixty times present atmospheric pressure, close to that of the sterile atmosphere of Venus and Mars. In the surface waters there were also marine plants, able to grow in the salty water. These algae produce a high percentage of the atmosphere's oxygen from photosynthesis. But 65 million years ago many of them were also wiped out. On land the loss of all dinosaurs is perhaps the best known mass extinction at the K-T boundary, but a wide variety of reptiles and amphibians also became extinct. The fossil record of the western United States shows that a fifth of all mammalian species also died out. But there were survivors: crocodiles and alligators, frogs, salamanders, turtles and many mammalian species. Yet many new species of animal and plant appeared. In fact at first there was dramatic change in the flora covering the Earth, reminiscent of the aftermath of a forest fire. The forests and flowering plants virtually disappeared with the dinosaurs. There was a big decrease in angiosperm pollen and flowering plants, which were replaced by carpets of ferns and grasses – the fern spike. At one time fern spores accounted for 99 per cent of plants. After this 'spike' the flowering plants returned with only a few species lost.

Palaeontologists distinguish between normal background extinctions and mass extinctions. In the Phanerozoic era the average life span of a marine genus was 11.1 million years, but there was considerable variation between species. Jurassic bivalve genera survived for 20 million years, whereas each ammonite genus lasted only 500,000-700,000 years. The vague explanation for these 'natural' extinctions is over-speciation, whatever that means.

Palaeontologists argue about the reality of the 'big five', whether they are a true reflection of what happened to life, whether there were mini-extinctions between them. Should we really be considering the 'big seven', to include the calcium and oxygen holocausts? Whatever the truth of the 'holocaust' hypothesis, it is clear from the fossil record that many life-and-death rubicons have been crossed for thousands of individual species and groups, responsible for the process we call evolution.

And what of modern times? The manifesto of the Green Party claims that one species is becoming extinct every five minutes. But this problem has been recognised for centuries. Mauritius, Réunion and Rodrigues are three islands in the Indian Ocean. In about 1507 Portuguese sailors reported that they had found flightless birds on these islands, the most famous of which was the dodo, *Raphus cucullatus*, found on Mauritius. By 1681 exposure to man and his animals caused it to become extinct – to be lost from the Earth's fauna forever. The two other species of Raphidae on the other two islands had also disappeared by the end of the eighteenth century, *Raphus solitarius* on Réunion in 1746 and *Pezophaps solitaria* on Rodrigues in 1790. The World Wild Life Fund lists over 200 species of animals and plants on the edge of extinction. Each species is on the verge of its ultimate rubicon. How many of the five million or so estimated species

Albert Einstein

1. Three crisis resolvers: (a) *top left* Max
Planck (1858-1947); (b) *above* Albert
Einstein (1879-1955); (c) *left* Peter
Mitchell FRS (1920-1991)

2. Living light — glowing and flashing rubicons: (a) *left* a luminous toadstool; (b) *below* the luminous jelly-fish *Aequorea* — the luminous cells are at the base of each tentacle; both photographs from Harvey, *Bioluminescence* (1952).

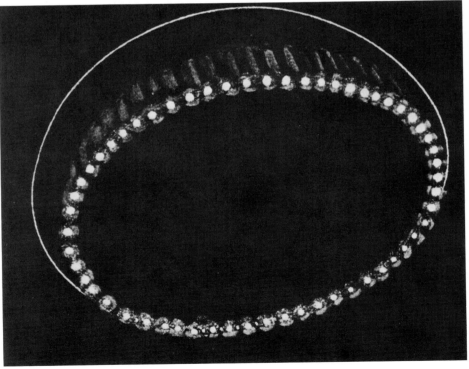

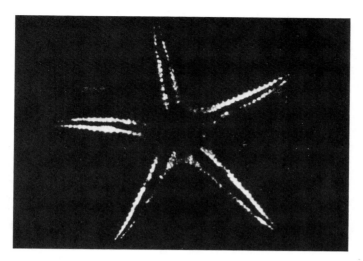

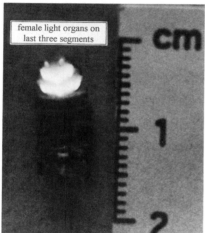

female light organs on
last three segments

3. Living light — glowing and flashing
rubicons: (a) *above* a luminous starfish; (b) *left*
the glow of the female glow-worm (found in
the last three segments in the female and the
last in the male); (c) *below* female glow-worms
glowing.

4. Two pioneers of calcium: (a) *above left* Humphry Davy FRS (1778-1829), who discovered the element; (b) *above right* Sydney Ringer FRS (1835-1910), the first to show a role for calcium in allowing cells to cross the Rubicon.

5. (a) *left* Lewis Victor Heilbrunn (1892-1959), a pioneering protagonist of calcium as a universal provoker of rubicons inside cells; (b) *below* a calcium oscillation in a human bleach-producing cell (a neutrophil), with thanks to my colleagues Dr Eryl Davies and Dr Maurice Hallett. Light areas = high calcium occurring in the cell after 80, 220 and 315 seconds; dark areas = low calcium occurring at 140 and 265 seconds. The calcium provokes rubicons in the cell responsible for removing agents which may damage the host.

| addition of stimulus | 80 sec | 140 sec | 220 sec | 265 sec | 315 sec |

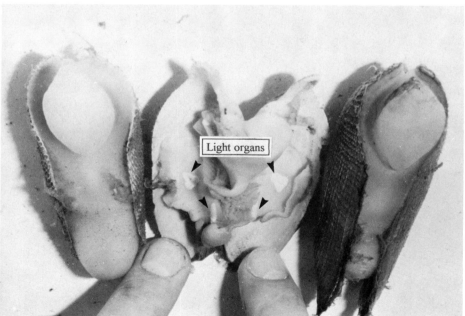

Light organs

6. The common piddock *Pholas dactylus*: (a) *top* piddock holes with the biochemist's tool for getting the piddocks! (b) *above* the piddock itself and its light organs. In the wild tapping the rocks results in a spectacular cluster of rubicons as the piddocks squirt a luminous secretion from their holes.

7. Two pioneers in the study of living light: (a) *right* Robert Boyle FRS (1626-1691), who discovered that air (oxygen) is essential for a glowing or flashing rubicon; (b) *below* E. Newton Harvey (1887-1959), scholar and protagonist of luciferin-luciferase rubicons.

8. Three nineteenth-century pioneers of evolutionary theory: (a) *above* Charles Robert Darwin (1809-1882), aged about 46, and Emma Wedgwood (1808-1896), at the time of her marriage to Charles in 1839; (b) *below left* Jean-Baptiste de Lamarck (1744-1829); (c) *below right* Alfred Russel Wallace (1823-1913).

9. (a) The sixth dimension — think-paths where the brain can receive inspiration, cross the Rubicon and generate a new idea: *above left* Darwin's sandwalk in 1993; *above right* the author's 'round' in Anglesey with Snowdon in the distance.

9. (b) Return across the Rubicon for an ecosystem: Cosmeston country park, South Wales: *above left* as a rubbish tip; *above right* a spotted orchid grows where the rubbish once lay.

10. Some organisms that have crossed the extinction rubicon: (a) *left* a trilobite, Canada, 500 million years ago; (b) *above* an ammonite, Germany, 250 million years ago; (c) *below left* a fish, Wyoming, 300 million years ago; (d) *below right* a redwood leaf, California, 25 million years ago.

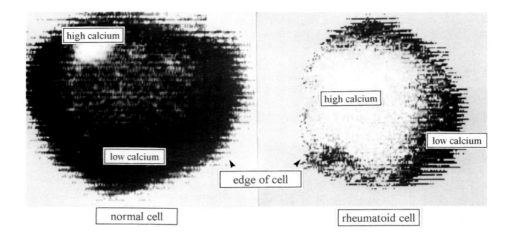

11. Lighting up the chemistry of the living cell: (a) *above* the calcium cloud in a normal and in a rheumatoid bleach-producing cell, with thanks to my colleagues Dr Eryl Davies and Dr Maurice Hallett. Light areas = high calcium, dark areas = low calcium. (b) *below* the chemical microscope.

Alpha chain

VLSPADKTNV KAAWGKVGAH AGEYGAEALE RMFLSFPTTK TYFPHFDLSH GSAQVKGHGK
KVADALTNAV AHVDDMPNAL SALSDLHAHK LRVDPVNFKL LSHCLLVTLA AHLPAEFTPA
VHASLDKFLA SVSTVLTSKY R

Beta chain

VHLTPEEKSA VTALWGKVNV DEVGGEALGR LLVVYPWTQR FFESFGDLST PDAVMGNPKV
KAHGKKVLGA FSDGLAHLDN LKGTFATLSE LHCDKLHVDP ENFRLLGNVL VCVLAHHFGK
EFTPPVQAAY QKVVAGVANA LAHKYH

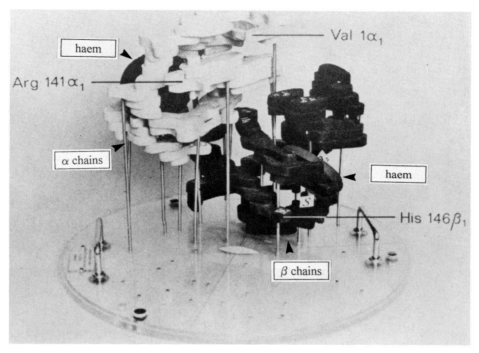

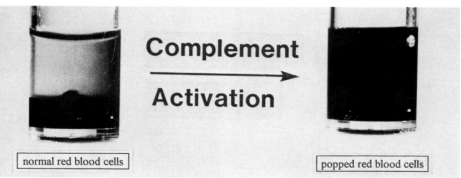

12. A protein in five dimensions — haemoglobin, a protein made up of four sub-units (two α and two β) and two haems (the part which actually binds the oxygen carried in the blood): (a) *top* in 1D — the primary sequence, each letter = an amino-acid; (b) *centre* in 3D — Arg, Val and His represent the amino-acids arginine, valine and histidine, from Perutz and Teneyck, *Cold Spring Harbor Symp. Quant. Biol.* 36:296 (1971); (c) *above* in 5D — the release of haemoglobin from red blood cells after crossing the Rubicon as the result of rocket attack (complement).

13. (a) *right* Peter Forsskål (1732-1763);
(b) *below left* Robert Chambers (1881-1957),
pioneer of micro-injecting cells, from
R. Chambers and E.L. Chambers,
Explorations into the Nature of the Living
Cell; (c) *below right* Frederick Gowland
Hopkins FRS (1861-1947) in the laboratory
of the Department of Biochemistry,
Cambridge.

of insects are on the verge of extinction we can only speculate on. Most haven't even been identified or classified, because they live in the inaccessible jungles hidden from the prying eyes of the taxonomist. By contrast man has made a positive contribution to Nature: the domesticated animals and the thousands of flowering plants and trees which adorn our parks and gardens. How many new species are being formed by natural processes? How many will be created as the result of genetically engineered animals and plants escaping or being released into the environment?

There have also been selective extinctions induced by natural forces. For example, there was a mini-extinction of mammals in the middle of the Pleistocene (1.64 million – 10,000 years ago), including the mammoths, the large marsupials and the sabre-toothed tiger. The last mammoths died out 12,000 – 18,000 years ago. But these selective extinctions were not always synchronous in different parts of the globe. The large marsupials disappeared from Australia several thousand years before their relatives in North and South America.

Extinction and the formation of species are evolution. The result of a mass extinction was that some species survived to evolve into new ones, while some disappeared for ever, the dinosaurs and ammonites being the most obvious. Why? As David Raup puts it so eloquently: bad genes or bad luck?

Raup and Sepkoski found that mass extinctions seem to occur regularly, every 26 million years or so. This implies a common extra-terrestrial cause. In 1980 Alvarez and colleagues proposed a dramatic cause of such mass extinctions, a large asteroid or meteorite colliding with the Earth and causing a dust cloud covering most of it, perhaps for millions of years, resulting in a loss of light and low temperatures. These would have effects on both marine and terrestrial species. The dinosaur enthusiasts are still arguing about the idea, for which some scientific evidence has been obtained. Bad luck?

As in the pathology of cells, the DNA of each extant species has been under physical, chemical and biological attack throughout evolution. Ice ages, drought, radioactivity, thermal warming, meteorites and dust clouds lasting millions of years, movement of the land masses by plate tectonics, and changes in sea level are some of the physical changes responsible for extinction. Oxygen, calcium, acidity and organic pollution by plants are examples of chemical attack. The spreading of DNA through viruses and other vectors allows bits of genes to be transferred from species to species, with consequential harmful or beneficial results.

What do these extinctions mean at the molecular level? Were molecular processes also lost for ever during mass extinctions, or at any other time during evolution for that matter? From the fossil record it seems not, though of course we cannot be certain about the reactions and molecules which made up the soft tissues. The fascinating thing about evolution at the molecular level is that it seems to be continually increasing the diversity of the gene pool. Yet 3,000 million years ago a mirror image of life may have existed, though there is no evidence that it did.

This has been a section of central importance to Rubicon. The appearance of chemical and structural processes enabled a species to survive a holocaust. Those that failed to evolve oxygen protectants, calcium pumps, DNA umbrellas, or a *milieu intérieur* to protect their cells from environmental change crossed the rubicon and became extinct. Those which crossed these beneficial molecular evolutionary rubicons moved on to the next bank. There the oxygen and calcium protectants evolved into new molecular processes, enabling those that crossed the next rubicon to carry oxygen around the cell and body and to use calcium as a means of controlling their behaviour. Rubicon argues that defence against attack has been a key force in the molecular evolution of cells.

Odd balls

The problem of how the insect wing could have evolved is a classic one for 'natural selection' and one Darwin himself addressed (first edition of *The Origin of Species*, pp. 449-56: 'Rudimentary, atrophied, or aborted organs'). The pathway from a bump on the body to a wing which can actually support flight must have taken thousands of tiny steps over millions of years. How could each step be selected for, when the advantage is only conferred when the insect can actually fly? The proposal is that either the intermediary structures confer another benefit as they evolve or the mutations are passive. It is still a worry, though – one which Darwin recognised in a number of phenomena, including bioluminescence.

The origin of bioluminescence is a fascinating puzzle. As Newton Harvey wrote in 1952: 'It is apparent from the previous classifications that no clear development of luminosity along evolutionary lines is to be detected but rather a cropping up of luminescence here and there, as if a handful of damp sand has been cast over the names of various groups written on a blackboard, with luminous species appearing wherever a mass of sand struck.' There are millions of individual species of beetle; yet only a few thousand are luminous. There are rock pools where several species of hydroid, the fixed stage of a jelly-fish, grow. They are all closely related; yet only some are luminous.

For luminescence to be susceptible to the forces of natural selection the organism must have evolved a chemical reaction capable of generating visible light, with a pathway to make both the luciferin and the luciferase catalyst. It needs a cell to house the reaction and a control mechanism to make it flash or glow. Unless the light generates a response in the beholder it is useless. Additions such as filters, lenses, energy transfer and colour modifications can improve the luminescent display under the forces of natural selection. But the origin remains a mystery.

You will have gathered that I find luminous animals fascinating. It is my hope that, by discovering how some of these evolutionary novelties occurred, we may learn some new principles about molecular evolution which can be implanted into the Darwinian scheme of things. Let me give you an example.

The first luminous protein isolated from a luminous jelly-fish was from *Aequorea forskalea*, now *victoria*. *Aequorea* occur in many parts of the world, but in 1962 Osamu Shimomura, working with Johnson and colleagues at Friday Harbor laboratory on the West coast of the United States, isolated a protein which flashed when calcium was added to it. The DNA coding for it was cloned in 1985, and we now have a complete amino-acid sequence – 189 amino-acids with three calcium-binding sites very similar to other calcium-binding proteins. So the protein could have evolved from a calcium-binding protein or another enzyme which handles the amino-acids phenylalanine and tyrosine.

The chemical which generates the light in the jelly-fish is called 'coelenterazine', and is bound tightly to the protein. This type of bioluminescence is the most common chemistry responsible for bioluminescence in the sea. It occurs in seven phyla: radiolarians (Protozoa), the hydroids, jelly-fish and sea-pens (Cnidaria), the comb-jellies and sea gooseberries (Ctenophora), shrimp, ostracods and copepods (Arthropoda), some squid (Mollusca), some fish (Chordata) and very recently an arrow worm (Chaetognatha). All aeons apart in evolutionary terms. Yet the chemistry responsible for firefly and glow-worm light has only been found in the luminous beetles. A fascinating problem for chemical evolutionists to explain.

When I first began working with coelenterazine, I discovered something which at first was a nuisance but on reflection highlighted something very interesting. In the summer the sun shines brightly into our lab. One day I left an ice bucket containing some coelenterazine near the window but was called away for an hour or so before I could continue the experiment. On returning I noticed that the nice bright yellow solution had faded considerably, and on measuring precisely how much coelenterazine was left I discovered that more than 80 per cent had disappeared. This compound is thus highly unstable. Evolution has had to solve this problem of chemical attack. It has succeeded in two ways. First, the luminous cell stores the compound attached to a sulphate so that oxygen cannot get at it, and secondly, by binding proteins to it these put a cage around it, preventing it from being oxidised until the flash is required. Fascinatingly enough, using genetic engineering to take just the last amino-acid – proline – off the end of the protein has disastrous effects for this protection. Instead of lasting for days or even months, the protein complex loses its ability to generate light when triggered by calcium within a few hours. Another way to stabilise the coelenterazine is to remove water, as is the case in a granule.

Bioluminescent proteins are very weak enzymes. They are thus primitive catalysts and solvent cages. They have much to tell us about the evolutionary origin of catalysis, a key feature of the molecular basis of life. We can now formulate three possible rubicon sequences for the evolution of a bioluminescent system – each rubicon being selected for by a Darwinian-Mendelian mechanism. Each is testable by genetic engineering.

This brings us to what is perhaps the greatest problem of contemporary biology, molecular evolution. How can we marry what we know of the molecular structure of life with natural selection?

From molecules to Darwin

In 1955 Frederick Sanger (b. 1918) published the first complete amino-acid sequence of a protein. Insulin, he showed, had 51 amino-acids made up of two chains linked together, themselves joined together in two places. He received the Nobel prize for Chemistry in 1958, and became only the fourth person to win two Nobel prizes when he shared the Chemistry prize in 1980 with Paul Berg and Walter Gilbert, for sequencing DNA. This opened up a new era in molecular biology, for tens of thousands of DNA sequences have now been analysed from which the protein sequence can be predicted using the genetic code.

However, this confronted the neo-Darwinists with a serious problem. The mutation rate in DNA and proteins was too rapid for every one to be selected for by natural selection. Thus, in 1967, the Japanese molecular geneticist Motoo Kimura proposed that a large number of these DNA changes must have been the result of being fixed randomly, being neutral or nearly neutral mutations.

We now know the amino-acid sequences of tens of thousands of proteins. These can be drawn up into evolutionary trees, leading back to a precursor. But the origin of the precursor is a mystery. There are few, if any, established examples of a protein with one function evolving into another. This then is the central dilemma, not the evolution of proteins, cells and organisms, but their *origins*.

Richard Dawkins (b. 1941) elegantly showed how a sequence of small changes can lead to a new sense in a sentence or a picture. But the problem is that if you do this with a protein you generate rubbish on the way, which will be rejected. Imagine the well-known party trick of lining up twenty people and starting a message at one end, which is passed on by whispering (Chinese whispers). By the time it gets to the other end it is completely different. But it still makes sense. Each person has heard a different message, but every time a word was nonsense their brains converted it to sense. There is no known mechanism by which this can occur in DNA during evolution. So, for example, suppose our precursor protein is:

The cat sat on the mat,

and is going to evolve into

The dog hid in the car.

This involves changing four words letter by letter:

cat → hat → hag → dag → dog;
sat → sad → sid → hid;
on → in;
mat → cat → car

Not only are some of these words rubbish but virtually each new sentence is rubbish: The hat sat on the mat, The hat sad on the mat, The hag sad on the cat, and so on. If natural selection is to work step by step, the precursor process, whether a protein, a cell, or an organ structure, must maintain its integrity. One could postulate that the DNA was first duplicated and only the duplicate mutated. Each rubbish mutation won't matter because the original bit of DNA is still intact. But this is not a Darwinian mechanism. Darwin, and his followers, were adamant that each small change must be selected for.

Motoo Kimura argued that many of the amino-acid mutations in proteins were 'neutral', neither good nor bad. Therefore they can be maintained within the gene pool. The essence of the idea seems to be true. Neutral mutation theory can explain how different variants of a particular protein evolved: for example, the small number of amino-acid differences between the haemoglobin in a mouse and whale. But neutral mutation still has not given us a pathway from one protein to another with a different function, or from one cell to another. Natural selection works on events, rubicons.

Attempts to convert one protein into another have usually failed. In the 1970s attempts were made to alter the substrate specificity of a bacterial enzyme by growing up the bacteria under conditions where many mutations were generated and in a medium containing unnatural nutrients. Only in those bacteria where the enzyme had mutated would the growth rate increase, so these would eventually dominate the culture. A nice idea. But it didn't work. What happened was gene duplication, and it was bacteria that contained more than one copy of the enzyme gene which were selected. No bacteria were found with an altered enzyme.

Now we have genetic engineering enabling us, in theory, to jump a hundred million years in a day. Many proteins have now been mutated, and key amino-acids identified. But we still have no route for the evolution of a new protein. The evolution of novelties is the problem. What we must look for are the rubicon sequences. Each leap will be susceptible to natural selection, but we need a mechanism to get to each bank.

How evolution works

There is no getting away from it: evolution depends on sex. And sex depends on the transfer or union of DNA from different sources. Even bacteria have sex! They contain plasmids, upon which genetic engineering technology depends. Changes in habit and structure must be inheritable, and this means they must be implanted in the DNA and then into the germ line. This is where Lamarck's ideas went wrong. Even if changes in muscle or other tissues acquired during weeks, months or years of activity are reflected in somatic mutations in your DNA, there is no way of passing these on to your children unless they can get into the sperm or egg DNA. This is why Darwin, who recognised the significance of Weissman's distinction between somatic and germ cells, invoked the idea of pangenesis.

For evolution to occur we need mechanisms for generating, randomly, mutations in the DNA, for sorting these changes within a genome, and for transferring them to other cells. Then natural selection can do its best, or worst. Also, mutations must be maintained within the population until the right molecular rubicon is crossed for natural selection to act on.

There are plenty of ways for mutations to occur. Radiation damage has been a plentiful source of DNA mutations over 4,000 million years. They can also occur every time chromosome is replicated. What is remarkable is how accurate this is. In fact the enzyme which replicates the DNA, DNA polymerase, has evolved a spell-check programme to proof-read the DNA after it has replicated it and correct any mistakes. But the enzyme from thermophilic bacteria is not so choosy. Mistakes can occur. The one from the heat-stable bacterium *Thermus aquaticus*, which lives in thermal vents, we use extensively in genetic engineering. This enzyme is no good at spell-checking, unlike the one in its cold-temperature relative *Escherichia coli*, the common bug in our gut. The result is that mutations occur every few hundred additions to the DNA. But not all the mutations do any damage. Some are synonymous, and do no harm. Others generate nonsense, missense or stops in the protein, and will be lethal. Ten mutations needed to change one sentence to another would take approximately 250 million years on the basis of a mutation rate in *E. coli* of 4×10^{-10} per base pair and 10^{-11} in eukaryotes.

Other mutation mechanisms include oxygen damage and UV, X-ray and radioactive radiation, all producing cleavage, chemical modification of bases and point mutations. Two thousand million years ago radiation from radioactive elements in the Earth's crust was some four times what it is today. And there was little or no ozone later to protect life from the mutagenic radiation from the Sun's rays.

Molecular evolution and disease

We have already seen that the intracellular signalling system has played a central role in the evolution of multicellular organisms. Without it none of the events we associate with animals and plants would occur. Yet we know virtually nothing about how this key element of cell biology evolved. This system is a prime target for gene therapy of inherited diseases, and those where particular genes make the individual susceptible to, or at risk of, a particular disease. Cell-signalling also plays a vital role in many of the other major diseases, including rheumatoid arthritis, heart disease, multiple sclerosis, cancer and infections. The exciting possibility now exists, using modern genetic manipulation and protein engineering techniques, to prevent these diseases by genetic targeting. Similar approaches are being explored in agriculture and pest control. However, unless we understand the molecular pathway responsible for the evolution of the cell's signalling system, the long-term effects on man and the environment of this genetic manipulation will be unpredictable. It is therefore essential that we unravel the molecular sequence occurring over hundreds of millions of years which selected particular signals for specific functions and events in man, other animals and plants.

The importance of understanding the molecular pathway of evolution cannot be overestimated. If gene therapy and the manipulation of genes making people susceptible to diseases such as atheroma, asthma and diabetes are to be effective without disastrous consequences for man and the environment, the reasons for the maintenance of these genetic predispositions in the human gene pool must be established.

A major problem in elucidating the molecular pathway of evolution has been the difficulty of developing an experimental system in the laboratory enabling evolutionary processes, which originally took hundreds of millions of years to occur, to be studied in a manageable time-scale. The evidence for molecular evolution has therefore had to rely heavily on analysis of protein and DNA sequences, in relation to the geological record. Although this has given us important insights into the evolution of protein families, the mechanisms responsible for the evolution of cell and organ shape and behaviour remain a mystery. And yet it is these upon which natural selection acts. Furthermore, at the molecular level it is clear that Darwinian-Mendelian selection as applied to selection of species does not work. The only hypothesis so far presented to resolve this crisis in biology is the Neutral Mutation Hypothesis of Kimura.

The central question in evolutionary biology therefore remains: How did step-by-step changes in DNA occur, which remained within a population over millions of years until a combination occurred which was then, and only then, able to take them across the Rubicon and make them susceptible to the forces of Natural Selection?

And there is another chemical puzzle about evolution. Try shaking hands with yourself in the mirror and you will get a glimpse of what I mean.

Left, right, left, right, left

Are you right-or left-handed? The human body, and the bodies of millions of animal species appear at first sight symmetrical. Cleave them down the middle and you end up with two halves, identical from the outside except that each is the mirror-image of the other. Of course inside there is much less symmetry. The lungs and kidneys are evenly positioned, but you have only one heart, on the centre left, and the liver and gut are spread all over the place. The brain appears to be symmetrical, but examination of its functional activity reveals that some things go on the left-hand side and others on the right. This principle of handedness is found also at the molecular level.

Louis Pasteur (1822-1895) is perhaps best-known for his pioneering work on vaccination, particularly in animals with anthrax and human rabies. Yet he was a major contributor to establishing the infectivity and wide-ranging occurrence of bacteria. His work saved the beer, wine and silk industries in France, bedevilled by bacterial contaminations. He also helped to resolve a problem highlighted by Mitscherlich in 1844, which turned out to be a discovery of a central chemical feature of life, chirality.

Let's do an experiment. It is fun to make crystals. Make up a strong solution of common salt, copper sulphate or alum and allow it to evaporate in a saucer. Within a day or so the water will have gone and you will be left with small elegantly shaped crystals. Attach these to a piece of cotton and you can make them grow bigger, provided you are careful to suspend them only in a super-saturated solution. Each 'salt' has a uniquely shaped crystal. Now repeat the experiment, only this time use sodium tartrate or lactate. Use two sources if you can, one extracted from living tissue, the other made chemically in the lab. You will find what René Haüy (1743-1822), Eilhard Mitscherlich (1794-1863), John Herschel (1792-1871) and Augustin Fresnel (1788-1827) and Louis Pasteur were fascinated by – not just beautiful crystals but two sets one the mirror-image of the other (Figure 10).

Take a ball of plasticine and four short pencils, two red and two black. Stick them in the ball so that they are evenly distributed. The points form a tetrahedron. Now write on a piece of paper various sets of triangles with the vertices labelled red or black. You will find that the three-dimensional ball can rest on the flat triangles several ways round provided there are two blacks or two reds in each. Now change a black pencil for a yellow and a red for a green. You will find that only one combination of colours on the triangle will fit. Swap round a yellow and a red pencil and you will need a different triangle, a mirror-image of the first. This is what we find in certain key biological molecules. They are handed, or chiral.

What the eighteenth- and nineteenth-century physicists and chemists discovered was that such chiral molecules will rotate the plane of polarised light, to the right or the left, dextra- or laevo-rotatory. Hence we designate biological molecules with at least one chiral carbon atom D- or L-. The amino-acids in our proteins are L-, whereas glucose for energy and ribose in RNA are D-. The enzymes which react with these, like the triangles on your piece of paper, will only react with the appropriate chiral shape. They won't react with its mirror-image. We saw in Chapter Two that bacteria use some D-amino-acids in their walls. These are thus resistant to the animal enzymes – proteases – which try to break them open, because these enzymes only recognise the L-forms. As Pasteur showed, a laboratory chemical reaction may yield a racemic mixture of a compound: that is, both left- and right-handed molecules. But try growing bacteria on them and

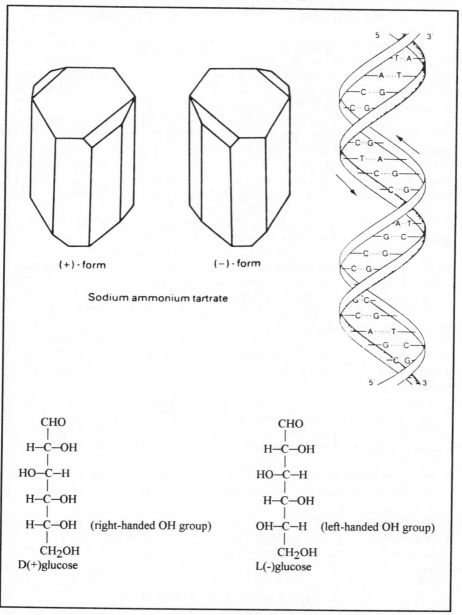

Fig. 10. Left- and right-handed crystals and molecules. *Top left* Left- and right-handed tartrate; *top right* A right-handed DNA helix, like a cork-screw turned by the right hand, both from *Chemical Evolution* by Stephen Mason, reproduced by permission of Oxford University Press. *Below* Left- (L-) and right-handed (D-) glucose (D-glucose = the molecule in our bloodstream).

only the correct-handed molecule will work. We cannot live on left-handed
(L-) glucose!

The rubicon for selecting chirality in life must have occurred very early
on – perhaps even before the first cell. Few science-fiction writers have yet
to grasp the implications of this. Is there a mirror-image of life on Earth
somewhere else in the Universe? Only one form exists now on Earth. The
cause of this Rubicon selection is unknown.

Life on Earth began some 3,500-4,000 million years ago. The problems
of the chemical and biological evolution which have occurred since have
fascinated both scientists and non-scientists for centuries. The creative
chemical forces responsible for the staggering changes in the chemistry
and forms of life over 4,000 million years stimulate excitement, joy, wonder
and creative thoughts in us all. Evolution is *the* universal principle which
unifies biological science. It is also a unifying force between the scientists
themselves, for over the past centuries many distinguished physicists,
geologists and chemists, as well as biologists, have expended much mental
energy on the mechanisms responsible for the evolution of life on the planet
and on how this relates to the chemical and physical evolution of the Earth.

Much has been learnt about evolution since Darwin first published his
scholarly text on natural selection in 1859. However, as we have seen,
many controversies still remain. There is still no consensus to explain the
mass extinctions which can be identified from the fossil record, including
the demise of the dinosaurs some 65 million years ago. But, more important, there is a major problem in relating molecular and cellular
information about evolution to the principles of Darwinian-Mendelian
selection.

There are five key questions concerning the molecular and cellular
evolution of organisms which must be answered if we are to discover a
unifying molecular evolutionary principle analogous to natural selection,
which acts at the level of individual organisms, populations and species:

1. What were the events which led to the origin, and then development of
   the three fundamental cell types in Nature: bacteria, archaebacteria
   and eukaryotes?
2. What was the origin of the genetic code and, in particular, why are there
   essentially only 20 amino-acids in proteins, and how did particular
   triplets in the genetic code become specifically linked to each amino-
   acid?
3. What was the origin of chirality in biological molecules? In particular,
   why were D-sugars and L-amino-acids selected?
4. How did proteins evolve to carry out specific functions either inside or
   outside cells? In particular, what were the origins of protein and RNA
   catalysis, without which there would be no life?
5. What were the molecular mechanisms responsible for the evolution of
   cell and organism shape and organisation?

The answers to these questions need both a new experimental approach and a new conceptual framework. Rubicon!

Gradual changes include the accumulation in the primaeval soup of what were to become biological molecules. These were not rubicons, until the chemical conditions arose for the first cells to form. Key molecular rubicons were: selection of chirality, i.e. D-sugars and L-amino-acids; selection of particular triplets for particular amino-acids in the genetic code; selection of ATP, as in the inner fuel, as opposed to GTP; formation of the outer membrane, the formation of cell walls (carbohydrate, calcium carbonate or silica); photosynthesis system I leading to photosynthetic bacteria; photosynthesis system II leading to plants and oxygen in the atmosphere; oxygen detoxification; DNA organisation and control including insertions (e.g. introns between exons) and the replacement of negative control in prokaryotes by positive control in eukaryotes; calcium handling and signalling including the origins of cyclic AMP, inositol phosphate, and channels; receptors and binding proteins leading to the development of eukaryotic cell function; oxygen transport proteins, leading to organisms with several organs – the metazoa; calcium phosphate instead of carbonate, leading to the bones of vertebrates; the origin of external regulators, i.e. hormones and neurotransmitters; the origin of particular macro-molecules, in particular collagen, responsible for determining the regular shape of cells and multi-cellular clusters; the development of defence reactions, including removal and repair of damaged DNA, proteins and membranes; and specialised defence molecules such as antibodies, pore-forming proteins and bleach-producing reactions. Several of these molecular rubicons were crossed after the first eukaryotic cells had formed. Bacteria, for example, do not use cholesterol and steroids.

And then there were a host of key cellular evolutionary rubicons: the first cell; the prokaryote-archaebacterial divide; formation of the first eukaryotic cell, and the organelles within it, involving several separate rubicons such as chloroplasts separating animal from plant cells; the evolution of cellular events – meiosis, mitosis, movement (amoeboid and flagellate), secretion, photoreceptors and vision, bioluminescence, programmed cell death; the development of specialised cells to house these events, including the development of sex, the development of the body's defence, specialised organelles such as peroxisomes and lysosomes, and specialised cells such as lymphocytes and neutrophils; the origin of the three germinal cell types – ectoderm, mesoderm and endoderm; the origin of multi-cellular tissues; the senses – communication, sound, language, pheromones, bioluminescence; the origin of the human brain, which clearly has the ability to do things no other species can.

You can see from this list that throughout evolution molecular and cellular rubicons abound, each one enabling the next stage of biological development to occur. The molecular rubicons were not restricted to the first 1,000-2,000 million years of biological evolution. New macro- and micro-molecules enabling new functions, under specific control processes, occurred and then developed under the guidance of natural selection.

The wheel of fortune

In *The Blind Watchmaker* Richard Dawkins quotes Paley's famous analogy and refutes the argument that such a complicated structure as an animal or plant must have had a designer. 'No,' says the modern theory of Natural Selection; 'mutation is a random process.' The timing of change occurs by chance. But only those changes which improve the survival, and thus reproduction, of the individual or population will increase within the population. Dawkins illustrates how this can occur by describing a computer programme which starts from a small dot on the screen and changes shape by random events in the programme. However, the programmer has included selective pressure on certain types of structural change, and after a few hours a shape looking like an insect appears. Very elegant. But it doesn't explain how evolution worked at a molecular level – the origin of new molecules remains a mystery.

Thus, looking back over 4,000 million years of problems, we find rubicons in abundance. What the evolutionary biologist needs to do is to identify the banks of these evolutionary rubicons and then discover the mechanism and timing of the crossing. The crossing may have taken millions of years, and may have involved stopping on islands on the way. As we saw with extant living systems, so in all aspects of evolution Rubicon is in action, from individual molecules up to whole ecosystems: the origin of a new gene, a new protein, a new process, a new cell, a new tissue or structure, a new species, a new taxon, or a new ecosystem.

There are, however, three important differences between the rubicons in evolution and the rubicons crossed by present-day organisms. First, the time-scale of the crossing is at least thousands, if not millions, of years, instead of seconds, minutes or at most a few years; i.e. within the lifetime of the individual organism. Secondly, when present-day animals and plants cross the Rubicon they are expressing the genotype they inherit, whereas in evolution crossing the Rubicon produces a new inheritable characteristic. Thirdly, the key to understanding the nature of evolutionary rubicons is to identify the point at which the characteristic becomes susceptible to the forces of Darwinian-Mendelian selection – the point at which a characteristic of life, whether it be an individual molecular species or the behavioural pattern of several species within an ecosystem, becomes implanted in the gene pool and is then improved. The heretical question we must address is whether natural selection, valid as it is for some evolutionary rubicon pathways, has always been the mechanism responsible for stabilising or removing a particular characteristic from the biosphere. The initial problem about the theory of natural selection still exists. How can it give rise to novelty – new forms and characteristics –

when many of the intermediary forms would be eradicated by natural selection itself?

What then is the answer to the famous question: which came first, the chicken or the egg? In evolutionary terms the answer is the egg, because dinosaurs preceded birds and dinosaurs produced eggs. But this really sidesteps the thrust of the question. One still has to ask, which came first, the dinosaur or the egg? To answer this we must identify the pathway of evolutionary molecular, cellular and organism rubicons which went from a group of cells reproducing asexually to a species reproducing by using a calcified egg.

So evolution and natural selection are facts. Mutations in DNA and their inheritance are facts. That dinosaurs are extinct is a fact. But these facts alone do not explain how evolution occurred! Ignore the polemics: whether or not there should be a finite probability of finding the missing link between ape and man; or whether archaeopteryx really was the precursor of the birds; whether the dinosaurs were wiped out by a meteoric dust storm or AIDS. The exciting challenge is to cross the same rubicon that Darwin has identified for us, natural selection by experiment – only now using a technique unknown to Darwin: genetic engineering.

5

Rubicon Challenges Gaia

The language of birds is very ancient, and, like other ancient modes of speech, very elliptical: little is said, but much is meant and understood.

Gilbert White (1720-1793).

THE GARDEN OF EDEN

One swallow does not make a summer, nor two or three trees a forest. Gilbert White (1720-1793), a cleric living in the small Hampshire village of Selborne, is recognised as the first great British naturalist. Walking daily through the woods and countryside near his house he made many seminal observations about animal behaviour and plant biology. Some of these were made in letters, particularly with Thomas Pennant (1726-1798) of Flint in North Wales, a distinguished biologist of the day and a Fellow of the Royal Society. Gilbert White was persuaded to publish these letters in 1789 as *The Natural History of Selborne*. But where did all those swallows and martins go in autumn? He looked around, thinking they must be asleep somewhere. The migration rubicon was yet to be discovered.

So when do swallows decide that autumn is coming? When do we decide that spring has begun and winter is over?

It is pretty obvious that we cannot survive on our own. We live in a complex society and depend on the activities of many others to survive and maintain our life-styles. But the life of *all* organisms is affected or dependent on others, even of solitary organisms in an Antarctic pond. For the air and the Sun's rays penetrating the upper ozone layer are all dependent on life. But when should a cluster of animals, plants and microbes be considered as an ecosystem? When is an ecosystem dead? What can an ecosystem do, and what tells it to do it? These are all rubicons that need to be explained.

In this chapter we shall consider the Earth, and the ecosystems within it, as a living organism. An ecosystem is a group of interacting organisms where the interactions are essential for the survival of the overall habitat and for the functions which the ecosystem can fulfil. Like an individual organism an ecosystem contains 'tissues' and 'cells'. These respond to signals generated within the ecosystem or external signals generated by the seasons, the weather and other physical and chemical factors. There are also eco-pathogens, and defence mechanisms trying to keep the ecosystem 'alive'. An ecosystem can spring back from apparent disaster, whether precipitated by man or by Nature herself.

At the centre of the ecological argument is Rubicon – the fifth dimension of ecology. As with a real cell, tissue or whole organism, so the establishment, survival, function, reproduction, defence and death of an ecosystem depend on a sequence of thresholds interspersed by gradual physical, chemical and biological change. Our job therefore is to examine ecological events and identify the rubicon sequence that enables them to happen. As with the life and death of organisms, so the physiology and pathology of the environment will be much easier to understand if we look on life and death not as single events but as sequences. Only when the eco-signals occur at the right level, in the right place, at the right time will the ecological event occur.

What then is an ecosystem? What distinguishes a live ecosystem from a dead one? Is a garden or compost heap an ecosystem? Can we predict the effect of pollution? Is it all really doom and gloom? What do we mean by pollution anyway? The Earth herself has generated some of the greatest acts of pollution ever – the oxygen holocaust, the great variety of toxins produced by animals, plants and microbes, and greenhouse gasses. Do we need to worry about them or not?

Though the idea of the 'economy of Nature' can be traced back at least to the eighteenth century, the word 'ecology' was first used in 1866 by the German biologist Ernst Haeckel (1834-1919). In 1866 he coined the word 'oekologie' (from the Greek *oikos*, 'household', 'home' and *logos*, 'study') to describe the branch of biology dealing with the interactions between organisms and their environment. Ecosystems are literally 'environmental houses'. There is no limit on size. Some are very big, some very small. A small rock pool, a pond, a lake, an estuary, an ocean, a forest, a copse, a river basin covering hundreds of square miles, an island or a whole continent can all be considered as ecosystems. Conventionally a cluster of organisms is regarded as an ecosystem when we can show that the interactions between them control the environment in which they live, and that flow charts and cycles of energy, nutrients, organic and inorganic chemicals and organisms can be drawn up embracing the whole system. Consumers and producers are identified. But the boundaries, and the decision to regard a group as an ecosystem, often appear subjective. Rubicon argues that the ecologist should look for the 'rubicons' within a group of organisms which are triggered as a result of their interactions.

How many trees do you need to form a forest? The area containing a group of trees may contain literally hundreds of distinct species of animals, plants and micro-organisms and yet may still not be a true ecosystem. A community in itself is not an ecosystem. A newly planted garden, a hot water spring, a high-salt lake, a farmer's field contain anything from a hundred to a single species. Yet none is a true ecosystem.

Have you ever moved into a brand new house? My family did this some four years ago. The back garden was pretty sterile, just a rough patch of uninspiring brown earth. No trees, no flowers, no grass, no birds, no insects and, what's more, no worms. In order to make a nice, sunken flat lawn, with a rockery around it, I had to dig out tons of soil. Not a worm in sight. I checked the contract I had signed with the builders and, sure enough, no mention of worms! I should have read Darwin first. Darwin's last book *The Formation of Vegetable Mould, through the Action of Worms, with Observations on their Habits*, published in 1881 six months before his death, is a monument to the importance of these wriggly creatures.

After much observation and experiment Darwin concluded: 'Worms have played a more important part in the history of the world than most persons would at first suppose.' You can say that again! He estimated that in an English field of about an acre worms pass some ten tons, or over 10,000 kilograms, of soil through their bodies and bring it to the surface. This is equivalent to a layer of earth 0.2 inches (0.5 cm) thick over the entire acre. Darwin quotes von Hensen who, in 1877, estimated that below the surface of one field there might be more than 50,000 worms, a weight of some 350 pounds (175 kilograms) all busily sifting soil, aerating it and allowing mould and bacteria to improve the chemical composition for plants to germinate in it.

'Worms prepare the ground in an excellent manner for the growth of fibrous-rooted plants and for seedlings of all kinds,' Darwin tells us. Now my garden soil is full of worms. There are apple, pear and plum trees, shrubs, flowers and grass. All flourishing. I remember the excitement when, for the first time, we saw two of Britain's smallest garden birds flit across and land on the shed – wrens with their tails erect. In the summer the honeysuckle and buddleia attract butterflies, and bees and other insects abound. There are more insects in a healthy garden than there are in farmer's field. More than 1,800 have been found in one garden alone! The garden is now a mini-ecosystem. But what has brought about this change?

When does a group of organisms become an ecosystem? Is the term ecosystem a valid scientific concept at all, or is it a subjective view of Nature of little real scientific use? Is a garden an ecosystem or not? Is the sea made up of a single ecosystem or many? Just as we have had problems defining life, illness and death, so we have the same problem here. No group of animals, plants and microbes exists in isolation. Yet the interactions and geographical boundaries seem to make it appropriate to consider certain regions as defined and separate – a garden, a rock-pool, a field, the deep ocean, the top ten centimetres of ocean, a lake, a pond, a river, and so on. So can the application of the Rubicon principle to the environment and its evolution help?

An ecosystem is a network of physical, chemical and biological components whose interactions work in such a way as to maintain life. As with a cell, the reductionist can break down each ecosystem into its individual components – a list of species, the minerals and organic constituents, the climate, temperature, rainfall, sunlight and energy. These flow through the system. The analogue processes include carbon and nitrogen cycles, changes in the balance of numbers of particular species and the stability of the physical, chemical and biological components. But an ecosystem is clearly subject to thresholds – rubicons. These include the worry that it will become arid or sterile or be taken over by a mere handful of species, and its birth. In the Great Lakes of North America life is difficult to find. Over-farming in certain parts of the USA in the past century has resulted in arid zones and annual dust-storms. Why did these ecosystems cross a disastrous rubicon to become sick, or start on a sequence of death rubicons?

Walk a few hundred metres in any one of three directions from my house in South Wales on a July night and you will find three colonies of glow-worms, *Lampyris noctiluca*, apparently distinct. The females, which cannot fly, turn their undersurface upwards, often after climbing up a stem of grass, thereby exhibiting their amorous fire for flying males to find (Plate 3). On a typical July night one expects only a dozen or so, on a good night up to a hundred – far fewer than in the spectacular firefly meadows of the USA or tropical regions. There appear to be plenty of habitats of the right kind, moist grassy banks, in the regions between the glow-worm colonies; yet they remain distinct. Why?

The elegant orchid dune helleborine, *Epipactis dunensis*, can also be found in July and in flower. Yet, unlike the glow-worm whose colonies can be found all over southern Britain, there are only a handful of sites for this orchid in the whole of the United Kingdom. One is the Newborough sand-dune nature reserve, a kilometre or so from my Anglesey cottage, where I had the pleasure of writing this book. Why?

The crucial point is that in an ecosystem animals, plants, fungi and micro-organisms don't just live together, interacting and feeding off each other. The interactions cause groups of organisms to cross a series of physical, chemical and biological thresholds – rubicons. Any species managing to gain a foothold in a particular environment will modify the physical and chemical conditions, just as the worms did for my garden or species do in a rock-pool. And the composition of the entire atmosphere is of course dependent on the biosphere, while the climate and penetration of the Sun's rays are affected by the depth of the ozone layer. The question we must now ask is how do changes in these conditions cause an ecosystem to cross the Rubicon?

The garden of Eden is one ecosystem made up of mini-ecosystems. The key criterion for determining whether a particular environment has a distinct ecology is the ability of each system in its entirety to cross the Rubicon in response to external and internal stimuli, attackers or man's intervention.

A PLACE TO LIVE?

Anyone who has looked down from an aeroplane for the first time will have been struck by how clear are the boundaries of the towns and villages. The gardens, the fields and woods which surround them appear from thousands of metres up to be discrete. Yet on the ground they seem to straggle and to have very diffuse edges. Each of these domains will house its own community of animals, plants and micro-organisms. Ecology, which provides a conceptual view of an animal and plant community, emphasises the interactions of organisms with one another and the non-living components of the environment in which they live. But in contrast to our view from the aeroplane, it is on the ground that the boundaries of what we call ecosystems appear sharp and easily definable. From above we see that no such ecosystem is isolated from another. No colony of glow-worms is really separated from another. Nor is a community itself necessarily an ecosystem, however well defined it is.

Ecology has emerged in the latter part of this century as one of the most popular branches of biology, and to some it is the most important. But its roots lie in the eighteenth-century concept of the 'economy of Nature'. This was a comprehensive approach to life on Earth and embodied the belief that, although Nature appears to be always in flux or disordered, there is an underlying pre-ordained constancy and harmony. This harmony is in evidence in the writings of the early naturalists. White's *The Natural History of Selborne* was one of the first books to describe Nature and to ask questions about the changes and interactions within it. One particular puzzle to White, as we have seen, was the fate of swallows and swifts in winter. The perceptiveness of his observations can be clearly seen from this poem:

A naturalist's summer evening walk

Gilbert White, written between May 29 and August 30 1769. To Thomas Pennant, Esquire:

> ... equidem credo, quia sit divinitus illis Ingenium.
> Virg. Georg.

> When day declining sheds a milder gleam,
> What time the may-fly haunts the pool or stream;
> When the still owl skims round the grassy mead,
> What time the timorous hare limps forth to feed:
> Then be the time to steal adown the vale,
> And listen to the vagrant cuckoo's tale;
> To hear the clamorous curlew call his mate,
> Or the soft quail his tender pain relate;
> To see the swallow sweep the dark'ning plain
> Belated, to support her infant train;

To mark the swift in rapid giddy ring
Dash round the steeple, unsubdu'd of wing:
Amusive birds! – say where your hid retreat
When the frost rages and the tempests beat;
Whence your return, by such nice instinct led,
When spring, soft season, lifts her bloomy head?
Such baffled searches mock man's prying pride,
The God of NATURE is your secret guide!

While deep'ning shades obscure the face of day
To yonder bench, leaf-shelter'd, let us stray,
Till blended objects fail the swimming sight,
And all the fading landscape sinks in night;
To hear the drowsy dor come brushing by
With buzzing wing, or the shrill cricket cry;
To see the feeding bat glance through the wood;
To catch the distant falling of the flood;
While o'er the cliff th' awakened churn-owl hung
Through the still gloom protracts his chattering song;
While high in the air, and pois'd upon his wings,
Unseen, the soft enamour'd woodlark sings:
These, NATURE'S works, the curious mind employ,
Inspire a soothing melancholy joy:
As fancy warms, a pleasing kind of pain
Steals o'er the cheek, and thrills the creeping vein!

Each rural sight, each sound, each smell combine;
The tinkling sheep-bell, or the scent of kine;
The new-mown hay that scents the swelling breeze,
Or cottage-chimney smoking through the trees.
The chilling night-dews fall: away retire;
For see, the glow-worm lights her amorous fire!
Thus, ere night's veil had half obscured the sky,
Th' impatient damsel hung her lamp on high:
True to the signal, by love's meteor led,
Leander hasten'd to his Hero's bed.

Interestingly enough, as with ideas about the origin of the cell, the first
real scientific ecological observations were made by botanists. Early in the
nineteenth century plant geographers, following Alexander von Humboldt
(1769-1859), tried to correlate vegetation throughout the world with climate. They noticed distinct, mutually dependent communities containing
distinct species of plants, which were associated with particular environmental conditions. Much observation, not available to Gilbert White, who
lived in Oxford or Selborne for most of his adult life, became available from
the explorations of Linnaeus' pupils, from Joseph Banks with Captain
Cook, from Darwin on the *Beagle*, from Hooker and Huxley. Two seminal
publications at the end of the nineteenth century signalled the beginning
of modern ecology: the first (1895) by Eugenius Warming (1841-1924)
Plantesamfund ('Plant Communities'), the second (1898) by Andrea Schim-

per (1856-1901) *Pflanzengeographie auf physiologischer Grundlage* ('Plant Geography upon a Physiological Basis'). These books were a synthesis of where plants grow, i.e. plant geography, and their growth and reproduction, i.e. plant physiology.

Life has invaded every nook and cranny of the planet – the soil, caves, streams, rivers, lakes, rock pools, the deep sea, and the air. Not even the most hostile environments need be sterile. Algae can grow in concentrated sulphuric acid. Bacteria, algae and fungi can live at the extremes of both acidity and alkalinity, from pH 0 to pH 13. There are bacteria that grow in hot water springs above 90°C, and even sulphating bacteria that live and reproduce at 104°C, above the boiling point of water. And some bacteria, invertebrates and fish can survive and flourish in conditions of extreme cold, below 0°C, even down to -23°C. Yet if the temperature of a human being drops below about 30°C or rises above 42°C it soon dies.

The aim of the ecologist is to explain in scientific terms the distribution and abundance of species in particular environments: why they are found where they are in the numbers there, and how these are dependent on measurable environmental factors and how the organisms control the non-living domain. The balance of species and their numbers can be dramatically altered by a relatively small change in the physical or chemical surroundings. Conversely, a small change in the distribution of organisms, even the loss or appearance of a single species, can have a dramatic effect on both the biosphere and the physical and chemical conditions embraced by it.

But before considering the rubicons which determine 'a place in which to live' and which enable ecosystems to form and be maintained, we must shoot for the stars. We must look back at the planet Earth, or ocean if you wish, and take a global view – the garden of Eden, the entire Earth as one ecosystem, one ecosphere.

IS THE EARTH ALIVE?

'I consider the Earth to be a super-organism and its proper study should be by physiology.' Thus remarked James Hutton (1726-1797) in a lecture to the Royal Society of Edinburgh in 1785. Hutton was a Scot with a broad interest in natural science. He began his professional life in the law, and then, because of his interest in chemistry, tried medicine for a few years, studying at Edinburgh, in Paris and in Holland, where he qualified as MD in 1749. After developing, with his friend James Davie, a cheap method of making sal-ammoniac (ammonium chloride) used in dry batteries and in flux for soldering, he made enough money to become a farmer. By 1765, with a good income from the farm and the company making sal-ammoniac, he was able to devote more time to his science. He is regarded as one of the founders of geology as a science.

Two seminal papers by Hutton were presented in March and April of 1785 and published in 1788 in the Transactions of the Royal Society of

Edinburgh. They laid out his views on the Earth as a living organism: 'Theory of the Earth; or an Investigation of the Laws Observable in the Composition, Dissolution, and Restoration of Land Upon the Globe.' This led to a two-volume treatise published in 1795, *Theory of the Earth*. Hutton's ideas were not in keeping with those accepted by the scientific establishment and were vigorously attacked. What's new?! The key idea was that the forces eroding and moulding the rocks of his day were the same as those aeons ago. They were 'uniform'. But they took an enormously long time to produce observable effects. Nevertheless, by studying the forms and changes in rocks observable in his day, one could predict their origins and fate. As Hutton argued: 'In examining things present we have data from which to reason with regard to what has been. Time is to nature endless and as nothing.' The science of geology was born. Changes in the surface of the Earth were caused by familiar forces of wind, water, ice, land movements, volcanoes and earthquakes, sedimentation and life. The laws of Nature were constant, uniform. This was contrary to the widely held importance of water in moulding the Earth's topography – floods, upheavals, tidal waves and the like causing massive movements of land and fossils. Charles Lyell (1797-1875), a dominant figure in British science in the nineteenth century and, as we saw earlier, a mentor to the student Darwin, was to use the concept of 'uniformitarianism' extensively in his Principles of Geology – the present is the key to the past, the past is the key to the present.

Lamarck also had a holistic view of the Earth. He had a keen interest in meteorology and geology. He looked at Nature as a whole, and made many observations on the environment. Believing that environmental changes had consequential effects on the physiology of life, he remarked that, 'fluctuations of temperature open and close routes by which transpiration takes place ... changes in atmospheric humidity either rob us of our natural heat or maintain it'. The first insight into environmental rubicons.

Imaginative and visionary as Hutton and Lamarck were, the idea that the Earth is alive has come to the fore again recently as a result of 'Gaia'.

James E. Lovelock is a self-funding scientist living in Cornwall, not far from where Peter Mitchell established his hypothesis – chemiosmosis – explaining how the power-houses inside cells make their fuel, ATP. Lovelock is an original thinker and inventor. He invented a device known as 'the electron capture detector', which has had a major impact on environmental analysis, particularly of the atmosphere. Before working as an independent scientist from his home in Cornwall, he was consultant to the Jet Propulsion Laboratories in Pasadena USA, whose objective was to develop ways of detecting life on Mars and other planets. Life would have to exist in a fluid form, but would not necessarily need the vast water masses of the Earth. Rejecting ATP analysis and other tests for bacteria and fungi in the Martian soil, Lovelock realised that the atmosphere would hold the key to detecting life. It was in the gas exchange in the atmosphere central to life on Earth that one should look for evidence; not for life forms themselves, but for chemical conditions on a global level which could only be maintained if there was life present.

As a result he predicted that there was no life there, because the Martian atmosphere was at equilibrium. Just as we see in a live cell or organism, so for a planet to be alive the chemistry surrounding life must be in dynamic flux. Once it reaches equilibrium it is dead.

Professor Lovelock first presented his Gaia hypothesis in 1969 to a scientific meeting on the origins of life on Earth. But it was his two books, *Gaia: A New Look at Life on Earth* (1979) and *The Ages of Gaia: A Biography of Our Living Earth* (1988), which re-created the ideas of Hutton and Lamarck. The Earth is alive! It was a new conceptual framework for understanding and predicting the effects of changes in the number of species and the distribution of organisms on the environment, and vice versa. To Lovelock the Earth ought to be considered as a whole – a living organism. What was new about his hypothesis was that the Gaian saw the Earth as a giant homeostatic organism. Just as the homeostatic regulatory processes in our body maintain the physical and chemical conditions for life, so the homeostatic regulators embodied in the physics and chemistry of the Earth on a grander scale respond to any disturbance so as to maintain the conditions for life. This is no religious or vitalist hypothesis. Nor are the forces of Gaia altruistic, for in order to maintain the conditions for life one or even thousands of species may have to made extinct.

In the early Greek cosmology Gaia (poetic form of 'Gê', and Latinised as 'Gaea'), the daughter of Chaos, was the personification of the Earth. She was the wife of Ouranos, the god of heaven, and the mother of various offspring including the Giants, Titans and Furies. Cronos, the youngest Titan, became the father of Zeus, who overthrew his father and succeeded him as the supreme god. Gaia was thought of as the original holder of the oracular shrine at Delphi. She was the giver of dreams, and the nourisher of plants and young children. For this reason, the Nobel-prize-winning novelist of 1983, William Golding (1911-1993), author of *Lord of the Flies*, and Lovelock's neighbour in Cornwall, suggested her name for the theory in order to immortalise Lovelock's hypothesis of the 'living Earth'.

What is the essence of the Gaia hypothesis? Is it an hypothesis at all, or simply a restatement of the balance of Nature, as some critics say?

There are many features of Gaia which are in close harmony with Rubicon, particulary the need to take a holistic view of Nature if we are to define the problem. Lovelock writes: 'As a scientist I observe, measure, analyse and describe phenomena. Before I can do these things I need to know what I am observing.' In the first Leslie Cooper Memorial Lecture at Plymouth on 10 April 1989 he argued, convincingly, that to understand the Earth we need physiology as well as the conventional approaches of the geochemist, geophysicist and biologist. He showed how discoveries about the atmosphere can be made – the importance of dimethyl sulphide, a gas emitted from seaweeds and other marine algae, as greenhouse gases, for example.

A lot of the high-energy radiation from the Sun, including visible light, is reflected back into space off the Earth's atmosphere. But some gets through and beams down to the Earth's surface, where it is absorbed and the energy converted to heat. The surface warms up. Very little of the radiation passing down through the atmosphere is absorbed, unless there are holes in the ozone layer. Molecules with particular bond structures, such as carbon dioxide and water vapour, absorb low-energy infra-red rays. These rays are generated when the surface warms up. The more carbon dioxide, the more of this secondary radiation is prevented from escaping back into space. The atmosphere warms up. So the Earth's surface as a whole gets hotter. It has been estimated that, at the present rate of global warming, the average temperature of the Earth by the year 2100 could increase by 5°C. At the poles the rises in temperature may be much higher. The reason this is called the 'greenhouse' effect is that we use a greenhouse deliberately to allow the carbon dioxide generated by the plants to act as a heat sink, warming the 'house' for seedlings and exotic plants to flourish.

The concept of an average temperature of the Earth is a little difficult to grasp, when at the poles the temperature is sub-zero and at the equator more than 40°C (100°F). The idea of 'mean temperature' is really meaningless. What matters is the weather and oceanic rubicons crossed as a result of gradual changes in temperature. The melting of the Antarctic ice will result in losses of islands, estuaries and so on. Some areas will change from being fertile to being arid, as a result of prolonged drought. In others the ecology will be dramatically transformed as a result of floods caused by excessive rainfall. Loss of food for an animal will lead to extinction from certain areas. We must relate the temperature of ecological zones to the stability of the biosphere. The surface of the ocean varies enormously all over the world. One hundred metres from my house it is about 10°C, and in summer it may warm up to 16°C. In the Arctic or Antarctic it may go below zero, without freezing. In the Baltic in winter it may be around zero and yet in the summer be high enough for a pleasant swim. In the deep ocean, however, the temperature is quite constant. A flow of water from the Antarctic keeps it at about 4-6°C. Many of the creatures which live here are much less adaptable to temperature fluctuations than those on the surface.

Gaia also provides a holistic view of the evolution of life over 4,000 million years, and of the way it has moulded the chemical environment on land, sea and air. But the hypothesis has been severely criticised. Criticisms range from 'Oh, but that's obvious. We knew that already. What's new?' to 'There are no mechanisms for selecting such self-compensating forces on a global level. Evolution by natural selection works at the level of individual species.' 'Gaia,' it is said, 'isn't even a real hypothesis; rather it is a framework for looking at the interactions between the physics and chemistry of the Earth's surface and atmosphere, its oceans, and the biology.' As such, it does a good job. Lovelock's books and articles are a joy to read. But I must take Gaia to task over one crucial issue – *homeostasis*.

Lovelock latches on to this concept because, as I pointed out in Chapter Two, it is so entrenched in physiological thought. Yes, we should use physiology to examine the Earth. Yes, we should consider the Earth as 'alive', one giant organism. But *no*, we must reject the misconception of homeostasis. Rather Gaia, like any living cell or organism, follows the principles of Rubicon. Chemical, physical and biological events occur at a global level and are thresholds. Gaia crosses the Rubicon. The Earth does not spend its entire time moving smoothly in a graded manner, correcting small fluctuations in temperature, acidity, salt and organic concentration, as in a system aiming at 'stasis'. So, if we are to predict the future of our environment, we must apply the principles of Rubicon. Thresholds in eco-zones and the Earth as a whole must be identified. Then, as we did for individual cells, we must unravel the pathway of mini-rubicons and smooth change which took the particular ecosystem to the banks.

As we saw for cells and organisms, so events in the ecosystems of the Earth involve movement, secretion, uptake, disposal, transformation, reproduction and death. An ecosystem can also defend itself against attack. Animals, plants and microbes have evolved to protect both their internal and external environments upon which their survival and reproduction depends. Man's apparent destruction of certain environments illustrates this *par excellence*.

An ecosystem is continuously under physical, chemical and biological attack. Physical attackers include fluctuations in temperature, wind, ice, glaciers, water movement, land movements, earthquakes and volcanoes. Chemical attackers include rain (acid or not) and changes in water or soil composition. Biological scavengers and polluters are everywhere. The attack may be a rapid burst of 'fire' lasting minutes, hours or days, or it can take millions of years, for example plate tectonic movements. There is no inherent reason why defending forces should have evolved in the purely physical and chemical processes of the Earth. However, evolution has led to protection mechanisms in living organisms. Populations of species move to find food, or to escape the ice, drowning or a forest fire. As a result of environmental change, living organisms cross the Rubicon in vast numbers; so the ecosystem itself crosses a rubicon. The incredible changes in species that follow a forest fire are a shining example of such a rubicon. There are many cases of Gaia defending herself successfully against attack. But there are also cases of the defence failing to prevent the ecosystem crossing the ultimate rubicon. It dies, and like an individual organism it decays. The Great Lakes in the USA, the dust bowl of the mid-West, and, by natural forces, the conversion of a fertile plain into a desert of blustering sand are examples.

Lovelock tells us that 'the chain saw is a an invention far more lethal than the hydrogen bomb'. But is it? Certainly the Gaian method forces us to consider the importance of forests on a global scale. But how much oxygen/carbon dioxide exchange can a field of genetically engineered grass carry out, compared with a forest? Where are the rubicons? In fact the long-term danger is the massive loss of carbon as carbonate in the shells of invertebrates. Unless this carbon is retrieved, the Earth's atmosphere may no longer be able to sustain plant life as we know it. But we are unlikely to see this in our lifetime!

Lovelock's global approach has led him to identify some important new features in the atmosphere – the formation of rain clouds and the production of gases from marine algae, for example. In the early 1970s it was clear that there was a global problem about sulphur. Where was it all going? Careful measurement and calculation of the amounts of sulphur washed off the land into rivers and then down into the sea showed that there was a global discrepancy of millions of tons. There wasn't enough from weathering of sulphur-containing rocks, from extraction by plants, or even from man's burning of fossil fuels containing sulphur. There had to be a route back for sulphur from land to sea through the atmosphere. Rejecting the stink-gas hydrogen sulphide, Lovelock and colleagues showed that a possible candidate was a methylated form of the gas, dimethyl sulphide, the familiar smell of seaweed at the seaside. But there is also a dangerous side to such methylation reactions: the Rubicon consequences which have been seen in Japan. Bacteria in marine mud can convert toxic elements such as mercury, arsenic and lead into methyl compounds. These, like their sulphurous relatives, are volatile. The gases formed as a result of pollution from Japanese industry were absorbed by fish and other organisms. A discharge of methyl mercury by Japanese industry into the Sea of Japan crippled and killed several unsuspecting people who ate the contaminated fish. Such toxic methylations had occurred before. In the last century methyl arsenic produced by moulds on wallpaper pigments killed several unsuspecting sleepers.

The average amount of salt in the sea is 3.5 per 100 grammes. This has been about the level for millions of years. Yet day-in-day-out more salt is added to the sea from the rivers which flow into it. It has been estimated that this would be enough to double the salt concentration of the sea within 10-100 million years. Gaia to the rescue. The sedimentation of the salt which occurs continuously is not a simple chemical crystallisation, but a biological sedimentation. Tiny algae in vast amounts sink to the bottom of the sea taking with them carbonates and silicates.

But Gaia goes beyond this. It argues that homeostatic mechanisms, chemical feedback reactions, have evolved so as deliberately to maintain the chemical conditions within the atmosphere and sea compatible with life. Gaia will not commit suicide. The objection to this super-organism concept is that there was no mechanism in natural selection by which such processes could have been selected. So Lovelock invented the 'daisy-world' – a world in which there were black and white daisies. It is a fact of physics that black objects absorb more light-energy than white ones. A shirt is white is because it has reflected the light hitting it, rather than absorbing it as the black one has. Next time you are in a carpark in summer place your hand on the roof of a black car and then on the roof of a white one.

Thus black daisies will get warmer than white daisies, which tend to favour cooler temperatures, while the more black daisies cover the planet the hotter it will get. Using a computer model, Lovelock and Watson showed that these two simple daisies can establish a feedback system, keeping the temperature of the planet relatively stable.

The most important message of Gaia is that we need to think globally when trying to understand the interactions between the biosphere, the salts in the sea and the gases in the atmosphere. But my fundamental objection is not that feedback mechanisms have not evolved, but rather the application of the principles of homeostasis. As we saw in Chapter Two, for the human body this is a misconception. Small changes in temperature, acidity and salt can cause individual organisms, and thus whole ecosystems, to cross the Rubicon. What Gaians therefore need to address now is what combination, location and timing of small or large changes in environmental conditions will take an ecosystem or the entire planet to the banks of a rubicon and then across. Only then will we be able to predict, and thus prevent, the consequences for our lives, those of other life-forms and the aesthetic appeal of them, in a decade or a million years. A further objection is that there are many extreme environments in which no organism-interaction or global-protection mechanisms are required. Organisms have invaded habitats, adapted and competed to survive. They multiply and pass on their genes to following generations.

Gaia is a much more positive framework for the environment than the depressing scenario set by Rachel Carson in the 1960s. Lovelock has made predictions which have led to important discoveries about the environment. But, while I admire the idea and the elegance of the arguments in Lovelock's books, I must take him to task over homeostasis. Just as Cannon and his disciples were fooled into analysing falsely the self-compensating forces in the body, so I believe are those who follow the Gaia hypothesis. One organism cannot form an ecosystem. Daisy world is not the real world. Small changes can and do induce ecosystems and the Earth as a whole to cross the Rubicon. The challenge is to discover how an ecosystem reaches the banks of a rubicon, and what the mechanism and consequences of the crossing are.

AN ECOSYSTEM IN FIVE DIMENSIONS

A typhoon, a hurricane, a tornado, lightning, a tidal wave, a forest fire are all dramatic weather changes which can cause havoc to an ecosystem, resulting in many eco-rubicons being crossed by multitudes of species. The ecosystem is rarely destroyed. It is just altered, sometimes irrevocably. Even after a forest fire green shoots appear. There are even some plants that have evolved for such an eventuality. The heat triggers seeds buried in the ground to cross a rubicon, and they germinate. With the trees gone, the light now penetrates to the forest floor and provides the energy for the small plants to grow and produce their seeds. The forest then goes through a series of rubicons, returning after some years to its woodland state, where most of the light is captured by the green leaves on the branches on the tops of the trees. But *small* fluctuations in weather can also cause an ecosystem to cross the Rubicon. As we saw in the blood, small changes in temperature, salt and water can lead to threshold changes. The loss of a few inches of water over a winter or so leads to drought the following summer – the earth cracks and the reservoirs run dry, with consequential disaster for many plants and animals.

A breath of wind is necessary for tree seeds to spread and find a fertile spot. There is a beautiful lake-side picnic spot in the mountains my family often stops at on the way to Anglesey. There you will find a grand oak, probably several hundreds of years old. I leave you to imagine what rubicon was crossed when I discovered it. One October I found the ground littered with hundreds of acorns. Looking more closely, I found that those that had survived my visit had, to an acorn, little white shoots springing from them. I took a handful home, and all are now tiny oak trees in pots awaiting the identification of a site to establish my forest. Yet on returning to the oak tree the following spring I found that, unlike my potted acorns, none of the acorns I had left had developed into trees. I deny that this was my fault. On looking round I found some saplings but at a decent distance from the parent oak. Seeds need to travel a distance from their parents in order to develop into mature adults.

During 4,000 million years of Gaia, ecological rubicons abound, some brought about by purely physical forces, others by biological ones: atmospheric changes, plate tectonics leading to separation of the land masses, ice ages, flower pollination by insects and so on. The evolution of Gaia has been critically dependent on a sequence of rubicon crossings, creating the route to banks by an accumulation of gradual changes.

Rubicon is the fifth dimension of an ecosystem acting at two levels: events in the ecosystem as a whole, and the rubicon sequence which determines the timing and nature of these events. Each has an analogy with the rubicons in a cell or intact organism. Rubicons in the ecosystem as a whole include:

1. Formation of an ecosystem – the transition from a community to an ecosystem, i.e. its birth.
2. Change to a new balance, a new ecosystem – transformation.
3. Spread or contraction of an ecosystem – movement.
4. Secretion of DNA, in the form of animals, plants, microbes or seeds, from the ecosystem to outside – secretion.
5. Pollution of the ecosystem – pathology.
6. Death of an ecosystem – death

Rubicons within an ecosystem include:

1. A casual visitor establishing itself as a permanent resident.

2. Permanent loss of a resident species.
3. Establishment of a symbiotic relationship.

The causes of these rubicons include a phase change or separation, the seasons and the day-night cycle. And yet it is seldom that an ecosystem disappears completely. Why? Because, as in the cell or a whole organism, a true ecosystem has mechanisms defending it against attack.

THE PROPHETS OF DOOM

Many people of my generation can remember precisely what they were doing at 6 p.m. GMT on Friday 22 November 1963. I was on my way out to choir practice when the news came that President Kennedy had been assassinated. But who, I wonder, remembers what happened at about 9 a.m. GMT on Saturday 18 March 1967. I was on holiday, taking a week off before the last thrust of study before my final undergraduate exams, staying with my cousins in Plymouth. The news broke that a 970-foot oil tanker, the Torrey Canyon, had run aground on the Pollard Rock of the Seven Stones, some fifteen miles west of Land's End and only an ecological stone's throw from Plymouth Sound. Six of her tanks were torn open by the impact. By 30 March, after being bombed, the tanker disappeared from view. Much of its 117,000 tons of crude oil, originally bound for Milford Haven from Kuwait, had spilled into the sea. Havoc. Dead sea birds, fish, seals, and shellfish were everywhere. But perhaps even more damage was done by the ignorant panic-spraying of detergents in a wild attempt to disperse the oil. In several areas so much detergent had been sprayed that its smell was obvious. It was the detergent that killed vast numbers of rock-clinging limpets, leaving the algae on which they browsed to grow rampant. Within a few weeks some rocks were dominated by their bright-green foliage, and the carnage of oil plus detergent was there for all to witness on the beaches, in the rock pools, on the sea's surface and beneath it.

The Marine Biological Association, founded in 1884, and based at Plymouth, had never seen such activity! All scientists sprang into action, redirecting their research to help prevent an environmental disaster of unimaginable magnitude. The lucrative tourist industry of Devon and Cornwall was not happy either, to put it mildly. The beautiful sandy coves, the rocky shores rich in marine fauna and flora, were about to be destroyed, precipitating a devastating loss of income from tourists and holiday-makers.

Yet, go there now and you would never know that the Torrey Canyon had ever let loose her black death twenty-five years ago. Similar disasters have hit Britanny off the west coast of France, Canada and several other parts of the world. Yet Nature has sprung back. It defended itself. The environment may have been unpleasant for man for a while, but it has recovered. The potential devastation was miscalculated. Even as I write a massive oil spillage off the Shetlands has thankfully been dispersed by seas whipped up by gale-force winds. Yet there are cases of the ultimate environmental rubicon having been crossed owing to Man's carelessness or greed. The Great Lakes of North America are heavily polluted. There has been great concern that they might become virtually sterile as a result of toxic pollution from years of industrial effluent and other abuses by man of the lakes' waters.

What we must therefore consider when trying to predict the effect of a natural or man-made disaster is what rubicons will be crossed, in what order and at what times. As we saw for a tiny cell, so the signals that will trigger an environmental rubicon must reach their target. And what of Nature's defence? If we wish to restore an environment after havoc has been wrought, we must understand the molecular, cellular and organism defence-mechanisms which enable the particular ecosystem to cross the rubicons back to full health. And man can play his part in the recovery process.

Down the road from my house is the site of a mediaeval village. Cosmeston goes back at least to AD 1320, and was established in a pleasant rural environment not far from the sea. But the Industrial Revolution put paid to all that. In the 1890s a cement-manufacturing plant was built there. By the 1920s the output of limestone from the quarries topped 170,000 tonnes a year. And there was worse to come. Once the limestone had run out, the quarries were taken over in the 1960s as a rubbish tip. The area became an eyesore, a scar on the side of the beautiful Vale of Glamorgan countryside. Yet, thanks to an initiative set up by the local council, the area has returned across the Rubicon (Plate 9(b)). Now the 200 or so acres have become Cosmeston Country Park. It contains two lakes, breeding grounds for great-crested grebe, mallard, swan, coot and other wild fowl. The 200-year-old oaks in the woodland have been saved and are a habitat for woodpeckers, foxes, squirrels, pipistrelle and noctule bats, and fungi, while in the meadows and marshes can be found butterflies, spotted and bee orchids, *and* glow-worms! The most I have found here on one night is 105. But without one man's efforts to remove another man's debris this ecosystem might have been destroyed for ever.

The cult book for environmentalists in the 1960s was *Silent Spring* by Rachel Carson (1907-1964). Specialising in English at the Pennsylvania College for Women, Carson had always wanted to be a writer. But she had a life-time interest in wildlife and natural history. So, in 1929, she took her degree in biology and followed it with post-graduate studies in genetics at Johns Hopkins and then zoology at the University of Maryland. She became particularly expert in marine organisms, working at Woods Hole from 1951 to 1952. In 1951 she published *The Sea Around Us*, but it was for her prophecies of environmental pollution and disaster in *Silent Spring* (1962) that she became famous. She painted a depressing picture of environmental disaster and pollution. Though oil pollution in the sea was a worry, the great tanker disasters lay ahead. The main concern in the 50s and early 60s was the indiscriminate use of herbicides and insecticides, particularly DDT, which was sprayed over huge areas from the air. There was also concern about the heavy metals – mercury, cadmium and, of course, lead from petrol. What became clear, as the analysts dissected chemically the sterile eggs of birds and dead animals, was that these substances accumulated in organisms at the end of the food-chains. As Carson pointed out, 'What we have to face is not an occasional dose of poison which has accidentally got into some article of food, but a *persistent* and *continuous* poisoning of the whole human environment.' The poisons were getting into meat, milk and plant food.

But there was an analytical problem. Leslie Cooper was a marine chemist working at the Marine Biological Association Laboratory in Plymouth, where he became Deputy Director. As an expert in the chemistry of the sea, he was asked to participate in several public enquiries examining the environmental problems likely to arise from the building of large industrial plants at certain sites around the British coast. He pointed out at one such inquiry that the problem was that many of the chemical tests at the time were less sensitive than the biological indicators. The lawyers kept shouting, 'But the mercury is either there or it is not there!' This naïvety is based on the assumption that you can keep on going down in the sensitivity of an assay. But assays also have their rubicons. There is a statistical criterion for defining the detection limit – the smallest amount we can detect in the lab. But this may be greater than that at which accumulation occurs in a living organism. The converse also applies, particularly now that we have such exquisitely sensitive methods for detecting substances in biological fluids and the sea.

The fact that we can measure it doesn't mean that it is necessarily poisonous. All organisms have a highly sophisticated chemical defence against poisons. The key analytical question therefore is how much has to accumulate in a bird's egg to make it cross the infertile rubicon, and when do the defences fail to prevent a toxic chemical provoking damage to cell and tissue function, or even death? Now that the wanton use of DDT has ceased, the peregrines are on their way back on the sea-cliffs of Wales and other parts of the UK. They hadn't crossed the ultimate rubicon after all.

In 1933 the ecologist Ado Leopold gave a good analysis of the relationship of man to the environment when he wrote, 'The Golden Rule tries to integrate the individual to society; democracy to integrate social organisation to the individual. There is as yet no ethic dealing with man's relation to the land, which is still strictly economic, entailing privileges but not obligations.' Albert Schweitzer (1875-1965), the German theologian, philosopher, organist and missionary doctor in equatorial Africa, who won the Nobel Peace prize in 1952, identified two important things regarding man's lack of vision over the environment: 'Man has lost the capacity to foresee and to forestall. He will end by destroying the Earth. I am pessimistic about the human race because it is too ingenious for its own good.'

We live in an age in which society is ever more concerned about pollution in the environment caused by man's greed or thoughtlessness. The news-papers are full of articles, written to hype us up and make us buy newspapers, about the scandal of radioactive or other toxic waste, of metal ion pollution and the effects of acid rain, of the loss of ecosystems caused by modern farming methods, of the loss of breeding bird colonies likely to be caused by marine and freshwater hydroelectric schemes. It is salutary to remember that perhaps the greatest cause of pollution is the biosphere itself. All plants produce toxins. The food we eat, the water we drink, the air we breathe are all full of toxins, generated not by man's chemical industry but by animals, plants, fungi and microbes. But we are ready for them. We have detoxification mechanisms in the liver and all our tissues. But what if a pollutant was produced for which we had no defence?

One prospector thought he had a bonanza when the Chernobyl radio-active cloud came over. His Geiger counter went berserk. What a disappointment he had when he returned to civilisation. The sheep feeding on Welsh grass became too 'hot' to eat. But what will be the after-effects? The natural radiation on the Earth's surface and the radiation from the Sun are very different from those when life began on Earth. These will not kill Gaia, but they may take her across a series of rubicons which will irrevocably change the balance of life on this planet, including the demise of man himself.

The area of USA known as the south-western High Plains consists of a bit of Colorado, south-western Kansas, Texas, Oklahoma and north-eastern New Mexico. After a period of overgrazing, bad land management and poor rainfall, a severe drought occurred in the 1930s. The top soil, having lost its anchoring grass roots, got blown up into dust storms by heavy spring winds. The 'black blizzards' blocked out the sunlight and piled up in drifts. Thousands of families were forced to leave at the height of the depression. But the wind erosion was halted by the planting of windbreaks. By the 1940s much of the area had recovered. Now there is a worry in parts of East Anglia that excessive farming and over-draining of the rich soil may also cause dust storms. The dust storms in the USA were associated with a drop of only 10-20 per cent in average annual rainfall and an increase of only 0.8°C in temperature between 1931 and 1940. This was enough to precipitate a drought-rubicon. Similar effects of relatively small climatic changes have been observed in Africa, the Middle East and India. Droughts and floods are not necessarily provoked by complete loss of rain or monsoons. This is the message of Rubicon. Wiping out thousands of buffalo and replacing them with herds of cattle in parts of the West also had dramatic effects on the grassland habitats – they crossed a rubicon. What will be the long-term effects of the excessive killing of whales for a century or more? It is not simply the demise of one species that Rubicon must consider, bad as this is.

The view from the cliff top near where I live is spectacular. Across the Severn estuary is the splendid Somerset coast-line. In between are two islands, one – Flatholm – from where early in May 1897 Guglielmo Marconi

(1874-1937) transmitted to Lavernock point the first-ever wireless message over the sea. When we moved here four years ago the cliff top was also a mini-ecosystem, with shrubs, small trees, flowers, birds for the season – long-tailed tits in winter and great tits in summer – butterflies and other insects, small rodents and so on. But some residents couldn't see the view properly, so a bit of environmental vandalism was perpetrated. A cutting machine arrived one afternoon and cut everything down, and I mean everything, to a height of a few centimetres! Gone were the flowers, the birds' nests and flowering trees. All that was left was some motheaten-looking grass. Guess what? Within a few months the cliff underwent a disastrous rubicon – two substantial rock falls. As a result, the fence has had to be moved back several metres. Tree roots stabilise such cliff tops. Fortunately, a year later my annoyance had subsided a little. The ecosystem has returned this year, but it looks completely different. Yet is it? The flowers have been marvellous. There are far more of them and they are far more varied than last year. Tree shoots are to be seen everywhere. In three or four years the top will be as it was. I can't believe it. As I check this manuscript, I hear the noise of the scrub-cutting machine again. Will the environment department of the local authority never learn?

But it is not only man that is responsible for cataclysmic effects on the environment. Nature herself can be even more severe. The eruption of the volcano at Mount St Helens in the USA was such a catastrophe. Mount St Helens in the Cascade Range, south-west Washington, had been dormant since 1857. But on 27 March 1980 it awoke with a vengeance, with an explosive eruption of steam. And on 18 May it produced the largest volcanic explosion ever recorded in the US. The blast flattened forests and showered dust and debris over many miles. By October 34 people were dead, 32 missing and some 100 square miles (260 sq km) of forest obliterated. But Nature has fought back. Green plants are beginning to return to the sterile dusty slopes. The ecosystem which is re-establishing itself may be very different from the one destroyed by the explosion and ash, but it will at least be alive. This first rubicon has already been crossed, the environment has been reborn. Each new species, each copse, each live pond represents a mini-rubicon in which organism interaction has been re-established.

However, these arguments must not encourage complacency. Each bird killed, each tree chopped down, each whale harpooned is an individual tragedy. As a lover of Nature I have empathy with anyone who gets hot under the collar about people who destroy just to make a fast buck. But I urge him, in the interest of the objectivity upon which the credibility of his political lobbying critically depends, to take a positive approach. From every evil can come good. The marriage of Gaia and Rubicon gives, I hope, the necessary means positively to preserve the Earth which we inherited and leave it in a form from which future generations can derive equal inspiration.

Our selfish concern is that the ecosystems we enjoy and upon which our survival depends may be under threat. But, as with human pathology,

Rubicon argues that we must look at a sequence of thresholds. Our view of the physics and chemistry must not be dominated by the final result. Dust to dust. Rubicon, like Gaia, looks at each ecosystem and the Earth itself as it did at an individual organism or cell. Changes induced by man, climate, or Earth forces may be compensated for by themselves. But, as we saw for homeostasis in the body, small changes can induce rubicons in the individual components of the living system. Some may appear analogous to the body's defence, and restore the status quo after an attack. But others may send the ecosystem down a pathway of destruction, where there is no return across those rubicons which have been crossed.

Let us now turn to a positive rubicon between species in an ecosystem – symbiosis.

SYMBIOSIS

As you drive in to Snowdonia along the A5, after the tiny village of Capel Curig you will see on your left a mountain with two large rocks seemingly cemented on to a peak – Adam and Eve on the peak of Tryfan (the 'y' sounding like the 'o' in shove). As you climb up the heathery slopes to reach them, you will find an extraordinary yellowy-black organism splashed on the surface of some of the rocks. They are lichens which have found a way of surviving in some pretty inhospitable habitats. The marine environment of the Isle of Anglesey is rich in them, the rocks around the shore being coloured grey, orange, yellow or black with their life forms. Some even get wetted every day by the incoming tide. They are also responsible for some of the familiar colours on the trunks of trees in a forest. But when you examine these colours a little more closely you find that this array of colour is not caused by one organism, but rather by two in close harmony.

It was H.A. de Bary (1831-1888) who, after showing in 1866 that lichens were really a marriage between an alga and a fungus, proposed in 1879 that the word *symbiosis* should be used to describe such a union. Symbiosis comes from the Greek *sym*, 'together with' and *bios*, 'life'. W.T.P. Pfeffer (1845-1920) had described in 1877 a micro-fungus now called a mycorrhiza which F. Kamiensky (1851-1912) showed formed a successful partnership with certain trees. In fact we now know that for orchids to germinate in the wild they must fall on soil where the seed can be infected by such a mycorrhiza. Otherwise the thousands, even millions, of tiny, nutrient-poor seeds shed by the orchid pods will fail to get the food they need to grow into a mature orchid plant. The relationship is of mutual benefit. In a lichen the photosynthetic alga produces sugars which are absorbed by the fungus as energy-supply and produce vitamins, while the fungus captures water vapour from the air and provides shade for the light-sensitive alga.

Micro-organisms and fungi are found in symbiotic relationships in many natural and man-made environments. As schoolboys we tasted our first alcoholic beverage as the result of a symbiotic gelatinous complex of a yeast and a bacterium, the 'ginger-beer plant', fermenting sugar. 'Tea-cider' in the Orient is the ferment from sweetened tea by a 'mould' which forms on the surface – the symbiosis again of a yeast and a bacterium. As more and more such close and beneficial relationships were revealed, both big and small, symbiosis became synonymous with a beneficial relationship. But the more one found the more confused the story became. In some relationships both organisms seemed to benefit, while in others one or both suffered.

That not all symbiotic relationships are beneficial to both organisms was realised by a contemporary of de Bary, P. Vuillemin. Vuillemin thought of symbiosis as the phenomenon in which two organisms live together with mutual advantage to each other, but in 1889 he defined *antibiosis*, in which one organism acted deleteriously on another. What then is the difference between a symbiont, that we tend to think of as beneficial to the partner, and an organism that obviously damages the partner – a parasite or a saprophyte? Should the definition of symbiosis return to the original simple definition of de Bary in his phrase 'des Zusammenlebens ungleich-namiger Organismen' – the living together of two distinct organisms without distinguishing benefit or harm to other species. What Rubicon argues is that the close interaction between two distinct species, which is the essence of symbiosis, is best seen as a pathway of rubicons within two time-frames, contemporary and evolutionary. Let's look at some examples.

Symbiosis is particularly fascinating among micro-organisms, though there are many symbioses between microbes and higher organisms and between higher organisms themselves. The weird-looking deep-sea angler fish has evolved a remarkable method of attracting its prey. It hangs a luminous lure in front of its mouth. But unlike the luminous animals we have met in previous chapters the angler does not make its own light. This is achieved by symbiosis. The organ at the tip of the lure contains a dense culture of luminous bacteria. At 10^8 per millilitre, this is sufficient to produce a high enough concentration to switch on the genes responsible for the light-generating proteins. There are several other species of fish and squid which carry symbiotic light-emitting bacteria. The pony fish carries them in its gut, with living 'fibre optics' to take the light to the surface. Flash-light fish have large symbiotic bacterial organs just below the eye. By moving a flap of skin, or by rotating the organ they can generate a series of rubicons. The flashes tell their companions about food and predators. During the Israeli-Egyptian war in the 1970s soldiers, seeing lights in the water at night, lobbed in hand-grenades to kill the divers who they presumed were lurking in the water. Next morning, to their surprise, the beach was littered with dead flash-light fish. And such luminous symbiosis is not restricted to the sea. I have already discussed the parasitic infection of wounds and decaying bodies by luminous bacteria from the soil (above p. 45). One remarkable nematode, keen for attention by day and night, carries a culture of these bacteria in its gut. After infecting a host these make it blue-luminous by night, while it is red by day.

But how the initial infection rubicon is crossed in these symbiotic luminous organs is still unclear. The Rubicon sequence is as follows: infection of the egg, embryo, or young adult; appearance of the light organ; growth and development of the light organ; infection of the light organ, followed by growth of the bacterial culture till a critical concentration of the autoinducer results in visible light. As we saw in Chapter Two, potentially luminous bacteria are in the sea all over the world, and are often present in the soil. However, the bacteria in the light organs of the fish and squid which have such symbiotic relationships are difficult to culture, unlike those from the sea water. Furthermore, recent work on the DNA of the symbiotic luminous bacteria has shown that it is not the same as the DNA in the free-floating species. This suggests that the bacteria are different species, and that the symbiotic infection is passed on via the egg.

Examples of bacterial symbiosis are plentiful in both plants and animals. In 1887 H. Hellriegel (1831-1895) and H. Wilfarth discovered that the nodules on leguminous plants like clover can fix nitrogen, while the herbivores which eat the grass in which the clover often grows would not be able to digest this green food without symbiotic bacteria in their guts. Bacteria in the guts of cows, sheep and other ruminants convert sugar walls into nutrients. We cannot digest grass because we lack the enzymes to rubicon bacterial cell walls, and we do not have the bacteria that cows have.

And there are lots of examples of symbiotic algae and dinoflagellates. The delicate hydra which can be found clinging to a jam-jar of pond water can sometimes be green, or even brown from a Scottish loch, because of symbiotic algae. And there are also large organisms exhibiting symbioses. Birds sit on the back of wildebeest and peck off insects. Jelly-fish and corals exhibit many symbioses. One of the most famous is between ten species of tropical anemone and 26 species of fish, one called the clown fish. They live within the protective stinging tentacles of the anemone, immune because of a thin layer of mucus which protects them against the anemone's 'microsyringes' loaded with poison – the nematocysts. The anemone benefits because the clown fish drives away other fish that want to eat it. Other fish have similar symbiotic relationships with big jelly-fish. Green hydra, a relative of the jelly-fish – one of the few fresh water ones in fact – harbours symbiotic algae. Other Cnidarians have symbiotic relations with algae, fish and invertebrates: anemones find a moving support on which to grow on the backs of crabs and whelk shells with hermit crabs inside; zooxanthellae (flagellate protozoans) and zoochlorellae (algae) are required by certain corals, which is why the coral can only survive in shallow water where the light can penetrate. These algae and protozoa provide oxygen and nutrients, using the carbon dioxide and waste products of the host. Another mutually beneficial symbiotic rubicon.

Grass fires attract rollers and bee-eaters which swoop into the flames to capture fleeing insects. Certain kingfishers excavate their burrows into large termite mounds, some nesting in them. The number of termite mounds therefore affects the population of kingfishers. But birds can also help insects. In the nest of the African hornbill more than 400 individual insect species, mostly larvae, were found, and they were alive and kicking.

But the concept of symbiosis is not restricted to separate species. It exists within species and gives us clues to the pathway of evolution of multicellular organisms. The tissues and the sub-cellular structures are in symbiotic interaction from conception to death – once again sometimes beneficial, sometimes harmful, but never lethal or both would die. There are examples of symbiosis within populations of the same species too. What else are the players of the stock-market, advertisers and the banks but symbionts! Or are they parasites?

Finally in this section I return to Angelsey, where in spring and summer some fifty per cent of species of British orchid can be found. In June and July you may be lucky enough to find the exquisite bee orchid, *Ophrys apifera*. This orchid and several of its close relatives resemble various insects. The question therefore arises whether these shapes have evolved as mimicry to attract them. In fact the bee orchid probably got its name from the similarity of the hairy front lobe of the flower – the labellum – with that of the abdomen of the bumble bee, rather than its superficial similarity with the colours of a bee. As Darwin showed so beautifully in his book *The Various Contrivances by which Orchids are Fertilised by Insects* (1877), the nectar and shape of many orchid flowers have been adapted by evolution to enable insects to pick up pollen and self-pollinate or transfer it from one flower to another. In some tropical orchids only one species of insect will fertilise them. The evolutionary rubicons leading to this symbiosis must therefore have involved first the selection of a particular group of insects, then an individual species. Yet Darwin observed that the bee orchid is never visited by insects and looks like no known British bee. This orchid self-pollinates.

The interaction of one group of organisms with another is not sufficient for it to be called symbiosis. The symbiotic rubicon is crossed when the lives of two species become inextricably linked together. The union may be beneficial to both, or only to one, or it may be harmful to one. It may exist throughout the lives of both species, or it may be temporary. The symbionts may be outside cells or, as occasionally, inside. Once again there are rubicons to be crossed to get the symbiont into the right cell as the organism develops. There are two examples of inner symbioses that I want to end with: a multi-tissue organism and the cell itself.

AN ORGANISM AS AN ECOSYSTEM

No cell within a multicellular organism can exist on its own. And, as with an environmental ecosystem, the whole body is greater than the sum of the constituent parts. Each fungus, plant or animal is thus itself an ecosystem. Each tissue does something unique for the organism as a whole. But without the symbiosis between them they would each die, and quite rapidly. These symbiotic rubicons are crossed during development of the embyro and child. As the body ages or gets sick, the symbioses break down, resulting in illness or death.

And there are creepy-crawlies to be found all over our body. Our guts contain bacteria. The effect of losing them will be well-known to anyone who has experienced the after-effects of a heavy dose of antibiotics. Without bacteria in the stomach a sheep or cow would not be able to digest grass. It would starve. But the evolution of higher plants and animals has depended on the establishment of a different type of symbiosis, between the individual tissues. The evolutionary origin of multicellular organisms may have been via cell division and then differentiation. Alternatively it could have originated from a symbiosis between two or more cell types, some of which crossed a rubicon 600 million years ago enabling the two sets of DNA to merge together, the DNA coding for such symbioses being now incorporated into the chromosomes of every cell. A similar hypothesis is now the consensus for the evolutionary origin of the cell itself.

THE CELL AS AN ECOSYSTEM

When I was a research student there were two novel ideas that particularly inspired my colleagues and me. One was the hypothesis of Peter Mitchell about the working of the power-house of the cell, which I discussed in Chapter One. The other concerned the evolutionary origin of the eukaryotic cell. The human body and the bodies of other animals and plants are made entirely of eukaryotic cells. The most obvious feature distinguishing these from prokaryotes or archaebacteria is the compartmentalisation within the cell (Figure 2). Some prokaryotes (blue-green algae and eubacteria) have a double wall surrounding them, in between which are found enzymatic reactions. But once inside the heart of a bacterial or archaebacterial cell there is only one compartment. Things are very different inside a eukaryotic cell, whether it is a yeast, an alga, a protozoan, an animal or a higher plant.

The main DNA and RNA factory is housed inside the nuclear membrane. The endoplasmic reticulum acts as a calcium cupboard (above p. 98) and the Golgi apparatus processes proteins that are secreted from the cell. The powerhouse is in the mitochondria, and in plants there is a greenhouse, the chloroplast. Plants also have other compartments – for example, the tonoplast – and both animal and plant cells have a refuse department in the lysosome and peroxisomes. When the cell divides, these all have to be replicated, involving several rubicons. These rubicons involve membrane fragmentation, vesicle and DNA movement, and membrane fusion. The nuclear membrane disappears, allowing the two sets of chromosomes to separate and two new nuclear membranes to form. The Golgi apparatus shatters into hundreds of tiny bits, each daughter cell having its share of vesicles, which then re-cluster and fuse to form a mature Golgi once the

cell has divided. But there is something extra-special about the power-
house and the greenhouse.

To break up cells and separate their components requires that the tissue
in which they occur be homogenised and then the soup be spun very hard,
up to 100,000 times the force of gravity. Because the various compartments
inside the cell have different densities they spin down under different
forces. The nucleus spins down first, within five minutes at 500 times
gravity. About 10,000 times gravity is used to isolate the mitochondria, the
powerhouses, and 100,000 times gravity then spins down the calcium
cupboard, the remaining membrane vesicles and cell fragments. What is
left is the soluble part of the cell, the cytosol. The next thing to do is to
analyse what has been isolated. This involves measuring DNA, RNA,
protein, carbohydrate and a variety of enzymes.

When this was first done in the 1950s and 60s, all the fractions, as
expected, contained protein, carbohydrate and enzymes, though each
fraction had a different set. But the real surprise was that the fraction
containing the 'powerhouse' also had DNA and RNA. Likewise when the
'greenhouses' were isolated from plants, this fraction also contained DNA.
What's more, these fractions could make proteins. Yet the protein factory
inside the cell was supposed to be in the ribosomes found in the cytosol or
attached to the membranes of the endoplasmic reticulum. We found the
same thing in our biochemistry practical as students. We thought at first
that this must be an artifact. Thinking we must have broken some of the
nuclei during tissue homogenisation, we assumed that the powerhouse
fraction must have been contaminated with bits of broken nuclei and other
membranes, and thus DNA. After all it would have been surprising if this
rather crude sub-cellular fractionation were 100 per cent efficient. But
when we looked in the biochemical literature, we discovered that experienced researchers also found DNA and RNA in the powerhouse and
greenhouse fractions. There was something funny going on.

It turned out that both mitochondria and chloroplasts really do contain
their own DNA. This enables them to replicate like a cell within a cell. They
can also make some of their own proteins. So it wasn't an artifact at all.
But what was even more exciting was the discovery that this DNA and the
protein synthesis were like those found in bacteria. The DNA was circular,
as in bacteria. In animal and plant nuclei the DNA from one cell would be
two metres long if spread out in a straight line! In fact it is packaged into
a string of thousands of beads, which are then packed together into
cylinders. Each bead is a ball of DNA and protein. The protein is very
special and only found in the nucleus. It is very basic, and called a histone.
Another type of DNA protein found particularly in sperm is called pro-
tamine. Histones and protamines are not found in bacteria. Nor are they
found in mitochondria and chloroplasts. And there are other biochemical
properties of the powerhouse and the greenhouse which are much more
like those of bacteria. The antibiotics which inhibited bacterial protein
synthesis also inhibited it in mitochondria and chloroplasts, but not the

main protein factory in the eukaryotic ribosome. There are other properties I could list. But the message is clear. The molecular biology of mitochondria and chloroplasts is much more like that of bacteria than like that of the host cell.

What we thought was an artifact had told us something vital about the workings of our cells and could tell us something of their evolutionary origin. In 1970 Lynn Margulis published her now famous book *The Origin of Eucaryotic Cells*, in which she presented a convincing case that several of the organelles inside the eukaryotic cell originated as bacterial symbionts: the mitochondria from an aerobic bacterium, the chloroplasts from a blue-green alga, and a flagellum from a spirochaete bacterium. These endosymbiotic rubicons must have been crossed some 2,000 million years ago.

As Margulis has since pointed out, the idea of endosymbiosis was not new. However, through her books and experiments she has constructed a much more convincing case than was originally proposed. In fact it is so convincing that many modern texts don't even bother to discus an alternative. The case is made even more attractive when one discovers protozoa such as particular species of *Paramecium* that harbour hundreds of symbiotic algae within them. But is the symbiotic theory for the origin of the eukaryotic cell correct? There are several arguments one can make to undermine the Margulis hypothesis.

First, there is an obvious alternative, just as plausible and one she has not ruled out. The primitive cell first learned how to vesiculate and then trapped some bit of DNA and cytoplasm within itself so that it eventually evolved a degree of independence. Or, since the RNA and protein machinery of our cells are more like those of the archaebacteria than the bacteria, these two cell types fused resulting in an everlasting marriage. This was followed by capture of the bacterial bits into one membrane compartment, the mitos and chloroplasts, and the archae bit into another, the nucleus. There has been plenty of time for this to occur. Fossilized single-celled eukaryotes have been identified which are nearly 1,000 million years old. The origin of a eukaryote cell able to divide by mitosis is thought to be about 1,500 million years ago, some 2,000 million years after the first cell rubicon. The nuclear DNA of the cell has therefore had plenty of time to evolve major differences in its biochemistry from the DNA trapped within the inner compartments.

Secondly, there is a real problem with the DNA found inside the organelles of the eukaryotic cell. Not only are there differences in the genetic code with present-day bacteria but also, and crucially important, the DNA just isn't big enough. The genetic code, the template of the architect's plan housed in the nucleus, is held in the sequence of letters, the *bases* in the DNA, – A, G, T and C. These are of course in pairs, because DNA is a double-stranded helix. Add up all the base-pairs in our chromosomes and you get a very large number – 2.9 thousand million (2.9×10^9). In the fruit fly *Drosophila* the number is even larger, because it has giant chromosomes in some cells, whereas in small eukaryotes like yeast there are only 13.5 million base-pairs. Now compare these numbers with bacteria and viruses. *E. coli*, the bacterium in the human gut, has a single circular chromosome of four million base-pairs. The smallest prokaryotic DNA is found in mycoplasmas, which invade eukaryotic cells. These have DNA with 760,000 base-pairs. Even many bacterial, animal and plant viruses have DNA with tens or hundreds of thousands of base-pairs. Yet animal mitochondrial DNA only has some 16,000 base-pairs. In plants mitochondrial and chloroplast DNA can be 10-100 times bigger than this, but it is still far short of the DNA in the smallest known bacterium. Of course one can argue that most of the original DNA has been lost, and that of modern bacteria has had plenty of evolutionary time to get bigger. The mitochondrial DNA only codes for a few of its own proteins, and RNA. The rest of the proteins are coded for by the nuclear DNA. Made in the main protein factory, they have to be targeted to the mitochondria, or chloroplast.

So, if the mitochondrial or chloroplast DNA was not from a bacterium, where could it have come from? Where but from the origin of bacterial sex? Bacteria house small circular bits of DNA called plasmids. These can replicate inside so that one bacterial cell may have one copy of the main DNA but tens or hundreds of the plasmids. These plasmids can capture bits of DNA from the main DNA, and they are passed from one cell to another during bacterial sex. As we saw previously, plasmids are a vital ingredient in the genetic engineer's kitchen. Plasmids are usually a few thousand base-pairs in size, can contain a few genes and can replicate. All just right for the evolutionary origin of mitochondrial DNA.

So we are left with three possible rubicons for the evolutionary origin of organalles: (a) invasion or capture of a bacterium or blue-green alga by the presuming eukaryote, (b) formation of a membrane around a DNA fragment or plasmid within the cell, or (c) fusion of two cells. Of course the cell which first housed the DNA for the mitochondria or chloroplast is almost certainly extinct. This would explain why there are differences in the genetic code between organelle and central office DNA. If we are to sort this out, it is essential that we predict the Rubicon sequence for each hypothesis and are able to design experiments to test that the sequence is feasible. Unless a hypothesis is testable it remains speculation.

The idea that the cell evolved as an ecosystem, capturing its bits and pieces – the internal structures – from other organisms is an attractive hypothesis. There is much circumstantial evidence to give it credibility. But I believe it needs re-examining and modifying. There is no direct evidence to support it. I trust this re-examination in the light of Rubicon will not undermine the elegance of Margulis's previous arguments or her seminal contributions to the scientific literature. These have inspired several generations of students, including me, and will no doubt continue to do so. What we really need, as we saw at the end of the last chapter, are experimental systems which enable the researcher to jump several hundred million years in a day, within a single test-tube.

RUBICON CHALLENGES GAIA

The main message is that, as in a cell, or a tissue or organism, so in an ecosystem – the whole is greater than the sum of the constituent parts. It is useful to consider an ecosystem like an individual organism – each organism representing 'a cell', each environment, be it a stream, a copse, a field, or a forest, representing 'a tissue'. It is the interactions of the 'cells' within each eco-tissue upon which its survival and function depend. As with an animal or plant, loss of an 'eco-cell' may not be lethal to the 'eco-tissue'. Similarly the loss of a forest or stream may not necessarily lead to the ecosystem crossing the Rubicon and becoming a desert.

Like an animal or plant, an ecosystem can be signalled from within or from outside to do something. It may move, increasing or decreasing its size. It may secrete, throwing seeds or whole clusters of animals and plants into other regions. The migration of birds during the winter is an example. The ecosystem may transform. A field may become a wood, or a forest lose the bulk of its trees and become a bushy meadow. A rock pool may change from one dominated by green seaweed to one dominated by red. And an ecosystem can be killed. A lake can become sterile, or a grassy plain become a desert. But the death of an ecosystem comes long before the complete loss of all animals and plants has occurred. Once all interaction and symbioses are gone, the ecosystem is gone. It has become simply a shambles, a group of uncoordinated individuals competing in their folly for the sunlight or food, so that all may die.

As with cells, there are external and internal signals setting rubicon eco-sequences in motion: small changes in weather, in rainfall, in atmospheric temperature, the scent of the spring flowers attracting bees and other insects. And ecosystems, like individual organisms, have evolved defence-mechanisms against physical, chemical and biological attack – a flood, a fire, a drought, a volcanic eruption, an oil spillage, acid rain, the release of toxic chemicals, a swarm of locusts, dutch elm disease and other insect-born pathogens.

Rubicon uses the central principle of Gaia – the Earth is alive. The movement of air and the oceans over the whole planet means that, when considering the interaction of animals, plants and microbes with the atmosphere or the sea, we must adopt a global approach. That means considering the Earth as a single organism, one ecosystem. Rubicon accepts also the principle of Gaia that there are ecological forces that try to defend an ecosystem, and the Earth as a whole, against both small and big environmental change. But Rubicon rejects the misconceptions embodied within homeostasis, as it did for the whole human body. Small changes in water supply, gases and temperature can trigger enormous rubicons in individual eco-cells and eco-tissues. A small drop in water temperature and light in autumn signal major losses in planktonic animals and algae around our coasts. In spring the annual rhythm and the relatively small physical changes in environmental conditions signal the seaweeds and hydroids to start growing again, so that by mid-summer they are again infesting the rock pools and rocks below the surface, releasing millions of 'spores' to germinate at other sites. Big changes in weather or ground conditions are not always needed to precipitate a disaster. We saw that a 'small' reduction in water supply could lead to the disaster of the 'dust bowl' in the US; and that Nature can recover from volcanic eruption, oil spillage and drought.

In trying to define the boundary between physiology and pathology, in trying to decide what is living and what is dead, in looking back over 4,000 million years at the appearance of new species and the extinction of others, in the passion of environmentalists about the survival or destruction of ecosystems, in defining whether a symbiotic relationship is beneficial or harmful, we see ever-increasing confusion. The more reductionist detail we see, the thicker the jungle of jargon and foliage seems to get. Rubicon is a rationalisation. The pathway of rubicons enables each individual to cut through the foliage and discover the inspiration of the clear air, the sky and the expansive panorama ahead.

An ecosystem should therefore be considered in five dimensions: three spatial dimensions, time and Rubicon. Rubicon provides the framework for a five-dimensional geography. The challenge now is to exploit the power of modern molecular concepts and techniques to unravel the precise mechanisms enabling groups of organisms to cross the Rubicon, and thus form or destroy an ecosystem.

Long live Gaia.

6

The Biochemist Meets Humpty Dumpty

The other day I went back to the concert hall. The bulldozer was long gone. But to my amazement I found some students trying to put the shattered fragments of one of the double basses back together. Another group were sitting at the disorganised ivories of the keyboard of the once majestic Steinway grand, stringing crochets and minims together, hoping to reconstruct a tune out of them.

TWO NURSERY RHYMES

The origin of many nursery rhymes is unknown, but the fact that variants of the same basic story exist in many countries, in forms which are clearly not simply translations of each other, suggests that they have been popular for centuries. My seven-year-old daughter has a favourite. It begins like this:

> Humpty Dumpty sat on a wall
> Humpty Dumpty had a great fall
> All the king's horses and all the king's men
> Couldn't put Humpty together again

I doubt whether the author of this riddle rhyme, or the many parents who have recited it to their children would have expected to see it quoted in a book on science. Nevertheless its wisdom has much to tell the biochemist!

Biochemistry is about discovering the molecular basis of life. But much of the knowledge gained from biochemists over the past century has been based on experiments using a *grind and find* approach. To get at the sub-cellular structures, proteins and DNA ultimately responsible for a biological event, the biochemist has had to resort to the sort of bulldozer approach we saw in the concert hall in Chapter One. The biochemist extracts things from live cells, characterises them and tries to find out how they work, by getting them to do their thing in the test-tube outside a live cell. The conventional biochemist is a great maker and consumer of soup. Yet no one has ever put a cell back together again. No one has ever reconstructed a live cell from its isolated constituent parts or from the DNA template, which we are told contains all the information necessary to form and maintain the complete organism from whence it came. The nearest anyone has got is to transfer a nucleus from one cell to another, following destruction of the original nucleus in the recipient cell. Thus one frog can be born from the DNA developed inside another's egg. Clever as this experiment was it has been repeated for very few other cells. No, once we have broken the outer membrane of a cell, or homogenised a tissue, it is no longer alive. Nor can it ever live again. In the present state of knowledge, all the King's biochemists cannot put Humpty together again. Yet a cell broken into bits can carry out many of the reactions found in the live, intact cell. Or can it?

What has been lost when we break open a cell, or liquidise a complete organism? Can cell soups still cross the Rubicon? Are we following the mindless course of the proverbial visitor from outer space who, wanting to find out what was going on inside the nearest building to his space craft, blew up the building. And then, as the dust settled, painstakingly collected all the bits and pieces and analysed them, together with what came out in the drains. And what of samples taken from the body? Much of clinical biochemistry is based on the study of drains, for what else are the veins and the urine from which most clinical samples are taken? And yet a wealth of information has come out of purifying individual items from the biochemist's soup. Is there then a path to find through the reductionist's jungle? I believe there is.

The key is to re-examine the questions we are asking about living things, and to look very closely at the experimental approaches which have been used to investigate them. Rubicon helps us identify what differentiates the molecules and structures extracted from life from what they do inside the intact cell, organism or ecosystem. If we wish to find out the exact size and structure of a protein we think may be responsible for telling a cell to divide into two cells, then we must extract it. We must isolate the part of the DNA template which retains the information about its structure, enabling the new cell to make it as well. But if we want to know how this protein works what should we do, study it in the test tube or in the live cell? As always in science, if we get the question right then the path to the solution often presents itself readily, even though at that point the answer itself remains unclear.

Viva la cell!

Let's look then at what has been learned from the fragments of Humpty Dumpty. But keep in mind our quest. It is the secrets of life we are trying to uncover, not the puzzles posed by the laboratory magician.

Sugar and spice

What are little boys made of?
Slugs and snails
And puppy-dogs' tails,
That's what little boys are made of.

What are little girls made of?
Sugar and spice
And all things nice,
That's what little girls are made of.

A second nursery rhyme for the biochemist to digest!

This rhyme is of course about behaviour, not composition, a figurative use of the word 'made'. How cells behave is central to the theme of this book. We have already examined many examples of threshold behaviour – rubicons – in cells, cell components, extinct cells and organisms, and ecosystems. But what are cells made of, and does it matter anyway? If we extract things from cells will it help us to explain why a rubicon occurs?

It was clear early on in the chemical investigation of life, in the eighteenth and nineteenth centuries, that many of the chemicals extracted were unlike any previously encountered in the non-organic world or in the alchemist's flask. Studies on fermentation showed that the reactions taking sugar to alcohol could occur in broken cells. But until recently the big molecules of DNA or protein on which these processes depend in the cell could not be manufactured in the test-tube. Now we have DNA technology and genetic engineering. DNA and proteins can be made in large amounts in the test-tube, using biological reagents or synthetic chemicals. Although the real reason for analysing the chemical composition of living things is to explain how the cell works, we need to place some order on the myriad of substances which can be isolated from cells.

Understanding the true nature of chemistry and the evolution of the universe only became possible once the elements forming the periodic table (which, including man-made ones, now number about 107) had been worked out by Dmitry Ivanovich Mendeleyev (1834-1907). Mendeleyev was the fourteenth and last son of the Director of the Gymnasium at Tobulsk. He was a prolific author, writing more than 300 papers on subjects as diverse as art, economics and evolution. But his greatest and most significant achievement was to organise the true elements of Nature into a periodic table, which rationalised the relationships between elements with similar and dissimilar properties. Gaps appeared in the matrix, predicting the existence of elements as yet undiscovered. The discovery of potassium, sodium, calcium, magnesium and chlorine by Humphry Davy (1778-1829), at the Royal Institution in London, had already greatly extended the known elements, helping to make this possible. But to isolate potassium and sodium Davy had to electrolyse molten potash and soda, separating the two constituent parts from each other. His cousin, Edmund Davy, acting as assistant, describes Humphry's excitement on 6 October 1807: 'when he saw the minute globules of potassium burst through the crust of potash, and take fire as they entered the atmosphere, he could not contain his joy – he actually danced round the room in ecstatic delight.' So with life – electricity has played a vital part in separating the 'elements of life' from each other.

The dogma of molecular biology that DNA makes RNA makes protein could not have been worked out unless these molecules first had been extracted from living systems and their structures determined. Proteins are a linear string of amino-acids, folded into a 3D structure upon which the function of the protein depends. Each type of protein has a unique sequence. Once Sanger had proved, using insulin as the model, that every molecule of each protein has exactly the same linear sequence of amino-acids, the door was opened for a multitude of questions, some undreamt of before this discovery. How is the information for the protein stored within the cell? How and when is this information made available, and then translated into the appropriate protein message? This is where DNA comes in.

DNA consists of two chains of sugar and phosphate twisted together and holding hands. In a single chromosome there are literally millions of handshakes. In order to divide or transcribe the information in a particular stretch of DNA the hands have to let go for a second. These are chemical hands made of a link between two bases. There are four bases, GCAT. It is the sequence of these bases which contains the information coding for each protein. But only two types of handshake are allowed: A with T and G with C. All this vital information came from biochemistry initiated in the 1940s and 1950s. So the biochemist may not be able to put Humpty together again, but we need his skills to identify the building blocks of cells, and to find out what they can do.

THE ELEMENTS OF LIFE

Silver and gold have I none

There are 90 natural elements – from hydrogen, the lightest, to uranium, the heaviest. Living systems use some 27 of them. Unless an organism has a large crystalline skeleton, about half the dry weight of all organisms is carbon. The chemistry of life is dominated by the chemistry of this element. However, without a host of inorganic metallic and non-metallic elements there would be no life.

The five main non-metallic elements in the Earth's crust are oxygen, silicon, hydrogen, sulphur and carbon, in that order (Figure 11). In the atmosphere approximately 73 per cent of the air is nitrogen, 21 per cent oxygen and 5 per cent carbon dioxide, though this composition is very different from that 4,000 million years ago, just before life began. In the sea chlorine – in its charged form, chloride – is the predominant non-metal. All this is compatible with the main non-metals of life: carbon, oxygen, hydrogen, sulphur, nitrogen, phosphorus and chlorine. But there are some special uses for some other non-metals.

From Mendeleyev's periodic table we find on the far right the halogens: fluorine, chlorine, bromine and iodine. Nineteenth-century chemists discovered the presence of fluorine in bones and teeth. It is thought to be an

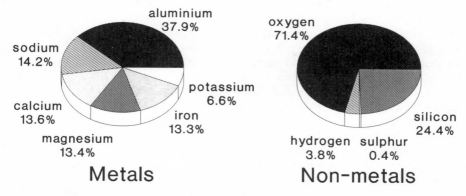

aluminium
37.9%

sodium
14.2%

potassium
6.6%

calcium
13.6%

iron
13.3%

magnesium
13.4%

Metals

oxygen
71.4%

silicon
24.4%

hydrogen   sulphur
3.8%   0.4%

Non-metals

Fig. 11. The elements of the Earth's crust.

essential element in strong teeth; hence its addition to the water supply in its charged form – fluoride. Fluorine does not seem to be used by living cells, but the other three halogens are. Normal bleach is made from oxygen and chlorine, but bromine is used by a special company of the body's army to make a different type of bleach. As we saw in Chapter Two, iodine is required to make thyroid hormones. Every child has the chemistry of silicon to thank for the sandy holiday beaches. Sand is mainly a compound of silicon. And without the chemical reaction between the silicon in sand and the lime in cement we would have no concrete. But life has made much more elegant and beautiful structures from such chemical reactions. Silicon is used in the skeletons of many organisms, producing the beautiful shapes of some algae and protozoa. But silicon does not appear to have a function in man, though the excessive use of talc – finely powdered magnesium silicate – has lead to speculations about a role for silicon in breast cancer.

All life requires the element oxygen, but that does not necessarily mean that oxygen gas is needed. We need the gas, of course, as do all animals and plants. But there are many microbes which do not use oxygen gas itself. Similarly, though the brain and the other major organs of the body require a continuous supply of oxygen from the blood, there are several cells in the body which don't need it at all. For example, the red blood cells themselves are carriers of oxygen, and not consumers. Yet, even when oxygen itself is not used by an organism, the cell is still full of it. Oxygen is essential to the chemical structure of sugars, fats, proteins and DNA. Selenium is next down in the periodic table from oxygen, but is only rarely used in life. In mammals, and some other species, selenium is bound to an enzyme which is part of the defence of the cell against 'burning' by oxygen. This is particularly important in protecting DNA.

Metals are shiny, hard elements which, apart from mercury, require pretty high temperatures to melt them. But this is not the form in which we find them in life. Most children will have experienced what happens when you burn magnesium metal. The sparklers on bonfire night light up the cold November garden with their brilliant display. But take a piece of magnesium and drop it into some dilute hydrochloric acid. Within a few minutes, and after a lot of hissing as hydrogen gas comes off, the metallic lustre of the magnesium will have disappeared. The metal will have dissolved in the acid. But where has it gone?

It was Humphry Davy, famed for his miner's lamp, who realised that salts, as we call them generically, were composed of two parts – metallic and non-metallic. By passing a current through a salt it is possible to separate them. What we call salt in the kitchen is sodium chloride. Soda is the common name used to describe another salt of sodium found in the kitchen, the carbonate. Pure metals can be very reactive. Sodium and potassium catch fire spontaneously when exposed to the air. But metals are uncharged electrically, even though they can conduct electrons down a wire when a voltage is put across it. However, in salts the metals *are* charged electrically. But one doesn't get an electric shock when handling salt in cooking because the charge on the metal is exactly balanced by an opposite charge on the non-metal, the other half of the salt. In life, therefore, pure metals do not exist. They are found rather as salts.

In a salt crystal the metal is married monogamously to a non-metal – chloride for example in table salt. But when dissolved in the sea, the blood, or inside the cell, the metal finds itself surrounded by a variety of potential partners: chloride, bicarbonate, phosphate and proteins, to name but a few. The metal ions have a positive charge on them, the non-metals a negative one. This means that they can act as carriers of electrical currents. But, whereas in a metal wire the current is carried by electrons, hopping from metal atom to metal atom, across the membrane of a cell current is carried by the charged metal or non-metal ions. This is how a nerve can transmit an electrical signal from the brain to another part of your body, or vice versa. The rubicons of taste, smell, sight, touch and pain begin with an electro-chemical rubicon in the part of the body doing the sensing. This message is then passed to the brain, by the electrical impulses of the nerves. Life has exploited a rich variety of metals, some common in the Earth's crust, others more difficult for the prospector to find in large amounts. The most common metallic element in the Earth's crust is aluminium (Figure 11). London clay is full of it. Yet surprisingly there are no organisms which use this element. Rather, it can be toxic to many species, including man in whom it has been linked to Alzheimer's disease. After aluminium come sodium, calcium, magnesium, iron and potassium. All major metallic elements in all living things. Salts such as sodium and potassium chloride are responsible for determining and controlling the osmotic and electrical properties of cells. Calcium and magnesium are crucial to the metabolism and regulation of cell events. The transition metals iron, copper, manganese, zinc and cobalt are also used in man and many other organisms, acting as oxygen carriers and helping to catalyse reactions involving oxidation and reduction of the small organic molecules with oxygen itself or the chemical warfare department. Zinc also has an important role in the nucleus, helping certain signal proteins bind to DNA.

And once again there are some oddballs.

There are magnetic bacteria, and magnetic organs in some creatures, which can sense the Earth's magnetic field, thereby acting as a micro-compass. There are sea-squirts and clams which need the metal vanadium, but the role of this unusual metal in man is not clear. What is clear is that silver and gold, revered so much as a result of man's vanity, have been ignored by evolution. Silver and gold have I none; yet a single cell sparkles with chemical trinkets more exquisite, more elegant and more beautiful than the most craftily constructed piece of jewellery.

And what of the organics?

Organically grown

The organic components of life can be found both inside cells and in the fluids and supporting structures outside them. It is the responsibility of the outer membrane of the cell not only to act as a defence barrier, but also to maintain gradients of these components across the membrane. Here we find a liaison between the metals and the organics.

The outer membrane of all cells contains pumps, made of protein. One pushes sodium out and potassium in, and another pumps out calcium. Without these there would be no electrical activity in membranes, no nerve rubicons. Nor would there be any calcium-triggered rubicons. It is the calcium pump that maintains the ten-thousandfold gradient of calcium – ions, remember – across the membrane. And it is that which the biochemist's bulldozer destroys. No more calcium rubicons! The biochemist's soup has lost this vital feature of all live cells. Yet from the biochemist's soup thousands of organic molecules have been discovered, both big and small. The small organic substances in the cell include the building blocks for making the big molecules: namely proteins, nucleic acids, membranes and cell walls. These are built up from amino-acids, nucleotides, fats and sugars respectively. Some substances are also required to convert the energy in food, such as glucose and fat, into the intracellular fuel – ATP. These are the intermediary metabolites, which refine the dietary 'oil' into 'petrol' which the powerhouses – the mitochondria – inside the cell can then 'burn' to make ATP.

All living cells have ATP to maintain themselves alive and to carry out their specialised functions. A dead cell will have lost more than 90 per cent of its ATP, but many proteins and other molecules can still be fully intact.

And there are also tiny traces of other organics in cells, acting in catalytic molecules to enable proteins and DNA to work. These include soluble vitamins such as vitamin B_6 and B_{12}.

And what of fat?

Fat is familiar as a white, solid substance found on nice juicy meat on the butcher's slab, the bulk of which is removed before cooking. Alternatively, fats are seen as oils in cooking, or as hidden monsters in our foods causing our arteries to clog up if we consume too much of them. But chemical reactions do not often work well at solid surfaces. The chemical reactions of life occur mainly in the liquid phase. In solution, molecules can move about, so that they find their targets, their residences and their factory buildings. Fats are substances not soluble in water; yet in live organisms they are always in liquid form. But how does this tally with what we see on the butcher's slab?

Our tissues have to be at about 37°C if they are to survive. At this temperature the familiar white fat is liquid and colourless, just like the cooking oils near your kitchen stove. Only when the temperature of an animal fat drops ten degrees or so, to the temperature in a room, does it look like the white solid familiar on meat. At room temperature vegetable oils are liquid. Not surprisingly, since the organisms from which they have been extracted do not have the central-heating system of us mammals. But there are deep-sea animals which are cold-blooded and yet live very successfully at about 6°C, where our white fat would be solid. Evolution has solved this problem. The fats in these animals are made of unsaturated fatty acids. As a result they are liquid at the temperatures at which they live. But homogenise some liver and centrifuge it at 4°C, as the biochemist usually does. Look carefully at the ice-cold soup. On the top will be a white layer of solid fat. Do the same to the liver of a deep sea shrimp and the fat floating on top will be liquid. These shrimp have to live at about 6°C. Similarly, archaebacteria can live at extremes of temperature, acidity and salt because they have membrane fats different in chemical structure from those of the cells of bacteria, animals and plants.

The outer membrane of all animal, plant and bacterial cells is made of a mixture of fat and protein. But it is a different fat from the fat we have just discussed. This fat in the membranes surrounding all cells must be liquid for the proteins in them to work. Many of these have to float around to find the molecule they are seeking. Fat is an important solvent in the body. The fat-soluble vitamins, A, D and E, would not be able to be stored or to work without it. We need them for healthy bones and vision. And there is much solvent abuse in some people, as we saw when examining how cholesterol is transported around the body.

The backbone of the fat in membranes of animal and plant cells is composed of phosphate attached to a glycerol-fatty acid ester. If they are to survive, microbes which live in extreme environments, such as hot springs, acid and alkaline ponds, need a membrane with a different structure from animals and plants. Archaebacteria, as they were named by Woese, have a fat with an ether, as opposed to an ester, link. A bit of chemical detail, of considerable evolutionary interest.

Carbohydrates, on the other hand, are made of water-soluble sugars and do not dissolve in fat. Like 'salt', the term 'sugar' is generic and includes many substances other than the crystals we spoon on to our breakfast cereal, sucrose. Sucrose is made by plants. The main sugar made by our body is glucose. But since sucrose is actually two sugars, glucose and fructose joined together, we can metabolise it. By linking such small sugar molecules into long chains they can act as long-term energy reserves, glycogen in animal cells and starch in plants, or they can form the large molecules essential to the structure of the cell walls. Walls are rigid structures, placed outside the cell membrane to protect it. Our cells do not have walls, only spongy, delicate membranes. Glycogen and starch are made from glucose. The walls of all plant and yeast cells are made of another polymer of glucose, cellulose. It is this we extract to make paper. All bacteria also have walls made of carbohydrate, but from sugars different from glucose. There are more complex sugars which are also stuck on to the surface of several of our proteins, including many in the blood plasma and those sticking out of the cell surface. All these walls protect the cell membrane against osmotic damage induced by changes in salt outside. Although our cells do not have walls, carbohydrates do have a structural role in the body outside cells, in cartilage and the lubricant of the joint.

When you want to build a house you employ a builder, who will eventually arrive with a lorry load of bricks. But cells in organisms which have walls do things differently. They are more efficient, and more independent. They have their own building department, and can manufacture their own bricks. One of the fascinating puzzles about the chemistry of life is why carbohydrate chains do not play the catalytic role that proteins do or the information store that nucleic acids do. There are just as many varieties of combinations possible.

The human body is an integrated and highly organised chemical machine. The cells house the factories and workers which make this happen. They contain hundreds of proteins which are being continuously broken down, repaired and remade. Proteins do many things in and out of cells. But the two main categories are *structural* and *catalytic*. Without the protein collagen, outside cells, our bones would be brittle and crumble into a calcium phosphate dust and our soft tissues disintegrate into a squidgy mass of disorganised cells. The collagen network holds the cells in tissues together. It is also crucial to the structure of cartilage and, as we saw in Chapter Two, is a key battle-zone in arthritis. Nature discovered how to make its own version of reinforced concrete hundreds of millions of years ago. Add a shell from the beach to some dilute acid, e.g. vinegar. Bubbles of carbon dioxide will appear as the calcium carbonate – the hard part – dissolves, leaving the soft 'reinforcing' protein behind. The inside of cells also has a skeleton, the cytoskeleton, made of two proteins, actin and myosin. These proteins are responsible for cell movement and muscle contraction. Many hormones are also proteins – insulin and interferon, for example. No chemical reaction in the body could take place without the catalytic group of proteins known as enzymes. Without them we would not be able to digest our food, and our blood would not clot when we cut ourselves. Furthermore, our defence against infection is critically dependent on the ability of white cells in the blood to make protein antibodies which, with some of the other white cells, attack invading bacteria and viruses. It is this defence system which breaks down in AIDS. In rheumatoid arthritis the body's defence system attacks some of its own proteins. In type I diabetes insulin is missing. In inherited disorders like muscular dystrophy and cystic fibrosis mutant malfunctioning proteins are produced instead of the normal ones. All this is protein trouble. How then is a protein made? The bricks from which proteins are made are amino-acids, mortared together by chemical bonds. How and where this happens in the cell we will examine when we need to engineer proteins in the next chapter.

Some molecules are special to particular cell types or to individual species; others, such as DNA, RNA, protein and ATP are universal to all cells. As we saw in the last chapter, many organic biological molecules are also handed, or chiral. Many amino-acids and sugars in life have a mirror-image, which is not biologically active. The chemical reactions of the laboratory chemist tend to generate mixtures of each type, that is left- and right-sided molecules. But, if a biological catalyst is used, only one-sided molecules are formed. The mirror-image is excluded.

Thus the six major constituents of life are: salts, small organic molecules (metabolites), proteins, carbohydrates (sugars), fats and nucleic acids (DNA and RNA). These are the 'elements' of life. But there is one component missing: one so obvious that its importance can easily be overlooked, the most essential ingredient of all – water!

WATER, WATER EVERYWHERE!

'Water, water everywhere, nor any drop to drink,' cried the Ancient Mariner. Sea water is too salty for us, but the frustration of the mariner adrift at sea highlights the fact that if we starve ourselves the thing that will kill us is not lack of food but lack of water. Fifty to ninety per cent of the weight of all live organisms is water.

Lazzaro Spallanzani (1729-1799), an Italian physiologist, was one of the first to emphasise the fact that water was needed for all life. To demonstrate this he grew a plant and weighed accurately the plant and the soil. He ascribed the loss in weight of the soil to water gained by the plant. His conviction about the importance of water was confirmed when he showed that addition of water to dried extracts of luminous organisms made them glow again. But like many of his contemporaries he got things very wrong about semen. He believed that the wriggly spermatozoa were inessential parasites! Some organisms have gone to extreme lengths to survive when the water supply is low or non-existent. Seeds and spores of plants and fungi are stored dry. But they must not be too dry, for some metabolism must go on in most seeds if they are to germinate when fully rehydrated.

Go to your local home aquarium shop and ask for some brine shrimp, a popular food for you to feed to your tropical fish. The shopkeeper will not give you a bottle of live shrimp, but instead a tube containing eggs of the crustacean *Artemia*. Drop some eggs into a jam-jar containing salty water and in a couple of days the eggs will have hatched. The water will contain dozens of darting brine shrimp nauplii. Brine shrimp inhabit highly saline pools all over the world. Several 'freshwater shrimp' have the ability to survive in a drought. The dried-up pools on Dartmoor look lifeless. But once the rains come the pools, replenished with water, come to life. The cells in these animals can survive drying because they contain large amounts of a special sugar, a heptose.

Desert organisms have also evolved ways of combating shortage of water. Plants have waxy leaves to reduce water loss, and widely spread root systems to extract the small amount of water available from as large a volume of soil as possible. Spanish moss lives on surfaces such as telephone wires where there is no contact with the ground. It obtains its water from the air. Some organisms, such as the American desert rat, the kangaroo rat and the flour beetle seem not to need any water at all. The chemical reactions which process their food generate sufficient water to hydrate their cells and body fluids.

Micro-organisms too can adapt to drought. Species of bacteria from the genera *Bacillus*, *Clostridium* and *Spirosarcina* form spores when depleted of water. They transform into a dormant state by accumulating very large amounts of calcium and by making a substance called picolinic acid, to which the calcium binds. Addition of water wakes them up.

Organisms have adapted to many extremes of water condition. High acid or alkali, high and low salt, soft and hard water. One can even find organisms growing in distilled water. But perhaps the most extraordinary of all is the ability to live or survive at high and low temperatures. In hot water springs, such as those found in Iceland, New Zealand and Yellowstone Park in the United States, the temperature of the water can be more than 90°C, enough to kill most organisms. Yet there are bacteria which love to live here. They are the thermophiles. Some sulphate-reducing bacteria can grow and reproduce at 104°C. These thermophilic bacteria have given the genetic engineer an invaluable reagent, enabling him to make a DNA factory in the test tube, which will only work if one stage of the manufacturing process is at more than 90°C. And there are organisms at the other extreme of liquid water.

Fish and invertebrates in the Antarctic have their own antifreeze. In the Don Juan pond the ratio of calcium chloride to water molecules is one to two so that it doesn't freeze until the temperature falls to -45°C. This extraordinary water hole has a unique microflora. Microbes in this pond can metabolise down to -23°C.

Thus some organisms have found a way to live in these extremes of temperature. But, though they may be able to survive, living cells cannot exist or function outside the liquid phase of water, neither in steam nor ice. True steam is a vapour, and ice crystals are lethal for the membranes of live cells. Yet James Dewar (1842-1923), the inventor of the vacuum flask and a Director of the Royal Institution where Davy had worked earlier in the nineteenth century, showed that luminous bacteria could be stored for long periods in liquid air at -160°C, and glow and reproduce when warmed up in culture broth. Nowadays we regularly store bacteria, cell lines and antibody-producing cells in liquid nitrogen at -196°C, and then grow them again weeks or even years later. However, to prevent large ice crystals sending lethal frozen spears through the cells we add glycerol or other substances such as dimethyl sulphoxide (DMSO), as antifreeze. Some insects have already learnt how to manufacture DMSO for the same purpose. And, as we saw when identifying the organic components of life, it isn't only the water that needs to be in the liquid state. Fat must remain liquid too.

Although living cells require liquid water, the inside of a cell looks anything but liquid. The gel inside the cell restricts the movement of molecules and structures. This has led some, such as the physicist J.D. Bernal (1901-1971), to propose that a key to understanding the physical basis of life is the structure of the *water* inside cells. Could the water inside the cell be in a non-crystalline ice form? It could be layered, as it is in the sea, allowing nutrients and organisms to concentrate in particular regions. The gel could act like a molecular sieve, allowing one size of molecule to move in a certain direction and not another.

A change in the state of the water, and thus of the protein gel, is an important mechanism for causing local rubicons within the cell, while mechanisms for preventing the potential lethal rubicon of ice formation being crossed have been crucial to the survival and evolution of organisms living and evolving below 0°C.

The principal focus of molecular biology is on the big molecules. It is these that will explain how life works. It is these that join together to take the cell across its various rubicons. But let us not forget humble water, H_2O. Perhaps the simplest molecule of life, water, still has some surprises up her sleeve. Understanding water is as important to Rubicon as are the organics and inorganics to the molecular biology of life.

THE MOLECULAR PANACEA

Biochemistry and events

We have met Frederick Gowland Hopkins (Plate 13(c)) several times already. This chapter is focussed on the discipline he played such an important part in founding. The first International Congress of Biochemistry was held at the University of Cambridge in 1949 as a mark of the esteem in which he was held. So what started him off?

As a youth of 17, in March 1878, he collected butterflies, moths and beetles. One such insect was the little bombardier beetle *Brachinus crepi-*

tans, plentiful around North London and on the South Downs near East-bourne. Observing it squirt a violet vapour as a defence against potential enemies, Hopkins wanted to find out more about the substance. Though he could only obtain a tiny amount condensed on the side of a collecting jar, and with no chemical training, his life's course was set. For Hopkins it wasn't just the components but how they reacted and how they were formed that mattered when trying to understand the chemistry of life. In 1931 he wrote: 'The biochemist's data gain their full significance only when he can relate them with the activities of the organism as a whole. The whole is not simply the sum of parts. The part in the whole is no longer the same as the part in isolation.' His aim, like ours, was an adequate and acceptable description of the molecular dynamics in living cells and tissues. All we have to do is to put this vision, forgotten by contemporary biology, into a modern context. Hopkins often used the word *event*, a particularly impor-tant concept for Rubicon. In his Linacre Lecture of 1938 he said: 'We realise of course that *events* studied in isolation may be modified when proceeding in the environment of the whole cell (i.e. live cell). Our methods of isolation do not, however, create artifacts, though they may lead us to study potentialities rather than actualities.'

Would that the *in vitro* experimenters in the 1950s and 60s had read and acted upon this wisdom. The literature of that time is littered with artifacts, effects of calcium and other agents on isolated enzymes and sub-cellular structures at concentrations miles away from those that are found in the cell. The power-houses of the cell, the mitochondria, were incubated with solutions containing 1,000 or more times the free calcium which exists inside the cell. Had these investigators thought about the bio-in biochemistry much artifact and misleading interpretation would have been avoided.

To Hopkins it was justifiable to study chemical reactions in the test-tube containing cell fragments or even pure enzymes, provided that the event which occurred in the cell also occurred in the test-tube. I couldn't agree more. The trouble is that we can now see that there are many rubicons – events – which don't occur in the broken cell. In fact, unless we can visualise them in the live cell, we miss them altogether. Now, with modern knowl-edge of the events inside cells, we can see that Hopkins's criteria for certain grind-and-find experiments are not satisfied. We have already seen one wide-ranging example crucial to the control of cell behaviour, calcium. Without the outer membrane intact, the calcium gradient is lost and the agent acting on the outer surface, a hormone for example, is unable to initiate the first event, the first rubicon. The calcium switch does not work. So the cell event doesn't happen either. If you cast your mind back to the first two chapters you will find many more examples of the Hopkins event criterion, lost when the biochemist gets his hands on the blender and the soup ladle.

Molecular biology v. biochemistry

Molecular biology is playing an increasingly dominant role in biology. In fact, sadly, it seems to have taken over from biochemistry. Are we ashamed of calling ourselves biochemists? Certainly not! Yet it is right that there should be an emphasis now on finding out precisely how molecules work, either as individuals like an enzyme or in complexes as in a chromosome. But when we look at a protein in a crystal we must be able to justify the interpretation that follows. To discover the structure of a protein the X-ray crystallographer examines it as a crystal. But is the structure of a protein in this crystal the same as it is when free inside a cell, or in the membrane of the cell? Calculation of the energetics tells us 'Yes'. But can we be sure, when tiny changes in free calcium can have such dramatic effects on the molecular structure of a entire cell? Fortunately we now have both X-ray pictures of proteins and DNA, and pictures taken with another type of spectroscopy, NMR. If we put protein solutions in the core of a very powerful magnet, and send a radio message to the atomic nuclei of the atoms in the protein, a molecular picture of its structure can be obtained.

Molecular biology looks at the structures of related proteins obtained by these techniques, in one, two and three dimensions. It also involves investigating the structure and control of DNA, and how proteins are made and work. The various regions in the DNA have separate functions: the gene itself, the control regions, the processing of the RNA, structural regions of the chromosome and so on. Likewise with a protein. One domain might bind calcium, another binds to a target protein or bit of DNA, another catalyses a reaction in the cell, all within one protein. Just as the biochemist dissected the cell into components and reactions, so the molecular biologist dissects individual molecules.

The information gained is fascinating and provides more pieces of the puzzle. If only someone could fit them together again to form a live cell. No one has yet done this, even from the smallest bacterial chromosome, let alone from the 23 pairs of chromosomal DNA found in all human cells. It is perhaps revealing how much of the success of DNA technology has relied on the use of live cells, particularly bacteria originating from the gut such as *Escherichia coli*, as well as cells in culture originating from animal and human cancers, and the fruit fly *Drosophila*. This is no accident. For only in the live cell does the DNA, RNA or engineered protein behave as efficiently and effectively as it should.

Cell biologists study the structure and function of cells. Biochemists discover the molecules within cells and what they do. Molecular biologists tell us how they work. Or do they? All three disciplines have four dimensions but now need the fifth – Rubicon.

The boiling nitric acid phenomenon

The study of biology depends on description and measurement. Experimental systems are then designed in which to observe the phenomenon under investigation, under controlled conditions. Predictions of the effect of manipulations are made and more measurements carried out to test the validity of these predictions. The trouble with this approach is that it so often relies on so-called 'model' systems, and on describing the properties of cells, cell fragments and pure molecules under conditions light years away from any conditions to which they are subjected in life, or to which their ancestors were exposed during their evolution.

Amazingly, the alga *Cyanidium caldarium* can grow in concentrated solutions of sulphuric acid. But drop most living tissues into sulphuric acid, or any other powerful acid for that matter, and all sorts of weird and wonderful chemical reactions will take place! Gases will be emitted, colour changes will occur, molecules will be broken down and new ones formed. Extracting a biological molecule in boiling nitric acid might be a good way to isolate it, identify it and characterise its composition. But would such an experiment tell us anything about how it works in the cell? I think not. This is an artifactual experiment in the true sense of the word.

The scientific literature over the past few decades is full of such artifacts. I myself once had a tube containing reagents from five distinct groups of organism, i.e. phyla: a calcium indicator from a jelly-fish, red blood cells from a pigeon, antibodies from a rabbit, some human serum, and a virus. Crazy! Surely no one would argue that spending a lifetime describing the details of such 'model' systems would lead to any real understanding of life, even though apparently it might be the only way to study one of its key components.

Herein lies the dilemma. We do need model systems. We do need to extract and purify substances from living systems. We do need to observe the effects of what sometimes appear to be very unnatural conditions on the behaviour of living cells and tissues, and molecules. But where to stop requires great judgment and the ability to define the fifth dimension.

RHYME OR REASON?

A final rhyme, and reason perhaps, to end this chapter:

> Jack and Jill ran up the hill
> To fetch a pail of water
> Jack fell down, and broke his crown,
> And Jill came tumbling after.

Have we learned anything from breaking up cells? Yes, of course we have. A great deal in fact. We have identified the chemicals of life, the composition of the cell, the sub-cellular structures, the reactions and how they may be controlled in the cell. Here, to end with, are three examples highlighting the success and failure of 'grind-and-find'.

First, the membrane complex within the cell known as the endoplasmic reticulum. We saw in Chapter Three that this was first isolated by Marsh in 1951, and that in 1963 Ebashi showed that it had powers of calcium accumulation. This led to the identification of the inner calcium store responsible for triggering muscle contraction. By the early 1980s it had been established as the calcium store in all other cells, release of calcium from the store being the way the cell generates its calcium switch. Secondly, the refuse disposal department in the cell, the lysosome predicted by DeDuve in 1949, was eventually isolated in the 1950s and 60s as a result of careful sub-cellular fractionation. It had been missed in the microscope. And thirdly, careful chemical analysis of isolated mitochondria and chloroplasts showed that they each contained their own DNA. Before this analysis it was thought that all the DNA in the cell was in the nucleus. The appearance of small amounts of DNA with isolated mitochondria was originally dismissed as an artifact, a contamination from DNA thrown out from broken nuclei. But it turned out not only that mitochondria contain their own DNA, but that it is circular like that of bacteria and codes for some of the mitochondrial proteins. When mitochondria divide, their DNA replicates. It was no artifact!

There are many other examples of vital information about living cells that could only have been found by breaking open the cell. But what haven't we found? What haven't we learnt? What has been lost, and, so aptly described by the author of Humpty Dumpty, is never to be found.

Five crucial features of life are lost in the broken cell or pure system:

1. The events of life, of tissues, cells and even sub-cellular structures.
2. The polarity and organisation of structures and chemical reactions within tissues and individual cells.
3. The heterogeneity of each cell and the structures within them.
4. The concentration of reactants and the gradients of substances on either side of the cell membrane.
5. The physico-chemical environment surrounding the sub-cellular structures.

Broken cells no longer move, secrete, divide, transform, or see. They no longer sense and behave as the live cell once did. The calcium gradient across the outer membrane of the cell is lost, essential for its ability to transmit a signal from an agent acting at the outer surface into the cell.

The position of structures and chemical reactions is also crucial to whether an event occurs in a live cell or not. All cells, even free-floating ones, are polarised. For example, in the exocrine pancreas the hormone cholecystokinin, which stimulates enzyme release into the gut to digest your food, acts at one surface of the exocrine cell, while secretion of the enzymes occurs at the other end. This is lost in an homegenate, as is the heterogeneity in the timing and magnitude of the response of each cell. The biochemist can only measure a mean chemical change from thousands or millions of cells. But when you look at each cell individually you find that the timing and magnitude of each rubicon is different in each cell. Not only does homogenisation turn a tissue into a soup, but also the data obtained from it are scrambled.

Two standard characteristics of a biological event occurring in a tissue or a population of cells are: (a) the dose of stimulus required to produce a maximum response, and (b) the time it takes to reach maximum. At half the maximum dose of stimulus, or at a time when the measured response of the tissue is half maximum, have all the cells been stimulated to half their maximum potential or have only half the cells been switched on? Without answering this Rubicon question it is impossible to explain fully the real biological phenomenon. Single-cell analysis is essential if the complete sequence responsible for provoking the ultimate end response is to be elucidated.

You are watching a football match with ten thousand other people — men, women, children, youths, young adults, parents and old-age pensioners. All are of different weights, heights and speed afoot. The loud-hailer suddenly announces that there is a bomb scare. Many people on one side of the stadium hear the message loud and clear, and run as fast as they can to the exits. On the other side, away from the loudspeakers, only a few people hear. The rest remain in their seats. The chemical police are waiting outside trying to estimate how many people have got out, how quickly the crowd inside is moving and how many are left inside. You can't answer these questions by weighing the bulk of human mass that is now outside the ground. Furthermore, assessing the total mass left inside will not help you identify where the information must be targeted to get the rest out. You need to know the polarity of the stadium. So with a cell.

Many phenomena depend on the movement of sub-cellular structures and chemical clouds drifting through the cell to reach a target, or on the direct targeting of substances to a particular site within the cell. The proteins of the nucleus are only found here. They have been targeted, as have the proteins for the other sub-cellular structures. In the homegenate, proteins are found all over the place; for not only has the cell membrane been split open but the membranes of some of the organelles have been damaged or destroyed. In other words, evolution has taken care to ensure that the molecules needed to control a cellular event are in the right place at the right time. But all the King's horses and all the King's men cannot put the substances which have spilled out into the soup back into their rightful places again.

The concentrations of reactants and enzymes in a broken cell system will never be the same as those in the original cell. For example, in the cell some proteins are at concentrations several thousand times that in a tissue homogenate. The act of homogenising a small volume of cells in a large volume of liquid dilutes and separates out the components of the cell.

Instead of being close neighbours, some molecules or houses are now miles apart. Nor can the environment in which proteins and sub-cellular structures find themselves in the cell yet be mimicked in the test-tube. The cytoskeleton, its attachment to membranes and structures, and its gel-sol conversions are all lost. The gradients of salts and other substances across the cell membrane are also destroyed. Consequently the electrical potential and calcium gradients are gone for ever.

Even Hopkins was aware of the smallness of some of the amounts in a single cell. He estimated that the number of sacchase molecules in one yeast was as little as 15,000. He also pointed out the smallness and lightness in weight of cells: 500 million *Bacillus* (now *Escherichia*) *coli* weigh only 0.1 mg. Yet this smallness can be deceptive. If we relate the amount of a substance in one cell to the amount of water, we get the concentration, which is what matters in terms of reactivity. Then we find that enzymes and regulatory proteins inside can sometimes be much higher than those outside the cell. In contrast, in the test-tube the situation is often reversed: the enzyme concentration is usually several orders of magnitude lower than the substrate: otherwise the basic assumption inherent in the enzyme kineticist's favourite equation, derived by Michaelis and Menton, becomes invalid.

So there we have it: the polarity and organisation of the reactions and structures within the cell, the cytoskeleton, the concentration of metabolites and proteins, the gradients of ions and other substances across the outer membrane, necessary for maintenance of the electrical properties of the cell and its signalling system – all these have been irreversibly changed or damaged in the broken cell. In fact, all the King's horses and all the King's biochemists and cell biologists cannot put our Humpty cell together again.

A poem by William Wordsworth sums up our distress:

The Thorn (1798)

Our meddling intellect
Mishapes the beauteous forms of things:-
We murder to dissect.

Enough of science and of art
Close up these barren leaves
Come forth, and bring with you a heart
That watches and receives.

Now that we have identified most of the principal characters in the performance of a cell and know the plot, what we need is to find out how the actors with their particular characteristics work in the cell, and how they came to be selected. There is still a lot to learn about the minute detail of biological molecules. What is going on at the active centre of an enzyme, for example? But is this question only of chemical interest, or will the knowledge gained from answering it really help us to understand how the molecule works inside a cell? Much of the enzymology of the 1950s and 60s was an *in vitro* artifact of no real relevance to the evolution and workings of a live cell.

We still can't really explain why a leg moves when we want to run, or how insulin is secreted into the blood when we eat sugar, or why and how a cell divides, or how it transforms into another with a different function when it does. We know so much detail about these processes from fragments and morsels that we can hardly see the wood for the trees. Inevitably there is a point beyond which reductionism can no longer go. From chemical substance, to molecule, to atom, to electron, to ... Where do we go from here?

So how can we possibly investigate the chemical mechanisms responsible for a particular phenomenon if experimental measurements and manipulations cannot be correlated at the same time with the event in the live cell? We need a technology to measure and manipulate the fifth dimension. We must view Rubicon in action. The wisdom of Hopkins, already quoted at the beginning of this book, says it all:

> All true biologists deserve the coveted name of naturalist. The touchstone of the naturalist is his abiding interest in living Nature in all its aspects.

Viewing the Rubicon

MEASURE AND MANIPULATE

An alternative to the bulldozer

How is your JCB driving going? In case you have forgotten, let me remind you of the chaos the bulldozer created in the concert hall when we tried to find out what was going on during a rehearsal behind closed doors! Let's try again. How could we find out what's going on inside without causing chaos?

How about sending in a TV camera and a microphone on a computer-controlled robot? You manage to get it into the organism without letting any of the sound out. You find a small unfastened window at the back of the building. Ideally, the camera should remain unseen when it enters the auditorium. In fact the conductor notices it, and stops the rehearsal almost immediately. You seem to have failed to get your indicator in without stopping the performance. Luckily, however, the conductor soon recognises it as belonging to the TV company who are to record the performance that night, and so resumes the rehearsal. So you have located your indicator in the right tissue, without too much disruption this time.

The camera and microphone switch on automatically, and send a TV signal via the robot's transmitter to your receiver outside the building. Your first task is to check that you are in the right cell. Yes, it's the Llangaffo Philharmonic Orchestra. Not very well known, but one should learn a lot from this tissue as it develops. The individual groups of cells are in close harmony for an end-response, the overture to Mozart's *Magic Flute*. But let's not get too carried away by the beauty of the music. This tissue can do more than one thing. It will be able to play a concerto and a full symphony, when commanded by its DNA instructor – the conductor. I wonder how we could change its instructions?

The music stops and the orchestra has a rest. Time to move through the programme to the concerto, Brahms's *Second Concerto for Piano and Orchestra in B flat major*, Op. 83, one of your favourites. The soloist has been primed, the necessary genes have been expressed through years of practice, and the manager of the orchestra has been down to the dressing-room to tell him it is time to come on stage. The pianist is on red-amber. So our first rubicon of the concerto response is crossed, the entry of the soloist – the principal player. Then the intracellular signal is released – the conductor sweeps down his baton, and the orchestra switches to green. The first rubicon of the end-response begins – eight haunting upward notes from the French horn. Once six of these notes have reached their target the soloist also switches to green and crosses his first rubicon. The full end-response begins. There will be lots more rubicons, at various times in different parts of the orchestra, as the piece develops.

Analysis of the video signal tells you who is playing and how loud the music is, how many instruments are playing at any one time and how long the piece is. At the end of the three movements the conductor issues a break, for the whole orchestra to have a drink and recover from an exhausting forty-five minutes. This cell works strictly to union rules, the last bastion of the closed shop! After a ten-minute break the rehearsal continues, with a repeat of the first movement. Was it really a horn playing in those opening few bars, or a trombone? Fortunately, the robot has an arm on it which you can control from outside. Quickly you remove the music from the music stand of the principal horn player, and much to the conductor's annoyance those haunting opening six notes before the piano entry are missing. Silence. The 'cell' has failed to be activated by the signal; the conductor's baton has gone unnoticed. The conductor stops the orchestra. In great haste you replace the horn's music and instead remove the music from the trumpet section. This time the concerto starts properly, though the trumpet section look a little distraught. As the rehearsal develops, you play a little game, removing one by one the music from the stands of different instruments. But there is a real problem with the strings: eight desks of firsts, six of seconds, four of viola players, six of cellos and five individual double basses. Trying to alter the music of the whole first violin section all at once is going to be a tricky problem – particularly as you don't want the robot to go crashing through the orchestra, stopping the music entirely. So the robot looks a few pages on, and alters the composer's instructions. At bar 200, mutes are to be placed on the bridges of all violins, so that you can monitor whether this changes the colour of the sound.

So by listening to the effects of manipulating the orchestra selectively, without major disruption, you can answer all your questions – apart, that is, from understanding the inspiration behind this wonderful piece of music. None of its beauty has been lost by your invasion, and by watching the orchestra intact you have learnt far more than you would have from just examining the score, or each instrument individually. In fact you wonder why you even thought of using a bulldozer in the first place.

Now let's translate this scene into a cellular context. What do we want to see in cells? What should we measure and manipulate?

The first problem is that an ordinary camera will be no good. There are plenty of microscopes available for watching individual cells. Shining light through the cell lights up the structure of the cell. But we want to light up and manipulate the chemistry of the cell. We will therefore need a very special detector and robot placed inside the cell. Of course, the camera we used to view the orchestra in action was noticed and the rehearsal stopped for a second or so, but essentially it was non-invasive. The performers were aware of its presence, but the quality and timing of the music was unaffected. This is precisely what we want from an indicator of the chemistry of the live cell. It must produce a signal detectable from the outside, but must not damage or alter the phenomenon under investigation. It certainly must not kill it off.

What are we looking for?

First, we want to watch the gang of four in action. Cast your mind back to Chapter Three. A crucial member was calcium, the others being cyclic AMP and the chemical signals derived from fats in the membrane – IP3 and DAG. We want to watch the signal starting, and then follow its course through the cell. And we need to check the fuel supply in the part of the cell where the action is – ATP. How much fuel is being consumed, and are there sufficient reserves? Ideally, the intracellular robot should have a fuel gauge and an electricity meter which doesn't consume any significant power from the cell.

But the ability to monitor the end-response of the cell is vital, so that it can be correlated with the signal. When the conductor of the orchestra signalled his baton the violins immediately started to play. This is necessary if we are to believe that the baton was the initial signal switching the violins to green for GO. But the trumpet section remained silent, only beginning to poop away several seconds later. The end-response of the tissue had begun before this particular cell started playing. The baton was therefore not the actual signal for the trumpets to start. They got this from the sound of the music. When the trumpet players sensed that the right point had been reached, or had counted the number of bars correctly, they started. A nod from the conductor gave them confidence that they were in the right place.

So with a cell. If we can measure the calcium change inside the cell and show that the lights switch to green before the cell starts to move or secrete, we have tested one criterion. This must be satisfied if calcium is to be identified as the primary intracellular signal, setting the rubicon sequence off. So that's the first thing we want to view and thus identify: the primary signal. Then we need to watch this signal as it moves through the cell. When it reaches a possible target, we ask whether the music has started. Has the cell moved, secreted, divided or died? If we stop the signal reaching this target, what happens then? As we saw when our robot switched the music around, so we watch to see whether the cell still undergoes its end-response. Or it might be delayed. On the other hand, the cell might respond louder or softer. All these modifications will give us information about how the rubicons are triggered in a particular cell. The movement of calcium through the outer membrane must also be watched. Tiny electric meters are now available to measure the electric currents in a minute patch of membrane. Channels open and close, i.e. they cross the Rubicon. The selectivity for calcium can be determined.

We shall see that all this is possible for calcium. But we still don't have methods for viewing and manipulating definitively the other possible signals, cyclic AMP, IP_3 and DAG, in live cells. But there is now a remarkable technology emerging for watching the next step in the Rubicon sequence, the modification of the target proteins. We can watch, in live cells, the activation of the proteins responsible for putting phosphate onto target proteins.

We also need to watch genes being expressed in individual live cells. Sometimes these rubicons are steps on the way to the final response, for example in cell transformation, division or programmed death. But at other times they tell us what makes the cell ready to respond to the signal. Some cells may not go because there is no fuel. Others may not go because the signalling machinery is not in place. In the orchestra's case, some instruments were not able to play because they had no music, while others simply weren't watching the conductor. They missed the instruction to GO. Others even forgot their instruments.

Changing the music

What if we don't have a 'camera' to view the signal in the live cell? Then we have to resort to indirect experiments. We add things to the outside of cells which we think manipulate one section of the rubicon sequence, and see what it does to the end-response. But even when we have a camera it is important to make predictions about the effect of changing the musical score, or the instruments, on the final outcome of the orchestra. So what sort of things can we manipulate from the outside?

We can remove the calcium. We can add things which will block proteins in the membrane, or activate them in the absence of the conductor. There are substances which penetrate the cell. For example, *ionophores* will let calcium into the cell. And there are agents which will open the door of the calcium cupboard inside the cell. There are also substances which will fool the cell into sending other signals, such as cyclic AMP. We have met some of these scurvy knaves already. Cholera toxin and pertussis toxin (whooping cough) are two such toxins which can set a signalling sequence going, without having to add the natural primary stimulus – a hormone, for example. There is a host of plant and animal substances, as well as chemicals from the drug industry, which will 'poison' or 'provoke' a specified component of the signalling pathway when added to the outside. Some generate the first signal. Some prevent it. Others activate the phosphate workers, thereby altering the amount of phosphate on a key rubicon protein. Okadaic acid blocks the enzyme which removes such phosphate. Another is a tumour promoter, belonging to a class of compounds found in certain desert plants. It is called a phorbol ester, and activates a phosphate handler called protein kinase C.

What we really want to do is get round the barrier of the outer membrane, without damaging it. There are dexterous scientists who can now use minute syringes to inject things into a single cell just a few millionths of a metre in diameter. This means that large proteins, such as antibodies, RNA and DNA, can be injected into a cell. But what about the whole tissue or organism? How can we view the chemistry of Rubicon here? We will see that genetic engineering is set not only to revolutionise how we view the Rubicon, but provides a vision for an alternative to the chemical poisons in treating disease. Transgenic animals and plants enable us to test hypotheses in a way impossible with the human animal.

Manipulation involves acute and long-term removal or activation of signals and other parts of the Rubicon sequence. Drugs may send the players to sleep, or antibodies block their view. Removal of the DNA or RNA, or giving a new piece of DNA, will change the musical score with predictable effects, if we have got the right picture of a Rubicon sequence. But surely all this measuring and manipulating must do some damage?

As Heisenberg (1901-1976) realised for the electron in an atom, any scientific investigation must affect the components of a phenomenon in some way, however small. The trick is to use indicators which cause minimal disruption, and manipulators which cause disruption only to selected components of the cell. Give the orchestra cyanide in their coffee during the break and it will kill them all. The music stops for ever. Adding cyanide to a cell to show that the phenomenon is killed when the cell is killed tells us nothing more than we knew already. But use an agent which selectively removes calcium from the endoplasmic reticulum or mitochondria, and then show that this has no effect on the phenomenon, and we have learnt something. Negative answers can be as important as positive ones when measuring and manipulating cells. The secret is to get a clear yes-or-no answer to a specific question. So much of the present experimental approach in medical research fails to be at the cutting edge.

The penetrative investigator has to ask: 'Is this really a definite way to answer my question? Or will the result of my experiment be manipulated to fit a preconceived picture?' Science is as much about asking questions as about finding answers. So, in seeing how we can light up the chemistry of the living cell, let's be clear exactly what questions we are asking, and put these into a Rubicon framework.

A shopping list of questions

Let us assume that the phenomenon we are studying has been described in such a way that we can now ask questions about the mechanisms involved. The cells responsible have been identified and the external stimuli responsible for triggering an end-response have been characterised. Secondary regulators and drugs have also been found which can either enhance or diminish the phenomenon. Two distinct sets of pathogens have also been discovered. One, a group of viruses, stops the phenomenon occurring at first but after a while appears to enhance the effect of the natural stimuli. The other, a group of proteins belonging to the body's defence system, stimulates the cells in their own right but inhibits the effect of the normal stimuli. Consider, for example, the release of bleach from cells in the joints of patients with rheumatoid arthritis. Why are these cells here? Why are they doing what they should not be doing?

There are eight sets of questions we must answer if the Rubicon sequence is to be viewed in its entirety:

1. What is the primary signal inside the cell generated at the cell membrane when a stimulus or pathogen acts? Is it calcium, or one of the other intracellular signals?
2. How is this signal generated and then removed? Is there, for example, an internal store that releases it, or is it generated at the inner surface of the cell membrane?
3. How does this first intracellular signal work? In particular, to where does it have to move in order to provoke the next rubicon? What are the protein-modification rubicons required to generate the end-response, and where in the cell do they occur? Is protein phosphorylation required, for example? If so which kinase-phosphatase system does the cell use?
4. How do the pathogens work to interact with this signalling sequence? Are signalling sequences generated by pathogens friend or foe, i.e. are they part of the damaging process or a signal for the cell to defend itself?
5. How do the drugs which affect the phenomenon work? By controlling the number of cells crossing the rubicon? Do they affect the time at which each crosses? Or do they alter the level of the ultimate end-response? Can we identify, from the characterisation of the rubicons caused by the pathogens, potential target sites in the signalling sequence for therapeutic attack or enhancement?
6. What are the priming mechanisms, via gene expression in the nucleus or otherwise, responsible for determining the number of cells which have the capacity to cross the end-response rubicon? And which components in the intracellular sequence are expressed?
7. How does the complete system develop from the embryo, and in the adult if the cells involved turn over continuously?
8. How did the Rubicon signalling sequence evolve?

To summarise: to answer these questions we need to measure and manipulate signals such as calcium in the cytosol, as well as inside organelles such as the endoplasmic reticulum, mitochondria and the nucleus. This will identify the source of any change in cytosolic calcium and whether it could be the switch for altering gene expression. We need to measure ATP as the energy source, in different parts of the cell, and its cousin GTP, which is required for signal transduction through G-proteins.

We need also to measure and manipulate covalent modification of proteins, such as phosphorylation, in defined compartments of the cell. And we need to do all of this while at the same time being able to measure and follow the end-response. In every case we need to be able to count the number of cells which have crossed rubicons for the signal generation, signal movement, covalent modification and end-response, to determine whether the time course, the magnitude, the dose-response relationships and manipulations work by affecting the number of rubicons crossed at any particular time, or by altering the level of the response at each stage in the sequence.

To do all this we need to light up the chemistry of individual living cells, to watch and quantify their individual sequences. Some may not even go at all, while some may only go half way. We cannot tell unless we can follow each cell. Measurements on cell populations will not give us this information. Rather, when one cell has crossed rubicon 6, another may have only just crossed rubicon 1. As a result, population data will be a mishmash of numbers that cannot be unravelled.

So what indicators have we available?

Litmus paper is a well-known indicator, testing whether a liquid is acid or alkaline. When immersed in an acid, such as vinegar, it turns red. When the liquid is alkaline – for example, washing soda – it turns purplish-blue. There are times when we shall want to measure the acidity of the cell – pH. But first we need to measure calcium. Furthermore, sticking a piece of paper into a cell wouldn't work.

It seems a daunting task even to think about how we could measure and manipulate chemical events in single live cells; cells so small that each on its own is invisible to the naked eye. More than a thousand would fit on to the head of a pin. But scientists are an ingenious bunch. The pathway of science has frequently required a combination of new questions, new concepts and the development of new techniques in order to forge a clear path through the jungle of facts produced by the herd. As often happens, someone has been here before. Their path may not have been as clear and straight as the modern one. However, we still have much to learn from past pioneers. Their vision from the past gives us a clear pathway for the future. In the first half of this century the principle of measuring and manipulating the chemistry of living cells was established by several scientists, including Chambers, Reznikoff, the Needhams, Loeb, and Heilbrunn and his students. Who? Their names have been forgotten by most teachers. Yet without the vision of these pioneers we wouldn't be where we are today.

THE PIONEERS

The story begins some seventy years ago with a pioneer of cell biology, Robert Chambers (1881-1957) (Plate 13(b)). Chambers was the mentor of Herbert Pollack, the first person to detect a change in calcium in a live cell. Born in Erzroom (Erzerum), Turkey in 1881, the son of a Presbyterian minister, his formative years were spent among the wild mountain tribes, the Koords (now spelt Kurds), and the Armenians. The latter, being Christian and refusing to pay oppressive taxes, were persecuted brutally between 1894-96 by the Turkish troops and Kurdish tribesmen. What's new?

Chambers obtained his PhD while working at Munich under the German zoologist Richard Carl Wilhelm Theodor von Hertwig (1850-1937). This was an exciting laboratory, for Hertwig was developing his now-famous germ-layer theory. The tissues of the body are derived from three fundamental cell types, a crucial rubicon during development of the fertilised egg from a clump of nondescript cells. Hertwig also described for the first time artificial development of sea-urchin eggs without the need for sperm. This is known as parthenogenesis, 'virgin birth'. Alcohol is one agent which will trigger it, a fact capitalised on by another pioneer of cell biology, Jacques Loeb (1859-1924), working in the United States. As if this wasn't enough, Hertwig also made important contributions to the study of the reproduction of the pond protozoan, *Paramecium*.

As it has been for many of us, the turning point in Chambers's career was to occur at a marine laboratory. Woods Hole, Massachusetts has been an inspiration for many American and foreign scientists. Here Chambers became fascinated with micro-manipulation of individual cells. By 1915, he was perhaps the leading authority on micro-injection and micro-manipulation of cells, and joined Cornell Medical College. But Woods Hole remained *the* place, where in the summer his most important contributions were initiated. The Marine Biological Association at Plymouth has a similar history of inspiration in British physiology and biology over the past century.

In 1923 A.B. Macullum, in a correspondence with Myra Sampson, wrote in the journal *Science*: 'A microchemical method for calcium would be a great desideratum.' Prophetic words indeed. Pollack, one of Chambers's students, reported in 1928 an experiment in which he had micro-injected a single amoeba, like those found in pond water, with the red dye alizarin sulphonate. Alizarin had been known as a dye since Egyptian times, but Pollack also knew that alizarin sulphonate could bind metal ions such as calcium. It precipitated calcium in the test-tube. As we saw in Chapter Three, Pollack observed a 'shower of red crystals' close to the site of pseudopod formation in the amoeba, and the movement stopped. He predicted that a rise in calcium inside the cell had something to do with generating the amoeboid movement which starts with a pseudopod rubicon. Not bad going for 1928: for even as late as 1960, as Ebashi pointed out in his Croonian Lecture to the Royal Society published in 1980, there was still much scepticism about the calcium hypothesis. Pollack's pioneering paper was visionary also because it laid down the criteria for an intracellular calcium indicator, including the need for it to be specific, sensitive and able to be incorporated into the cell without damage. At that time Pollack did not realise how low the intracellular calcium actually was, i.e.

some ten thousand times lower than the calcium outside the cell. If he had, he might even have bothered to try looking at it. But it was to be another forty years before a method, generally applicable to all cells, was developed.

The first attempts to manipulate calcium involved changing the medium bathing cells. Sydney Ringer (1835-1910) (Plate 4(b)), working at University College Hospital in London, was red-faced after realising the error in his first paper of using such a manipulation. His model systems were the isolated frog heart, which continues to beat as long as an oxygenated solution is perfused through the coronary arteries, and the sea-urchin egg. But the first experiments in which calcium was removed from the medium proved negative. The heart continued to beat, as Ringer reported in 1892. But he had no reason to be ashamed of withdrawing the original conclusion, for he himself corrected the mistake. And calcium is devilishly difficult to get rid of from water! Calcium is everywhere. Even distilled water can have up to a hundred times the amount free in the live cell! It will even leach off laboratory glassware. Leave some distilled water in a glass flask for a few weeks, and then measure how much calcium there is in it. You will find that it may be a hundred times or more that of the free calcium inside a live cell. However, we can get round the problem by adding an agent which binds tightly any residual calcium. These substances, or chelators as they are called, were invented in the 1950s and 1960s. Injecting them into a cell stops it crossing the Rubicon. One of the first such experiments was carried out by Portzehl, Caldwell and Rüegg in 1964. They stopped the muscle of a crab contracting by injecting a calcium chelator into the cell before attempting to excite it electrically.

But the pioneer of micro-injection of calcium into cells was Heilbrunn (Plate 5(a)). First he tried to show that calcium would cause muscle to contract by making tiny holes in cells with and without calcium outside. Then, in 1947, the classic experiment was carried out with a student, Floyd Wiercinski, the injection of salts into a frog muscle. Only calcium chloride stimulated contraction. Injection of water, sodium, potassium or magnesium chloride did not. Similar experiments had been carried out by two Japanese workers, Kamada and Kinoshita, in 1943. Yet it wasn't until the proteins responsible for making the calcium work and the source of calcium inside the muscle cell was identified that the calcium story was fully accepted by the scientific community.

Much of this pioneering work was done with very large cells, some a millemetre or more in diameter and sometimes several centimetres long. These were ideal targets for the early micrurgicalist's (the word micrurgical was often used in Chambers's day to describe the micro-surgery of cells) micropipettes. But what was really needed were techniques to light up the chemistry not only of giant cells but also of tiny cells of the type found in our bodies. A bleach-producing cell is less than 10 millionths of a metre in diameter. And as late as 1965 there still wasn't a method for measuring calcium inside live cells. The vision of Macullum (above p. 213) of the need for an indicator of free calcium inside a live cell was however about to be realised. And, as is so often the case in science the breakthrough to achieve this came from a surprising source – a luminous jelly-fish!

LIGHTING UP THE CHEMISTRY OF THE LIVING CELL
A luminous lung

Luminous jelly-fish have been described in some imaginative ways. Pliny described several luminous organisms in his *Natural History* written in the first century AD, including the bivalve *Pholas dactylus*, a lantern fish, the glow-worm and fungi. Jelly-fish were common in the Bay of Naples, where Pliny died during the eruption of Vesuvius in AD 79. Jelly-fish were called by the Romans *Pulmo marinus*, 'sea lung'. Pliny's description of the luminous pink jelly-fish, now known as *Pelagia noctiluca*, was translated in 1601 by Philemon Holland (1552-1637) as follows: 'Rub a piece of wood with the fish called *Pulmo Marinus*, it will seeme as though it were on fire: in so much as a staff so rubbed or besmeared with it, may serve instead of a torch to give light before one.' The scientific term for jelly-fish is *medusa* and was first introduced by Linnaeus because some species looked like a head with snaky curls dangling from it. Medusa in Greek mythology was one of the three Gorgons, whose head had snakes for hair and turned anyone looking at it into stone. The Swede Peter Forsskål (1732-1763) (Plate 13(a)) – Petrus Forskål on the frontispiece of his major work *Fauna Arabica* (1775) – was a pupil of Linnaeus in Uppsala. He had a particularly apt description of another luminous jelly-fish, the one that has such an important part to play in the calcium-signalling story some 200 years later (Plate 2(b)).

Between 1760 and 1763 he visited Arabia in search of unusual animals and plants. *Fauna Arabica*, written in Latin, lists the animals he found. Forsskål described a jelly-fish he called *Medusa aequorea* thus: 'Raso ligno, parum adeo in tenebris splendet', roughly translated 'If you give it a good crack with a stick it glows in the dark!'. Well, what would you do?

Osamu Shimomura, a pioneer of the chemistry of bioluminescence working with Frank Johnson at Princeton, collected at Friday Harbor Washington State thousands of these jelly-fish, now called by them *Aequorea aequorea* (or *forskalea* in the UK, or *victoria* on the West coast of the USA). In 1962 he showed that the cause of the light emission from this remarkable animal was a protein. Tightly bound to it were a small organic molecule and oxygen. All you had to do was add calcium and the protein complex flashed – a dramatic molecular rubicon. But, for us at this point in the story, the crucial observation was that the speed of the flash was dependent on the amount of calcium added – the less calcium, the slower the flash.

So in 1967 Ernest Ridgway and Chris Ashley injected this protein, extracted from the jelly-fish, into a giant muscle fibre from a barnacle. The free calcium inside the cell was so low that the aequorin, as it is called, didn't flash at all. Rather it glowed, ever so dimly. But the light was detectable by a special electronic tube (a photomultiplier) which produces a million electrons for every light particle hitting it. They then excited the muscle fibre electrically. To their delight, just before the muscle started to contract, the glow from the cell began to increase. In fact a small dim flash was recorded. When the cell was injected with a substance that bound calcium, a chelator, this stopped both the flash and the contraction rubicon – definitive proof that calcium was the trigger for muscle contraction in these cells. These are the cells that keep the plates across the top of barnacles closed when the tide goes out. Similar experiments were carried out in the 1970s by John Blinks and colleagues, who injected aequorin into a more difficult cell to study, a muscle cell from a frog, including one from the heart.

These experiments showed that it really was possible to light up the chemistry of the living cell. During the 1970s much was learnt about calcium as a rubicon trigger, though it was not given this title then. Calcium flashes were seen in all sorts of cells: muscles, nerves, photo-receptors, slime moulds, salivary gland cells and protozoa. But small cells proved very difficult. The problem was, how to get a protein into a small, mammalian cell without blowing it up.

We succeeded in getting a relative of aequorin, known as obelin, into a human bleach-producing cell. My colleague Maurice Hallett and I were able to detect changes in light signals from these cells when stimulated by a chemical attractant. We went on to show that there were in fact two independent triggers of the bleach-production rubicon, one caused by a calcium switch in the cell, the other by a different signal. This, we believed, had important implications for the rheumatoid joint, where these mechanisms were potential targets for therapeutic intervention. The end-response of the cell – the release of the bleach – was monitored by another light-emitting protein, this time extracted from the piddock *Pholas* (Plate 6). More of this in a minute. But the real technical breakthrough in measuring calcium inside cells came at the end of the 1970s from a young chemist, Roger Tsien. Tsien was an American visitor to the UK and working at the Physiology Laboratory in Cambridge, a lab which had an outstanding history of the study of calcium and other ions in controlling the behaviour of nerves and other cells. Experimenting with a young physiologist, Tim Rink, Tsien found a way of lighting up the calcium in any cell you wanted to look at, even tiny human cells. To understand the brilliance of the invention we must return to the phenomenon we have discussed several times already, light.

A light ruler

Without light we would not be able to appreciate the beauties of the Universe, and without light science would be nowhere at all. Walk into any physics, chemistry or biochemistry lab and you will find it full of instruments dependent on measuring light. There will be infra-red, visible and UV spectrometers, scintillation counters, NMR and ESR spectrometers, fluorimeters and chemi-luminometers, and of course a range of microscopes and video cameras. But only some of them detect visible light. So why discuss them collectively?

Whenever it is raining and the sun is out I always look for the rainbow: a spectacular arc of colour rubicons – violet, indigo, blue, green, yellow, orange and red. But this is only part of a much wider arc – the electromagnetic spectrum which includes not only visible, UV and infra-red light, but also gamma and X-rays at one end and microwave and radio waves at the other. Visible light is just a small blip in the middle.

In 1678 the Dutch mathematician, physicist and astronomer Christiaan Huygens (1629-1695) conceived of light as waves, while in 1704 Isaac Newton (1643-1727) proposed that it should be considered as particles. The problem whether light should be regarded as a wave or as a shower of energetic particles has remained ever since. By considering it as a wave with electric and magnetic components, James Clerk Maxwell (1831-1879) in 1868 was able to develop an electromagnetic theory of light which explained reflection, refraction, diffraction, polarisation and the Doppler effect. But the theory fell down, as we saw in Chapter One, when it tried to explain the relationship between the colour of an incandescent body and its temperature. Nor can it explain how light hitting the surface of a photo-sensitive substance can generate an electron, or the converse. When an electron beam in the tube of your TV set hits the inside surface of the screen, light is generated. To explain these latter two phenomena – to overcome the crises – required quantum theory and the concept of light as a stream of energetic particles – photons. The concept of photons originated in 1905 when Einstein succeeded in using them to explain the converse of the TV screen – the photo-electric effect where electrons are *generated* by light instead of the other way round. However, the term photon was apparently not used until 1926. Photons are also needed to describe the energetics of light emission from chemical reactions or fluorescence. The energy of these particles, or the distance between each hump of the wave if we look at it that way, varies enormously – in fact over thirty decades. Long radio waves have lengths of a thousand metres or more, while gamma rays emitted by radioactive elements have wavelengths of less than a million millionths of a metre. Yet all these waves or particles move through space at the same speed, the speed of light: about three hundred million metres per second (or 186,000 miles per second). At that speed you could travel round the world seven and a half times in a second.

Each region of the electromagnetic spectrum has found both scientific and practical application. Radio waves give us the sound and vision for radio and TV, but also nuclear magnetic resonance (NMR) spectroscopy. Microwave cookers have revolutionised the restaurant industry and give the scientist electron spin resonance (ESR) spectroscopy. Visible light gives us the electric light bulb, fluorescent strips and the TV screen: and it gives the scientist luminescence spectroscopy. Infra-red cameras enable survivors to be detected in the rubble of an earthquake. X-rays are used by the radiologist to see if your bones are broken or whether cancer is present, while the high energy of gamma rays is used for treating cancer, and gave the experimental scientist Mössbauer (b. 1929) spectroscopy. Of all these scientific applications there are two which enable the chemistry of living tissues to be lit up: NMR and luminescence.

NMR detects the chemical environment around nuclei – not cell nuclei but the nuclei at the centre of atoms. An over-simplified model of an atom is that of a nuclear sun with electron planets spinning round it. The radio sets in these atomic 'suns' change the frequency of the radio wave they receive depending on what other atoms are around it. This means that when chemicals find themselves in an NMR machine each atomic type has its own radio station. Hydrogen is the pop channel – everyone listens to it – while the serious channel is listened to by those wanting to hear what environment phosphorus is in, particularly in the form of phosphate. Thus a chemical picture of a tissue can be built up. Magnetic resonance imaging (MRI) is a particularly sophisticated type of NMR. It is an exciting, though very expensive, new technology now being used in medicine. MRI can win out over X-rays, particularly when one wants to examine the soft, non-bony tissues. A human arm, or even the whole body, can sit inside the enormously powerful magnet required for NMR, and the amount of ATP at a specific focus, for example the heart or kidneys, can then be recorded. Exciting as this new technology is, it has one major limitation for Rubicon. It is not very sensitive.

We have seen how tiny are the amounts and concentrations of the rubicon signals in individual cells. NMR indicators for free calcium have been developed for use in intact organs, and NMR signals have been recorded on single cells. But it is beyond the scope of NMR to detect free calcium and cyclic AMP in single cells, at the moment at least. Nor can NMR watch a chemical wave, lasting only a few seconds, moving across a cell. It takes minutes, or longer even, to generate an NMR signal. Transient calcium changes in cells are thus beyond the limit for NMR. But there is another way. This is to use the part of the electromagnetic spectrum where UV and visible light occurs. It involves a phenomenon we have already met several times, luminescence.

Encounters with natural light

In 1603 a remarkable stone was discovered by a cobbler and amateur alchemist from Bologna, Vincenzo Cascariolo. He found that a local stone he took from Monte Paterno (or Poderno) near Bologna, after special treatment produced a stone which could 'imbibe' daylight and emit it in the dark. The original stone was a heavy spar we now know to be a form of barium sulphate rich in sulphur. To convert it to the 'magical' stone it was roasted to drive off water and gases such as carbon dioxide and sulphur dioxide, a process known as calcination. Luminous creatures, shining flesh, glowing wood, stone and liquors that shine in the dark had been known for centuries. But here a new phenomenon had been discovered – the ability of substances to 'store' light. Many distinguished men were later to explore the slopes of Monte Paterno searching for the golf-ball sized heavy silvery stones which offered so much promise. Cascariolo's preparation became known as the Bolognian stone or phosphor. Knowledge of the stone spread rapidly throughout Europe, and many distinguished people tried to explain how it worked. A detailed description of how to make it was published by Pierre Potier (d. 1640), physician to the kings of France, in his *Pharmacopoea Spagirica* (1625) which dealt with inorganic remedies based on the teaching of Paracelsus, whom we shall meet in the next chapter. The remarkable thing about the Bolognian stone was that it glowed in the dark while being stone cold! It was 'luminescent'. If we are to understand the true nature of how we light up the chemistry of living cells today, it is essential to grasp the difference first between *luminescence* and *incandescence*, and secondly between *fluorescence* and *chemi-luminescence*.

Imagine you have taken your family on a camping holiday. It is a lovely, warm summer's night. The thunderstorm has abated, after a few flashes of lightning, and the bluish wisps of St Elmo's fire emanating from the tips of some of the masts of the boats in the bay have disappeared. The embers of the fire you lit some hours ago are still glowing. As you saunter out towards the sea's edge you glance up. The flickering lights of the stars are visible again. A satellite is speeding across the sky, a dot of moving light through the myriads of stationary ones. A bright flash temporarily lights up a small area of darkness, another meteorite glowing hot as it enters the earth's atmosphere. Above the horizon there is a spectacular luminous arc, transparent white with hints of green, red and violet. This is the first time you have observed the *aurora borealis*, the Northern Lights. As you move away from the lights of the camp, you notice bluish-green flashes on the strands of seaweed washed up on the beach, sparked off by being trod on. The rock pools and the sea itself sparkle as you wade along. A dead fish, glowing bright blue, is decaying on a rock.

Of these encounters with natural light, some are caused simply by reflection, some because the object is very hot, and some by the phenomenon known as luminescence.

Most people are familiar with the fact that when solids and liquids get very hot they emit light. Things start to glow red at about 525°C, and by 1,400°C are blue-white. As Newton wrote in his *Optiks* of 1704: 'And what else is a burning coal but red-hot wood? Do not all fixed bodies, when heated beyond a certain degree, emit light and shine?' By 1794, James Hutton proposed that the term *incandescence* (from the Latin *incandescere*, 'to become white with heat') should be used to describe the emission of light from bodies heated to high temperature. More than a century earlier Robert Boyle (1626-1691) had published a paper in the *Philosophical*

Transactions of the recently formed Royal Society, on the similarities and differences between 'burning coal and shining wood'. But it was not until 1888 that a German physicist, Eilhardt Wiedemann (1852-1928), decided to use *luminescenz* (from the Latin *lumen*, 'light'), to describe phenomena that produced light without requiring the very high temperature for incandescence.

Like the Becquerel family in France, the Wiedemann family in Germany devoted much energy to the study of luminescence. Eilhardt Wiedemann was the son of a professor of physics at the University of Leipzig, Gustav Heinrich Wiedemann (1826-1899). It was here that Eilhardt obtained his PhD and also became a professor, moving to professor of physics at the University of Erlangen in 1886. His early work involved studies on the polarisation and refraction of light, and the the colour of light from electric discharge tubes. He then became interested in what he was to call 'luminescence'. Interestingly he was also keen on the history of science, particularly Arab knowledge, publishing a booklet in 1890, *Die Naturwissenschaften bei den Araben*. Wiedemann at first divided luminescence into six categories, labelled with a prefix: photo-, electro-, thermo-, tribo-, crystallo- and chemi-luminescence. To this list we can now add sono-, radio- and pyro-. Light is energy, so the prefix tells us where the energy comes from. In photo-luminescence, more often referred to as fluorescence, the energy comes from light itself. When light is shone onto the photo-luminescent substance some light is absorbed and the substance then re-emits light, but at a different colour when it is shifted towards the red. The energy for tribo-luminescence comes from structural changes between molecules. Cracking some raw sugar or a peppermint will generate a flash. You can also generate a flash by stripping off a piece of sticky tape or the top of a self-sealing envelope. In chemi-luminescence, on the other hand, the energy for light emission comes from a chemical reaction. Such reactions use nearly all the energy available to generate light, in contrast to non-luminescent reactions where any energy freed generates heat. Thus all living light is caused by chemi-luminescence.

Paradoxically there are two types of luminescence which do need heat; pyro- and thermo-. Spill some salt onto the cooker while you are cooking and the flame will turn a bright yellow. This is pyro-luminescence. Thermo-luminescence on the other hand results from the gentle heating of objects which have been previously irradiated. This phenomenon has application in the dating of archaeological specimens. But that is another story. The issue at hand is that, if there are types of luminescence which need heat, is there really any difference at all between incandescence and luminescence? Why is luminescence such an important phenomenon for viewing the Rubicon, and incandescence simply a means of generating charcoal?

The answer once again lies in an orgasm. No, not a human one this time. But rather one of the smallest components in every atom in your body, the electron. The key to understanding luminescence is the electron and its excitation, something I mentioned briefly in Chapter One.

In 1891 G. Johnstone Stoney had suggested the name *electron* for the elementary unit of electricity. On Friday 30 April 1897 J.J.Thomson told an audience at the Royal Institution that he had measured how heavy it was. He had found that the electron was many times smaller than the smallest atom, hydrogen. This was an essential step towards the dissection of the atom itself. Each hydrogen atom has one electron. As we go through the periodic table, element by element, the number of electrons increases one by one, until we reach the last natural element, uranium, which has ninety-two. The other elements are man-made, but the same principle applies. The outer electrons in atoms can be excited. When these excited electrons drop back to the resting state they have to get rid of the energy. If the electron is in a luminescent substance this energy is emitted as a particle of light. So the electron in a photo-luminescent substance is excited by absorbing light, in a pyro-luminescent substance by heat and in a chemi-luminescent substance by a chemical reaction. By contrast in incandescence the energy for the light is generated as vibrational energy between the atoms.

Electron events are incredibly fast, beyond our real experience. Excitation takes a few thousand million millionths (10^{-15}) of a second, and the decay producing the light a thousand millionths (10^{-9}) of a second. This means that in the twinkling of an eye over a million atoms can release their particles of light.

Returning to the camp site we can now see that the glowing embers of the fire and the flash of the meteor were examples of incandescence, while the others were types of luminescence: St Elmo's fire – a form of electro-luminescence; the aurora – a form of radio-luminescence, as a result of bombardment of the Earth's atmosphere by particles from the Sun; and chemi-luminescence – the cause of the flashes in the sea, the hydroids on the seaweed and the bacteria on the decaying fish.

But there is still a problem about nomenclature – concerning the use of the word 'phosphorescence'.

The *Oxford English Dictionary* defines 'phosphorescent' as 'having the property of shining in the dark', and recognises the layman's use of the word to describe the many animals and microbes that can generate their own light, some of which we have encountered in this book. But in science the term phosphorescence has a more precise meaning. In a monograph published in 1640 entitled *Litheosphorus, sive de lapide Bononiensi lucem in se conceptam ab ambiente claro mox in tenebris mire conservante*, 'Stony light-bearer, or the stone from Bologna which amazingly keeps the light conceived within itself from the surrounding daylight once it is in the dark', Fortunio Liceti (1577-1657), professor of philosophy at Bologna, described details of many accounts of 'stony light-bearers', including the Bolognian stone. But the phenomenon needed a name. Heenig Brandt or Brand (d. 1692), a physician in Hamburg, was intent on making a fortune by alchemy. In 1699 he isolated a material by chemical reduction of urine. This also had the remarkable ability to glow with a blue light in the dark.

No previous exposure of light, heat or mechanical treatment was required. The substance was called *phosphorus* from the Greek *phos*, 'light', and *phoros*, 'bringing'. This first discovery of artificial chemi-luminescence – for this is what it turned out to be – Brandt appropriately called 'phosphorus mirabilis' – miraculous light-bringer – and is now a recognised property of pure phosphorus when exposed to the air. Like the discovery of the Bolognian stone, luck had played a major part. It is in the form having reacted with oxygen that we find phosphorus in the body, as phosphate. In science 'phosphorus' is restricted to the element itself, as applied in 1677 by another German, Johann Sigismund Elsholtz (1623-1688). But in the seventeenth century 'phosphor' or 'phosphorus' were used to describe a variety of luminous substances, not only the element phosphorus. Soon 'phosphorescence' became popular to describe any kind of 'cold' light, including light emitted by phosphorus and luminous animals. But this created a new problem because, as I have explained, the general word phosphorescence did not distinguish between a host of phenomena that produced light and that could be separated on scientific grounds. This is not merely a semantic point, for it has created confusion even among scientists.

Whenever I give a scientific talk I try to emphasise the essential differences between chemi- and photo-luminescence. Yet someone will invariably come up to me afterwards and ask for more information about 'these *phosphorescent* or *fluorescent* animals ...'. In scientific discussions the term 'phosphorescence' is used to describe prolonged light-emission from objects. What is happening is that an excited electron decides to stay excited and to take ages to drop back to rest. Phosphorescence, therefore, usually describes a slow photo-luminescence, as distinguished from 'fluorescence' which is used when the electron gets back to rest pronto. But in chemi-, and thus bio-, luminescence, the light decay is also slow. Why should we not describe this as phosphorescence? The reason is that it is the slowness of the chemical reaction, not the slowness of the electron, that causes chemi-luminescence to produce a glow. Even when a flash is generated the chemical reaction is a hundred million times slower than the speed of the electrons in going from 'excited' to 'rest'.

As Henri Becquerel, the discoverer of radioactivity, showed in 1858, true phosphorescence can last many minutes or even hours. You can buy such starlight displays for the ceiling of a child's bedroom. In fluorescence, on the other hand, the other type of photo-luminescence, the electron comes back to rest very fast. A fluorescent compound only glows while the light continues to shine on it.

Chemi-luminescence can be found in Nature in luminous animals, Will o' the Wisp, cold flames – for example, ether – and synthetic compounds. You can even buy luminous light sticks for golf at night, for fishing and to adorn yourself with at Hallowe'en.

The problem of nomenclature was cleverly highlighted by a cartoon which appeared in a newspaper article in 1987 about my work (Figure 12).

Fig. 12. Cartoon by Alder, *Sunday Times*, 12 April 1987.
© Times Newspapers.

Now that we have, I hope, clarified some of the terms, let's see how the phenomenon of luminescence can be used to light up the Rubicon sequence in living cells.

Light without fire

Fluorescent strip lights, invented in this century, are part of our way of life, in offices, homes and on the streets. But chemi-luminescence has been exploited by man for centuries, and in some remarkable ways.

An early account of how to use *living light* to illuminate things without needing a flame comes from Oleas Magnus (*c.* 1490-1557), Archbishop of Sweden in Uppsala. He travelled widely in Europe, but in 1523 as a Catholic he was forced to live in exile in Rome because of the Swedish Reformation. He described several luminous organisms. In his influential history of Scandinavia – *Historia de gentibus septentrionalibus* ('A History of Northern Nations') (1555) – he wrote: 'When it is expedient, or there is an urgent need, people of the far north use an ingenious method for lighting up their way through the forests in the dark, and when continuous night prevails before and after the winter solstice they place pieces of rotten oak bark at certain intervals on the proposed route in order that by their glow they may complete their journey.' We now know that this light is generated by a luminous fungus, a common cause of tree rot in Britain, the honey-tuft fungus or *Armillaria mellea*. During World War I soldiers prevented collisions in the trenches at night by placing similar pieces of luminous wood on their helmets or on their bayonets. At Arnheim in World War II paratroopers found such light so bright that they were forced to hide the luminous timber under tarpaulins, and luminous lures are still used by fishermen in some parts of the world. Portuguese fishermen use lines containing bits of luminous squid, and in the Indian Ocean flashlight fish inside bamboo attract larger prey. Dried ostracods made luminous by wetting provided some Japanese soldiers with a night-light to map-read.

These have now all been mimicked by the synthetic chemist. Sailors can buy chemi-luminescent light sticks as safe night-lights, and golfers have green night-time orgies with luminous golf balls. But competitive fishermen have been banned from using luminous flies – they are too efficient! Natives of Ecuador use luminous fungi in rituals, and suitors find each other by such beacons, while fireflies and luminous cucujus are sometimes used by Mexican women to adorn their headdresses.

But all this chemi-luminescence is used to illuminate, a replacement of a *hot* lamp. Light without fire. What we want to do is to cause a change in the intensity or colour of the light emitted as the result of a *chemical* change.

Since chemi-luminescence is caused by a chemical reaction, all we have to do is to link the chemical we want to view in the cell with one of the components of the chemi-luminescent reaction. We have already seen that this is easy for calcium and ATP. The jelly-fish chemical reaction glows or flashes according to how much calcium is added, and the one from the firefly glows or flashes according to how much ATP you add. Genetic engineering can increase the potential of these indicators enormously.

But fluorescent substances – fluors – produce, on the whole, much more light than a chemi-luminescent compound. Furthermore, the synthetic chemist can generate almost any fluorescent colour he requires. And the fluorescence goes on and on, unlike a chemi-luminescent compound which is consumed. The breakthrough for cell biology was to find a way of coupling a fluorescent compound to a calcium binder, so that when the calcium went up there was a change in the fluorescence. This is what Roger Tsien succeeded in doing. When calcium binds the spectrum changes. One fluor is *excited* alternately by light of two colours. Another fluor is excited by one colour, but calcium alters the colour of the light emitted so the *emission* is measured alternatively at two colours. As a result the ratio at the two colours can be converted to the concentration of calcium present. But Tsien added a further piece of ingenuity. Getting luminous proteins into cells was quite difficult, a real problem in fact. Giant cells, and sometimes quite small cells, could be micro-injected with solutions of the light-emitting proteins. And a variety of ingenious methods, with unwieldy titles such as 'cell ghosting', 'liposome fusion' and 'scrape loading', also achieved some success. I used some of these successfully myself. Now using DNA we can get the cell to synthesise its own light-emitter. But Tsien found a much more elegant way of getting his fluorescent indicators into cells without damaging them. It was an idea he got from the way some pharmaceutical companies had found to get certain drugs into cells, or across the gut into the blood stream.

Tsien's fluors consisted of two parts – the fluor and the calcium binder – cemented together by chemical bonds. The compound was an acid, and as such unable to penetrate the membrane of cells. It did not dissolve in the fatty *wall* at the centre of the cell membrane. But by chemical synthesis he was able to stick a chemical group onto the acid. This made the compound, now called an ester, rather difficult to dissolve in water, nor could it bind calcium any more. This requires that the acid groups be intact. But it was soluble in the fat. Tsien and Rink added this new compound to a population of cells and it dissolved in the membrane. As a result, some floated off inside the cell. Once inside the cell the esters met an enzyme which chopped off the ester group, with two important consequences. First, its ability to bind calcium was restored, and secondly, because it was now an acid again, it was difficult or impossible for it to leak back out of the cell.

Tsien has now developed similar indicators for sodium, magnesium, acidity and the target protein that reacts with cyclic AMP. Another is now available that binds the calcium target protein calmodulin, changing its fluorescence in the process. A novel observation, as the result of using the cyclic AMP indicator, is the ability to follow trafficking of this target protein into the nucleus. This is followed by rubiconing new genes.

But how are we going to see where in the cell, and from which cells, the calcium and other rubicons are being crossed? Enter the chemical microscope.

THE CHEMICAL MICROSCOPE

Calcium clouds and waves were first visualised in single cells during the 1970s with an image-intensifier pioneered by George Reynolds at Princeton. Thanks to Tsien and Lansing Taylor and the commercial exploitation of their technology, we now have chemical microscopes available which are capable of producing a picture of the calcium distribution throughout an entire cell (Plates 5(b) and 11).

Most academic scientists welcome the opportunity to share reagents and technology they have developed. But this can become so time-consuming that it is impossible to keep up with the demand. There is no doubt that biology today would be stuck without the development of molecular reagents on a grand scale by the private sector. It is therefore particularly frustrating that both Tsien's brilliant invention and ours replacing radio-isotopes such as iodine and phosphorus by chemi-luminescent compounds were offered to the government body, then the National Research and Development Corporation (NRDC), which was supposed to be responsible for capitalising on inventions in the UK. As has so often been the case, mediocre civil servants who had never discovered or invented anything in their lives failed to have the necessary vision. Recognising the big market potential of an idea in its early stages requires insight, vision and drive. Another two inventions initiated in the UK are now exploited at the million-dollar level by US companies. Now every cell biology and biochemistry department in the world uses Tsien's technology, or wants to use it. And it has clinical potential.

Let's get back to the science before my blood crosses the steam rubicon!

To view the chemi-luminescence and fluorescence inside cells a special type of microscope is needed. But the special feature is not so much the microscope itself, though this has modifications from a conventional one, but rather the *eye* which views the image. This eye is not human, but rather an incredibly sensitive video camera. Intensifiers were developed by astronomers, and the military. Nuclear submarine detection was one objective, would you believe, as they fire off the unsuspecting deep-sea luminous creatures. There are several types of camera used, some cooled in liquid nitrogen (*c.* -196°C) to make them sensitive enough. Some can even detect individual photon light-particles and then reconstruct a *chemical* image, far beyond the capability of the human eye, sensitive as this is. The camera generates a video signal every thirtieth of a second or so, made up of several hundred thousand bits of information. This signal is processed by a computer. But so much information can be generated in an experiment lasting several minutes, equivalent to several thousand individual sets, that a massive amount of computer memory can be required to store it, if one isn't careful. This problem has been solved, and the result is a computerised picture of the chemistry of the cell, presented in *pseudocolour* or as a mountain map, each colour or contour representing a different amount of calcium, or whatever chemical is being analysed.

A conventional microscope shines light through a cell and lights up the structures within. Luminescent indicators generate light from within the cell to provide a chemical picture of what is going on. We can watch this picture changing with time, correlating chemical changes reaching a site in the cell with a rubicon. This was first achieved with the jelly-fish protein aequorin in a salivary gland cell from the midge *Chironomus* in 1975. Rose and Loewenstein showed that when a calcium cloud hit the junction connecting two adjoining cells together the communication between them ceased.

Manipulating the rubicon

The conventional way of manipulating the chemistry of cells is to add drugs and other specially designed chemicals which are known to block or activate a particular reaction inside the cell. Antibodies, to block specific protein targets, and signalling proteins can also be injected into live cells. By manipulating and then measuring the signalling system, we can identify specific components of the cell required for the end-response. And Tsien and others have also invented another ingenious way of manipulating the signalling system inside live cells. Calcium binders and caged compounds capable of releasing a signalling molecule when flashed by a laser allow us to generate a signal rubicon or prevent it, and at a defined location in the cell. These manipulators can be incorporated into live cells in the same way as the fluorescent indicators. Flash a laser and the molecular animal is let out its cage to do its job. In the cage can be calcium, cyclic AMP, ATP, IP$_3$ and so on.

This combined technology for measuring and manipulating the chemis-

try of living cells has revolutionised molecular cell biology. But there is one
further technology, even more awe-inspiring in its potential. It is poised
to revolutionise medical research, the treatment of disease, and agriculture. It is protein engineering.

PROTEIN ENGINEERING

A new kind of engineering

To most people the word 'engineering' conjures up smoky chimneys, steel
plants with their red hot furnaces, road building, cranes, bridges and the
like. But there is a new kind of engineering, which has developed only
within the last decade: it has become possible to manipulate DNA in the
test-tube. Genetic engineering provides the tools and instructions to alter
the structure of existing proteins, and to construct new ones. The aim of
the protein engineer is to manufacture, starting from DNA, a new or
modified protein. But what properties do we want this new protein to have,
and how can this be achieved?

First we have to remind ourselves of how proteins are made, what they
do and how they do it. Then we shall see how they can be altered, i.e.
engineered, so as to be used to measure or manipulate something inside a
cell.

The bricks from which proteins are made are amino-acids. Some are
familiar in the kitchen – glutamate in a Chinese meal, for example. But
others such as proline are not in everyday use. There are twenty possibilities. Proteins are linear chains of these amino-acids (Plate 12(a)), some
with as few as a dozen or so, e.g. the hormone oxytocin, others, such as
apolipoprotein B and the protein mutated in muscular dystrophy, with
several thousand. But this linear sequence does not remain linear. Unlike
a house made of bricks, proteins are flexible and fold up to make a 3D
structure upon which its function depends (Plate 12(b)). It is upon this that
the properties of the protein depend. The shape of a hormone has to be just
right for it to attach properly to the outside of a cell and instruct it to move,
to release an internal component, or to reproduce by dividing into two. An
antibody has an intricately built cleft into which only the bacterial, viral
or human protein for which it was selected will fit. Similarly an enzyme
has a cleft which folds around the molecules of the reaction it catalyses.
Within each 3D structure there are regions with particular functions, like
the parts of the body. For example, an enzyme in the cell membrane which
is responsible for catalysing a particular chemical reaction and can be
activated by calcium may have as many as five or six different, but
interacting, domains: three or four for binding calcium, one for binding the
reactants and for catalysing the reaction itself, one for binding to the
membrane and another for interacting with its protein neighbours. The
engineer has to identify these domains and find a way of altering one to

suit his purpose, either to measure or to manipulate a process within the live cell.

Since there are twenty main varieties of amino-acid in proteins, the potential number of possible proteins is vast. To make proteins you need these *bricks*, the amino-acids, *mortar*, the chemicals within the cell, including our old friend ATP, *a builder*, known as the ribosome in the cell, and of course *the design or architect's plan* – this is where the nucleic acids come in.

DNA makes *RNA* makes *protein*. This is the central dogma of molecular biology. The plan for all proteins is found in the deoxyribonucleic acid, DNA for short. A copy is present in every cell in the body. The DNA template has to be converted into a form which can be understood by the builder – the ribosome. The DNA is thus first transcribed into RNA – ribonucleic acid, which is then transported out of the nucleus to the protein factory. In bacteria all this happens in one compartment.

The DNA template is made of a linear sequence of the letters A,T,G and C. In our cells there are 3,000 million of these split among twenty-three pairs of chromosomes. This is equivalent to five to ten complete twenty-nine-volume copies of the *Encyclopaedia Britannica*, though perhaps less than ten per cent may actually be read. Every few pages there is a set of instructions. These instructions are read by a set of proteins, which transcribe them into a computer program, the RNA. The RNA computer program also is a linear set of four letters, but this time they are A, U, G and C. The computer terminal on the ribosome reads this program in combinations of three. This is the terminal which reads the computer program, translating it into a protein sequence and manufacturing the protein itself. Each set of three letters represents one of the twenty possible amino-acids. Each triplet can only code for one particular amino-acid building block. However, some amino-acids have several triplets coding for them, while others have only one. For example, the triplets GUU, GUC, GUA and GUG code for the amino-acid valine, but only AUG is able to code for methionine – the amino-acid which starts all proteins. There are stops as well as starts. AUG is the start of a protein, whereas UAA, UAG and UGA are stop signals, telling the manufacturer, the ribosome, that the protein is finished and can be released to do its job. So how can we alter the protein, and make it something different?

Each time three letters are read the next amino-acid is added to the growing chain of the protein. So a program for a protein of 400 amino-acids is a linear sequence of 1,200 As, Gs, Cs and Us. Proteins can now be made this way in the test tube, but we still require the builder from the cell, the ribosome, and its gang of workers.

Consider again the phrase:

The cat sat on the mat.

Remove the second T and we have:

The cas ato nt hem at.

Complete rubbish. But now instead change the M of MAT to an H and we get:

The cat sat on the hat.

Still sense, but the cat is now doing something different from before. This is what we try to do in protein-engineering. We first isolate the DNA template responsible for a particular protein. Then we alter one or more of the letters, so that, after it is transcribed into RNA and this is translated into a protein, the new protein still makes sense to the cell but has a new or changed property. OK, we have a new protein, but how can we get to the right site in the cell, or even into the cell at all?

Here again we can learn from Nature. The enzyme which transcribes the DNA template into the RNA computer program, called RNA polymerase, is located only in the nucleus. The proteins which bind calcium inside the calcium cupboard in muscle cells are found only here. The proteins which keep the powerhouses of the cell going, the mitochondria, are found only here. The receptors, enzymes and pumps on the inner and outer surface of the membrane surrounding each cell which respond to signals from outside, are placed specifically here. Yet all are made in the same way, in the same protein-manufacturing plant. How do they get to the right spot? By targeting.

On one end of the protein, usually the first bit to be made, but sometimes the last, and occasionally in the middle, there is a sticky label with an address on it: 'Please send me to the nucleus', 'Please send me to the cell membrane', 'Please send me to the mitochondria', 'If lost do not return to sender but destroy', and so on. Nature has certainly evolved some beautiful solutions to some tricky problems. The protein-engineer can mimic this natural postal system. He can take the DNA for the protein he is engineering and put onto it the right targeting message, so that the protein when it is made goes to the required place. He can even fool proteins which originally were intended to go to one site and redirect them to another address. The address can also be specific for the country concerned, i.e. the cell. This is done by having the right promoter-sequence in front of the DNA template. It will only be expressed in the right cell.

It is even possible to set up a protein-manufacturing plant in the test-tube. Starting with the DNA, this is first amplified a millionfold in the test-tube, using a technique called PCR. This also enables the DNA to be altered and bits of DNA to be added to either end. The DNA is then transcribed in the test-tube using the enzyme RNA polymerase, and the resulting RNA added to a cell soup extracted from live cells. This lysate, from red cells which make haemoglobin or germinated wheat, has all the machinery to translate the added RNA into protein. So soups are useful after all, though less efficient by a factor of 100 to 1,000 than the live cell at making protein!

The protein can then be fully characterised. If it is suitable, the DNA is put first into a plasmid (the piece of DNA responsible for bacterial sex we met earlier) and then into a safe virus. The plasmid is grown up in bulk in bacteria, and then added to cells in tissue culture. Alternatively, the bacteria may be induced to make lots of protein. The protein, or the RNA, can then be injected into a cell. This is particularly useful if the cell being studied has finished dividing: for example, a bleach-producing cell.

Using this factory we and others have succeeded in engineering probes for calcium, ATP and the protein-phosphate enzymes in defined sites within live cells. Learning from nature is our philosophy. Nature tells us how to target. It also gave us a clue as to which bioluminescent systems to try. Just a few amino-acid changes in the beetle and jelly-fish proteins from various species cause the light to be a different colour. Thus luminous beetles can emit green, green-yellow, orange or red light. The same is true for the jelly-fish system, though less obvious to the naked eye because we don't have the right colour-receptors to produce the same colour rubicons in the blue region of the spectrum as we do in the green to red. Other groups of luminous organisms have a much more uniform colour distribution from species to species. Thus by finding the right target within either the firefly or jelly-fish protein we can engineer a detector which changes colour when the cell is signalled. Soon the cell really will change from red to green!

But how do we use these engineered proteins? And can we also use genetic engineering to manipulate Rubicon – to initiate, speed up, slow down or stop a crossing?

Transgenics

Transgenesis is the transfer of a gene or genes from one organism to another. The organisms may be as far apart as jelly-fish and man, or bacteria and sheep. Or they may simply be variants within the same species, as for the correction of inherited disease in man. The transfer may occur between cells in culture or in the intact animal. If the latter, the gene being transferred usually must get into the germ line. This can be done in animals by injecting the egg, and then carrying out *in vitro* fertilisation. Hormone and growth genes are but two successful examples of transgenic mice and pigs. But injecting DNA into muscle or spraying virus into the lungs also allows some of it to get expressed. The latter has been achieved in humans with the gene which is mutated in people who have cystic fibrosis.

In some plants, e.g. tobacco, there is a natural mechanism for incorporating foreign DNA into the DNA of the plant. For the bacterium *Agrobacterium tumefaciens* to attack a tobacco plant successfully it has to get some of its genes expressed in the leaf it is trying to infect. By fooling it to take in a bit of DNA we are interested in, the gene can be transferred to the tobacco plant. It even gets into the pollen cells and thus the seeds. Marc Knight and Tony Trewavas in Edinburgh have succeeded in expressing the jelly-fish protein in intact plants. When watered with the 'luciferin' the plant glows. When it blows in the wind calcium spikes are seen, triggering reactions which will lead to stem-strengthening. This is why the type of tree post is so important if you want to grow a strong tree. The sapling needs to bend in the wind, without snapping. Others have been expressed in plants (potatoes or tomatoes for example), the firefly and luminous bacterial systems.

The intriguing possibility now is to develop a luminous Christmas tree. But I'm not so sure about the idea of a cigarette that glows at both ends!

The DNA for these light-emitting proteins can also be expressed in human or animal cells in culture. These cells can also make their own light. All you have to do is add the luciferin to the cells making the engineered protein. We have also targeted the luminous proteins from the jelly-fish and firefly to defined sites within live cells. This enables calcium and ATP to be monitored inside the calcium cupboard, the nucleus and the power-house in individual cells. There should be enough light to enable one to pick up signals from single cells. Since the indicators have been targeted whole cell signals will be sufficient. By linking the luminous genes to 'signal boxes' in the DNA they can be used as *reporter* genes. Only in those cells responsive to a growth factor or cytokine will the cell light up. The timing of gene rubicons can be followed in hundreds of individual cells for the first time.

Genetic engineering can also be used to manipulate the chemical machinery of the cell, providing a unique way of looking at how cell stimuli, drugs and pathogens cause cells to cross the Rubicon. By using anti-sense RNA we can block the synthesis of a selected protein. By engineering human antibodies containing domains from antibodies originally generated in mice or rats it should be possible to kill cancer cells. This leads to the most exciting potential of all, the treatment of disease by targeted DNA.

There is still much technology to develop. But the door is now open to exploit protein engineering to view the Rubicon sequence in live cells, and in live animals without harming them. Some people may not like animal experiments, but medical research just cannot get on without them. However, I do subscribe to the view that a full re-examination of the real value and conditions of animal experimentation is required.

Magic bullets

What we need to kill off unwanted cells are bullets which can be fired to hit only the right target. Two methods are now available in the human body; one uses tiny fat bubbles called liposomes, the other DNA. The lipid bubbles are made so that they contain a toxin, lethal to any cell it strikes. By attaching an antibody to the liposomes you can target them to specific cells, e.g. the cancer you want to kill. That is the idea anyway. It works in some cases but does not seem to be the panacea hoped for. The vision for medicine in the twenty-first century is gene therapy and genetic targeting.

Nature has already learnt how to fire DNA at selected cells. It uses a virus. All you have to do is to use genetic engineering to make a virus which will target the cells you want to manipulate or kill. You engineer a protein, incorporated with the viral DNA, that will attack the host cell from within. Using DNA to treat inherited diseases such as cystic fibrosis and muscular dystrophy is now no longer just a dream. But whether we should play around with the gene pool which confers susceptibility to disease is not clear. We don't understand why these genes are still held within the gene pool. We eradicate them at our peril.

Biology has climbed a mountain in this century. A hundred years ago we didn't even know what DNA did, let alone expect to be able to manipulate it. Over the horizon there are exciting times ahead for those of us trying to view the Rubicon. Yet there are things we still can't see.

WHAT WE CAN'T SEE

In spite of this highly sophisticated technology there are processes we cannot see inside cells. The physics of light and the chemistry of the indicators place limitations on what we are able to see with a chemical microscope.

The wavelength of visible light ranges between about four and seven tenths of a millionth of a metre (i.e. 0.4-0.7μm). It is pretty obvious therefore that we cannot see things smaller than this, even with the aid of a microscope. Most cells in the body range from five to fifty millionths of a metre across: bacteria are one millionth of a metre. These can therefore be seen with visible light, as can many sub-cellular structures – just. But some vesicles inside a cell are too small to see in visible light, being only 0.1-0.2μ in diameter. This is beyond the resolution of the light microscope which, to all intents and purposes, can never go beyond the wavelength of the light shined through it. Hence the need for the electron microscope, which can magnify the image of cells tens of thousands of times, as opposed to about 2,000 times for the light microscope. Unfortunately, we cannot easily shine electrons through live cells and produce images, because the electron microscope requires a vacuum.

Thus the fluorescent and bioluminescent indicators can only resolve down to an area within the cell of about 0.5-1μ in diameter. This is enough to resolve the nucleus, the endoplasmic reticulum and mitochondria, provided the indicator is able to generate enough light photons. This depends on the concentration of the indicator and, in the case of the fluors, on how much light we are able to shine on them. We need to use high-energy lamps and lasers. But we must be careful not to use too much energy; otherwise the light beam will burn up the cell or bleach the indicator. However, if we can target the indicator to a defined site within the cell, we don't necessarily need to see the precise location of the light emission. Measurement of the signal from the whole cell will suffice, provided we have first proved beyond doubt that our indicator has located precisely to the site we want to follow.

There are many chemical processes that we still cannot light up in the living cell. Though bioluminescence depends on oxygen and its metabolites, we still can't visualise oxygen gradients inside live cells, though oxygen-binding pigments such as myoglobin can be used to give some information about the levels of oxygen inside cells. What is often forgotten or ignored is that the concentration of oxygen in water or laboratory solutions, naturally saturated by oxygen from the air, is about a hundred times that which cells see *in situ*. We would also like to be able to watch enzymatic reactions as they move across cells and the movement of molecules such as proteins, RNA and DNA. These are just some of the many exciting challenges facing the biological chemist and molecular cell biologist.

At least we now know that it is possible to watch the chemistry of a live cell without blowing it up.

Preventing explosions

The origins of my own city of Cardiff can be traced back thousands of years. Stone-age axes from 200,000 years ago, when Britain was still connected to the continent of Europe, bear witness to the early hunters of Wales. The first Celts arrived some time in the late seventh century BC, never fully conquered by the Romans or the Anglo-Saxon English! It was the Romans who first realised the full potential of a site at the mouth of the river Taff. A fort built some time around 75 BC marked the beginnings of what is now the capital city of the Principality of Wales.

By the end of the eighteenth century Cardiff was still a fairly small market town. But by the end of the nineteenth century it had become one of the busiest ports in Europe. The reason, coal! The iron from Merthyr Tydfil some twenty miles up the valley from Cardiff was also streaming down. From less than 2,000 in about 1800, the population had risen to 190,000 by the World War I. In 1914 Cardiff was the largest coal-exporting port in the world. But the increasing use of coal as a fuel was not without cost. When I first moved to South Wales the valleys were still blighted with black and scarred with tips and enormous bicycle wheels up in the air above the mine shafts. They seemed to be everywhere. The cities too were black with soot from coal fires. But, with some help from man, the environment has managed to return across the Rubicon. By 1968 the export of coal from Cardiff had all but ceased. Many of the mines were closing.

And what of the human cost? The tragic loss of more than 150 people, many of them school children, at Aberfan was fresh in everyone's mind. And the pathology of South Wales was still greatly affected by lung disease, pneumoconiosis and emphysema, pathological rubicons crossed as a result of inhaling a critical amount of coal dust.

Several of the valleys are now restored, almost to their former beauty, though a lot of investment is still required to improve the towns and restore their economy. But a new environmental rubicon looms. One of the most exciting waterfront-development schemes in Europe, in Cardiff Bay, will result in the construction of a barrage across the mouth of the Taff and Ely rivers. Nowadays health and safety at work are demanded by law, and the environmentalist lobby has a great influence on new industrial developments. But in the nineteenth century it was a different matter altogether. As the demand for coal increased there was one particular terror, a rubicon dreaded by all miners and their families. Explosion! This was caused by ignition of gas in the mine known as firedamp. It was a group of English miners who were to initiate the path to solving this problem.

On 25 May 1812 an explosion at Brandling Main, Felling Colliery, near Gateshead-on-Tyne killed 92 men and boys. Further explosions followed in the district. Northumberland and Durham had mined coal since Norman times, but this just couldn't go on. A group of clerics and mining experts decided to approach Humphry Davy (Plate 4(a)). After all he was *the* scientist of his day. Surely if anyone could find a solution it was he. The first contact was somewhat abortive because Davy was away abroad. But once he received a letter from a Dr Gray, the rector of Bishopwearmouth, he made arrangements to visit Newcastle as soon as possible. This was an applied problem of immense significance to human suffering, and of huge economic importance too. Even when there was no loss of life, explosions cost a great deal of money in lost revenue.

Miners had to have light. So there had to be lamps in the mine. But Faraday had yet to discover electromagnetic induction. So there were no dynamos to power electric light in the mines. Miner's lamps were lit by flame, and it was these flames and sparks from equipment that ignited the firedamp, triggering the explosion. Davy and Faraday set to work to see if they could find a way of controlling the explosion of methane, the principal component of firedamp. In only a few months they cracked it. The key was to place a metal gauze around the wick in the lamp. Imagine their excitement when, on placing a prototype safety lamp into potentially explosive mixtures of air and carburetted hydrogen, or firedamp, not only was there no explosion but the flame burnt more brightly. The lamp could get red-hot and still no explosion occurred.

After some refinements John Buddle, an expert in mining safety, tested the lamp. A year after Davy had been approached he wrote: 'It is impossible to express my feelings at the time when I first suspended the lamp in the mine and saw it red hot ... I said to those around me, "We have at last subdued the monster." '

The Davy lamp was modified further and has saved many lives. The remarkable thing was that it not only lit up the mines without causing an explosion, but also gave prior warning that one might occur. It was thus an indicator of firedamp as well as a lamp. It lit up the chemistry of the mines without blowing them up.

Hold up a miner's lamp to an audience in Wales, as I often do, and most will be able to name it as a Davy lamp. Yet few will know anything of Davy's immense contribution to science as a whole, his discovery of several elements and the nurturing of his protegé, Michael Faraday. This chapter has focussed on invention, rather than discovery. It is therefore, I hope, appropriate to end by reminding ourselves that a hundred and seventy years after Davy invented a safety lamp for lighting up the chemistry of mines, we can now light up the chemistry of calcium, the element he discovered, in the cell without blowing it up!

All this fuss about measuring chemicals while cells and tissues remain alive. Is it not simply a return to the outmoded and ill-conceived idea of a vital force? Rubicon sounds to me to be a repackaging of a concept which misled so many scientists in the nineteenth century. Isn't it just vitalism re-vitalised?

Well, let's move on and see.

8

Vitalism Revitalised?

Vitalism – the concept of a hidden life-giving force – has played a fascinating part in the evolution of science. Rubicon identifies the force which pervades all living things as the ability of the living unit to cross thresholds – necessary for life and not found in a dead molecule, a dead cell, a dead organism or a dead ecosystem. What then separates Rubicon from vitalism? Superficially this chapter is about what Rubicon is not and treads on dangerous ground – the border between science and non-science, between science and religion, bringing us to the apparent conflicts between religion and science. However, I believe that these arguments do have a place in book devoted to establishing a concept through the normal rigours of scientific investigation and argument. To understand the full potential of Rubicon in giving us a pathway to understand the difference between a primaeval soup and a living cell, between a dead fly and a live one, between an homogenate and an intact tissue, between an extinct and an extant organism, between an ecosystem and a jumble of species, it is necessary to examine some of the other ideas that have been put forward about the special features of life.

WHAT IS LIFE?

Vital force, entelechy, the anima and the *élan vital* are just four concepts introduced over the past two millennia in an attempt to rationalise a difference that seems, on the surface, obvious – the difference between the living and the dead. Yet no human has ever created a life form from chemicals, inanimate materials, primaeval soups electrified by lightning or the constituents isolated from broken cells. A piece of DNA is not 'alive'. It needs a cell to replicate and to carry out its functions.

Like most of us, the philosophers and scientists of the past tried to identify something which would confirm their inherent faith that there is something special about life. Indeed this faith is still with us, for there is much debate among biologists and paleontologists today about exactly when life began and how it arose. Yet Darwin believed that the search for the ultimate origins of life were inscrutable. So he argued to his close friend and confidant, the distinguished botanist, Joseph Hooker (1817-1911). To Darwin the quest for the origin of the first living microbe was as futile as the search for the origin of matter. The only problem worth addressing was whether a group of apparently related species had a common ancestor.

So is 'What is life?' a question for science at all? Shouldn't it be left to religion, philosophy or, worse still, politicians and the law?

No, science cannot go on ducking this one!

'It's great to be alive!', 'What a life!', 'There's a live match on TV tonight' – three common-or-garden phrases we all use frequently. In science too we find physiologists, pathologists, even biochemists referring to living and dead organisms and cells, day-in, day-out. Pick up any modern text dealing with evolution, and you will invariably find a statement somewhere stating, 'Life began around three and half to four thousand million years ago.' The *Oxford English Dictionary* defines life as 'the state of living; the sum of the activities of plants and animals; conscious existence; the period between birth and death.' Not much help to us, I'm afraid. But all this does highlight one aspect of the problem: the different uses of the word 'life' depend on the context. Gowland Hopkins (1861-1947) once said that 'Life is a thing that happens.' Another vague and scientifically useless statement. Perhaps he felt some sympathy with Norman W. Pirie (1907-1991) who, in a collection of essays by distinguished protégés of Hopkins published in 1938, argued for 'the meaninglessness of the term life and living'.

Pirie was co-discoverer of the composition of viruses. With Sir Frederick Bawden (1908-1972) in 1936 he was the first to obtain a virus in crystalline form. The virus they isolated in such pure form is known as tobacco mosaic virus, or TMV for short, and causes mottling on the leaves of plants, thus reducing crop yields. Now that the virus was pure they were able to make a precise chemical analysis. It was made entirely of nucleic acid and protein, six per cent by weight being RNA. In the mid 1950s it was shown that the infectivity of the virus resided in the RNA. The protein alone is not infectious. TMV is different from HIV in that the RNA itself acts as the template for replication, to make lots of copies. By contrast, in HIV the RNA has first to be reverse-transcribed to make a DNA copy, which then acts as the template for many HIV RNA copies. The British crystallographer Rosalind Franklin (1920-1958), now famous for her pioneering work with X-rays to find the structure of DNA, showed that the rod-shape of TMV's structure was a hollow tube covering the RNA nucleic acid. No doubt this simplicity and elegance of viral composition and structure influenced Pirie in his arguments about the difficulty of defining the difference between living and non-living. But, as with all viruses, TMV requires a cell to multiply. So should we call viruses 'alive'? An even greater puzzle has been presented by the discovery of so-called prions, responsible for diseases such as scrapie in sheep. These self-replicating protein moieties seemed initially to defy the dogma of modern biology that, to make a protein in living systems, you must first start with a DNA or RNA; it was the problem of deciding whether viruses and such things were alive that precipitated Pirie into rejecting the question 'What is life?' altogether.

But I cannot accept this.

We continue to use the terms 'life' and 'death' freely, not only in everyday language but also in rigorous scientific and medical discussions. The heated debate about brain death is not just about the ethical and legal problems associated with switching off life-support machines. At the heart of the problem is the inability of medical science to provide a definition of death applicable to all patients under all circumstances. It is frightening to think that people have recovered fully from the deepest of comas, where the application of certain criteria would have pronounced them dead. Yet it is clear that at the point of switching off a life-support device most of the cells in the comatose patient remain alive. Nor can we accept that the argument can be left to philosophers and clerics. As biologists we cannot simply dismiss as 'meaningless' the very essence of our discipline: *bios*. What we must do is transform what at first sight seems a semantic problem into a real scientific question.

In 1951 one of the founders of modern quantum mechanics, Erwin Schrödinger (1887-1961), famous for his 'uncertainty principle', published a monograph entitled *What is Life?* but with the sub-title 'The physical aspect of the living cell'. When such a distinguished mind entitles his last chapter, 'Is life based on the laws of physics?' surely the question is worthy of some serious thought? Similarly Jacques Monod (1910-1976), another Nobel Laureate, and a pioneer of molecular biology and co-discover of the link between DNA and the manufacture of proteins, took the question seriously. In his penetrating *Le hazard et la necessité* of 1970 ('Chance and Necessity'), he argued that 'although the molecular theory of the genetic code cannot – and will doubtless never be able to – predict or resolve the whole of the biosphere, it does constitute a general theory of living systems. No such thing existed in scientific knowledge before molecular biology. Until then the *secret of life* seemed to be essentially inaccessible.'

Throughout the history of science many of the major discoverers and inventors took the puzzle of describing the science of life seriously. They recognised in their time, as now, that something was missing from their understanding of living things. The lack of any obvious chemical or physical property separating the living from the dead led many to argue for the existence of some form of *vital* force, while others were vehemently opposed to such a vague and apparently unscientific concept. Louis Pasteur (1822-1895) attributed unique functions to living cells. Not even Niels Bohr, Nobel Laureate for first proposing a model for the atom, dismissed vitalism out of hand. Many distinguished scientists over the past four centuries have devoted a vast amount of mental energy to the question, without coming up with a satisfactory answer. Nevertheless their thoughts cannot be dismissed simply as the romantic wanderings of a mind that has run out of reductionist questions, or given up struggling with the energy of youthful contenders. If the understanding of natural phenomena were simple there would be no science.

It was the thinkers of ancient Greece who were the first to realise that there was a problem at all. Alcmaeon of Croton (*c.* 500 BC) was one of the first to practise dissection and the foremost pre-Socratic embryologist. He discovered the optic nerve and realised that the brain is the central organ of sensation. Could this alone explain the uniqueness of human existence? Archimedes of Syracuse (287-212 BC), rejecting the confused natural philosophy of Plato (428/427-348/347 BC), realised with Aristotle (384-322 BC) that it was important to marry mathematics with experiment if one was to understand the natural world. The quantification of science was under way. Thus for centuries our knowledge of biology has progressed by the reductionist approach of dissection into smaller and smaller parts, describing and measuring, measuring and describing. But as anatomy led to physiology led to biochemistry, the essential mystery of life remained. The greatest morphologist, physiologist or molecular biologist has never been able to answer clearly and succinctly the fundamental question of biology: What is special about the physics and chemistry of life and its functions, that separates it from other natural phenomena, and allows us to describe it with that ill-defined term 'life'?

If we still have trouble with the question, it is hardly surprising that scientists in the past have had trouble putting their finger on this crucial property, and turned to a *vital force*.

The problem became a practical reality when the US space agency NASA decided in 1975 to send a Viking space craft to Mars to find out if there was, or ever had been, any life there. Many extraordinary devices were constructed as potential *life detectors*. One included a 'Martian flea trap'. Wherever there are deserts there are camels, and wherever there are camels there are fleas! The universal function of ATP is as the internal fuel for cells. Without it no cell on earth can live. The measurement of ATP in Martian dust was thus proposed. An exquisitely sensitive method for measuring it was available, using the light emitted from firefly luciferase. This can detect the amount of ATP from a mere ten per cent of a single human cell. All very ingenious, but data obtained from telescopes detecting the infra-red emission from Mars already held the answer. As James Lovelock predicted from the near equilibrium state of the Martian atmosphere, there could be no life on Mars. Gaia only remains alive when the chemistry of life and its environs are kept far from equilibrium. But the Viking project went ahead all the same. Lovelock could not predict that there had never been life on Mars, only that it would not exist now.

There are four perspectives from which we can view the question 'What is life?': religious or spiritual, global, physico-chemical and biological. None of these needs be exclusive or competitive. Rubicon applies to them all. The physico-chemical approach looks for physical and chemical components and characteristics which are unique to life: the crystalline structures of bone, teeth and shells, the electrical potentials across cell membranes, DNA, protein, ATP and so on. The second law of thermodynamics, discovered in the last century, tells us that in an isolated system, as physical and chemical processes proceed, the system as a whole will become increasingly disordered. Yet life as it develops becomes more and more ordered, as the structures of an animal or plant grow. This apparent contradiction of the law of entropy is explained because, thermodynamically, life is an open system. It is not isolated from its environment. The processing of food by the cellular chemical factories provides the energy for this. When considered as a whole the disorder, or entropy, of the universe is still increasing!

As a geneticist, the biologist looks at life as a system capable of evolution by natural selection. Whereas the physiologist sees an animal capable of performing the functions of eating, metabolising food, excreting, breathing, moving, reproducing, responding to external stimuli and sensing, or a plant and some microbes capable of photosynthesis, the conversion of light into chemical energy. But it is as a biochemist that the biologist is closest to the physicist or chemist in the definition of life, looking at the chemical components and reactions of living systems, seeing objects with defined boundaries continuously exchanging chemicals with their surroundings. On the other hand the globalist looks at the entire biosphere: how the physics and chemistry of the Earth's surface interact with living things, indeed how the mass and composition of each are interdependent. Without life the chemical composition of the atmosphere, the seas and the land would be very different from what it is and be very close to chemical equilibrium. The oxygen-, carbon-dioxide- and sulphur-containing gases in the atmosphere are a long way away from chemical equilibrium, as are many salts and other substances in the sea.

One minute we are trying to measure billionths of a gramme of substances in a few cells, the next millions of tonnes produced by the biosphere at a global level. But in the end all these scientific views of Nature, even the global one, come back to the cell. It is cells which have invaded every nook and cranny of the planet Earth. It is cells which are responsible for controlling the amount of oxygen and carbon dioxide in the atmosphere. They combine to process millions of tonnes annually. The question 'What is life?' must therefore focus on finding out what makes a cell alive and when it can be considered dead. What chemical substances or reactions, or physical processes can we identify which break down catastrophically when death occurs? But the life-giving features of the physics and chemistry of life both at the cellular and at the global level are the rubicons it is capable of crossing. And what of the religious perspective on life? Even here we can find Rubicon in action.

RELIGION VERSUS SCIENCE

'If God did not exist, he would have to be invented,' wrote Voltaire (1694-1778) in 1769. Every group of humans and every culture which has ever existed bears witness to this truth. They have all found the need for a belief in some form of God, or supernatural being. Yet the unravelling of the elegance and logic of the natural laws of the Universe has turned many away from religion. It is unnecessary and illogical. Or is it?

Some, like Newton, moved towards a belief in a God; others, like Darwin, away from it. How can a scientist be true both to science and to his religious beliefs? How is it that there are brilliant scientists who are passionate Christians, Jews, Moslems, Hindus and so on? The misapprehension of a past curator of Down House, Darwin's house in Kent, sums up the apparent dichotomy. On arrival at the museum visitors were greeted with, 'Welcome. This is the house of Charles Darwin – the man who proved the Bible wrong.' In fact it was not his ideas about the descent of man but the death of his precious daughter, Annie, at the age of 9 and rows with the local cleric that turned him away from religion, He was ever conscious of his precious wife Emma, who maintained her Christian beliefs to the end. Yet her great fear was that, because Charles's ideas on evolution appeared to be at odds with the Bible, they would be separated in death. How ironic, and tragic, that her fears were to be realised. When Darwin died, at 4 p.m. on Wednesday 19 April 1882, the hypocrisy of the scientific nobility came to the fore. During his lifetime he had received few accolades for his labours – which consisted of nineteen books, hundreds of ingenious experiments, dozens of papers, and a brilliant concept. He must be buried in Westminster Abbey. That would salve their consciences. But how did Emma feel, I wonder? In the little churchyard in the centre of Downe, along the road from Darwin's house, you can see the grave of Emma Darwin, buried not with her beloved Charles but with his brother Erasmus.

And what of Samuel Wilberforce (1805-1873), son of the anti-slaver William Wilberforce, and Bishop of Oxford? What was he attempting to do at the British Association for the Advancement of Science held in Oxford on Saturday 30 June 1860 when he had the famous confrontation with Thomas Henry Huxley? The image we have been brought up with is that of a waffling, prejudiced cleric, ignorant of science, who tried to dismiss Darwin's *Origin* with emotional rhetoric. But is this true? Mary Midgley in *Evolution as a Religion* claims that Wilberforce was at the meeting not as a bishop representing the church but as a scientist, and vice-President, and spokesman for Richard Owen (1804-1892), President and vehement anti-Darwinian. Wilberforce had apparently carried out several worthy observations about birds. Owen stayed with Wilberforce the night before the meeting and is likely to have briefed him beforehand. Wilberforce was on his home territory and had a reputation for sermons cautioning against the wrong way to do science – of the 'foul temptation of speculation'. But Huxley and the new men of science couldn't stand such pompous clerics, regarding them as scientific 'amateurs' – 'Soapy Sam' was the nickname given to Wilberforce. He played into Huxley's hands when he facetiously asked whether it was on his grandfather's or grandmother's side that he was descended from an ape. Huxley responded: 'If then, said I, the question is put to me would I rather have a miserable ape for a grandfather or a man highly endowed by nature and possessed of great means & influence & yet who employs these faculties & that influence for the mere purpose of introducing ridicule into a grave scientific discussion I unhestitatingly affirm my preference for the ape.' Great laughter ensued. Such outbursts are not unknown today at scientific meetings! Darwin's most serious critics were not the Victorian clerics but some of his fellow scientists.

The point is that religion, however much you believe or disbelieve in it, is essentially anthropomorphic. It is about humans, their philosophy of life, their soul, their everlasting spirit after death. This alone makes it both too restrictive for science and also outside its domain. But then are the two philosophies in conflict? Can it really be true that Isaac Newton, the co-inventor of calculus who through his laws of motion, gravity, and light did so much to establish the path of modern science, was schizophrenic? Why else would he spend the later part of his life writing essays on religion? This is a rubicon which I do not intend to cross in this book. Suffice it to say that Alister Hardy (1896-1985), Professor of Zoology in the University of Oxford and pioneer of the study of planckton, in his two books *The Living Stream* and *The Divine Flame* showed how straightforward it is to be an evolutionist and a Christian.

The idea of transmutation of species was abhorrent to many of the Victorian laymen and scientists. Even Lyell was initially against the idea. But we believe modern man evolved from a primaeval ape. Whatever our conception of the afterlife, whether or not we believe that the animals will be there, Christianity and most religions accept that man is different from the rest of the animal kingdom. Man has a spirit, a soul. At what point in evolution therefore did man cross this rubicon and attain this unique characteristic which is the one above all that distinguishes him from all other animals, and where did he do it? In the Garden of Eden?

This is a question for us all to think about – deist, atheist and agnostic alike. The crossing of this rubicon is as much a problem for science as it is for religion. What was the evolutionary pathway leading to this striking rubicon – the awareness, through intelligence, that man himself has a soul, and that there is a God? This is a question we must eventually address if we are to understand fully how the human mind evolved, and how the various rubicons it crosses in its development and maturation – in life, in death, and during its evolution – occur. It was his difficulty in coming to terms with the rubicon between a soulless, inarticulate ape and a thought-ful, articulate man with a soul that made Lyell so resistant at first to Darwin's conception of natural selection.

If I look down a microscope I can see the cells and acellular material of which these objects are composed. The contents of these cells seem to be in a constant state of flux and movement. I can use the microscope to find even smaller objects, bacteria, which can divide under my very eyes. All these we call 'alive'. All have an active chemical metabolism. But only some have the capacity to reproduce, divide or respire, criteria believed by the biochemist to be universal properties of life. By these criteria viruses, bags of protein encapsulating bits of DNA or RNA, are not alive. But herein lies the heart of the problem. If we are to use the word 'life' in a scientific sense we must be able to define it. It must pass the test of any scientific term. A parameter or parameters must be identified that are both universal and unique to all those objects which we describe as *being alive*.

WHAT'S IN A NAME?

Vitalism embraces the idea that there is something special about living things that distinguishes them from inanimate or dead matter. The concept has appeared in the writings of philosophers, and in the experiments and theories of scientists for centuries, but under various guises. Vital force, vital principle, vital power, vital spirit, motive principle, *élan vital*, *force hypermécanique* or in more classical form, *vis essentialis impetum faciens* (essential force creating impetus) and *physis* ('Nature') are just some of the terms from the past few centuries associated with vitalism. But there were five particular terms covering over two millennia which lead to the full blown vitalism of the nineteenth and early twentieth centuries: the *entelechy* of Aristotle (384-322 BC), the *pneuma* of Galen (AD 130-200), the *archeus* of Paracelsus (*c.* 1493-1541), the *anima* of Stahl (1660-1734) and the *élan vital* of Bergson (1859-1941).

It all really started with the *entelechy* (*entelecheia*) of Aristotle, a concept defined in the *Shorter Oxford English Dictionary* as 'the condition in which a potentiality has become actuality', and was developed well into this century by Hans Adolf Edward Driesch (1867-1941). Empedocles (*fl.* 450 BC) argued that there were four 'roots' or elements which made up matter: a solid = earth, a liquid = water; a gas = air; and something even rarer than a gas, fire. He taught that blood went to and from the heart and that health depended on the right balance between the four elements. Aristotle added a fifth: *the 'element of life' = entelechy*.

Entelechy has since had two leases of life, one from Leibniz (1646-1716) in the seventeenth century, and the other from Driesch at the beginning of the twentieth. H.A.E. Driesch was a German experimental embryologist of some repute who eventually gave up experimental science to be a full-time philosopher, only to be forced into early retirement by the Nazis. In 1895, using sea urchin eggs, he separated the two cells which are formed from the first division, after fertilisation of an egg by sperm. As Roux had done with frog's eggs in 1888, he showed that both cells can develop into a fully active larva. Quite remarkable! In fact too remarkable for Driesch. He just couldn't see how one *machine* could be divided into *two machines* without the need for the mysterious and elusive ingredient of Aristotle's entelechy, the vital agent which Driesch proposed regulated organic development. This, in spite of Driesch's insight into the importance of the nucleus in influencing the cytoplasm of cells.

Hippocrates (*fl.* 420 BC), the father of modern medicine and medical ethics, believed that disease was a process subject to natural laws. He thought that the heart was the central organ of the body – the instrument of the soul. Blood comes from it, and from blood comes the *pneuma*, an air-like substance containing vital heat. The concept of pneuma was developed by Galen, who believed in animal and *vital* spirits, and that an element could be transmuted into another by changing the proportions of its primary qualities: hot, cold, dry and moist. Galen also believed that inhaled air was necessary to cool the excess heat from the heart, the immature pneuma passing through the heart to form the purest form of blood, that charged with pneuma. What else could one postulate without the concept of a chemical metabolism whose energy was converted into heat? Whereas we think of metabolism as an exchange or reaction of substances, Galen thought of metabolism as an exchange of *qualities*. The four 'elements' were combinations of these qualities: hot, cold, dry and moist. These were the primary qualities. Thus fire is hot and dry, whereas water is cold and moist. The secondary qualities included density, lightness and hardness. Galen's ideas had a profound influence on medicine until a Swiss doctor, Theophrast von Hohenheim, calling himself Paracelsus (*c.* 1490-1541), broke away from the components of the organism defined by Galen.

Paracelsus introduced the idea that digestion was not due to 'innate heat' but to an 'internal chemist' known as the *archêus* (Greek *archaios*, 'old'). As William Dampier cites in *A History of Science and its Relations with Philosophy & Religion* (1942), this was originally proposed by a Dominican monk, Basil Valentine, in the latter half of the fifteenth century The *archêus* was the force or energy by which the Ruler of the Universe determined all of its phenomena. Paracelsus was a medical chemist and an alchemist who turned to the preparation not of gold but of drugs. He and his disciples – the Paracelsian school – over the next century, believing that the *archêus* was the internal chemist, a *spiritus vitae* ('spirit of life') and an *arcanum* ('secret'), laid the foundation for the extraction of bio-chemicals from plants and animals. To them the art of the chemist was to separate the essence of the substances of life and leave the dead body behind. Thus, the *archêus* of man, born within and given us by God, separates the pure nutriment from our food, through digestion. This then becomes the food and nutriment of the whole body. Like a part of the body, or any other phenomena, the *archêus* was responsible for chemical change. J.B. van Helmont (1579-1644) was a particularly vociferous exponent of the *archêus*.

But the *entelechy*, the *pneuma* and the *archêus* lacked the credibility and discipline of the new order of Natural Science. They were not palatable to a Renaissance scientist trying to uncover the natural laws of the universe. The man regarded as the father of true scientific vitalism was the physician to the King of Prussia, Georg Ernst Stahl (1660-1734), the originator of the concept of the *anima*.

One of the key problems facing the early chemists was how to understand the phenomena of fire and combustion. We have already seen that Aristotle and others believed that the components of matter could in certain circumstances be separated. In which case something previously hidden could be released. Thus, when objects burned it was quite natural to think of something being released. This *something* had long been associated with sulphur, and Stahl decided to give it a name – *phlogiston* ('something burnt up'). Stahl's phlogiston theory dominated eighteenth-century chemistry. Even Joseph Priestley (1773-1804) believed in phlogiston. What else could he call the gas we now call oxygen and which was released when he heated mercuric oxide and which supported combustion, but de*phlogisti*cated air (see above p. 66)?

What, then, could be more natural than to accept that what was lost from chemicals extracted from living things, or lost in a dead organism, was another potential escaper – *anima sensitiva* ('the sensitive soul') or *anima sive natura*, as Stahl called it? The *anima* controlled the chemical and other processes of the body, and was not governed by the *ordinary* laws of physics and chemistry, as long as the body was alive. The sensitive soul was on a plane above physics and chemistry. All changes of the living body, though they might superficially resemble chemical and physical processes, were really different, being governed by the *anima*.

Stahl's mantle as the leader of the German vitalist movement was taken over at the end of the nineteenth century by the psychologist and philosopher Ludwig Klages (1872-1956). Klages was educated in physics and chemistry, but between 1895 and 1915 was regarded as leader of the German vitalist school which argued that the laws of physics and chemistry alone could not explain life. In 1935 he published *Geist und Leben* ('Spirit and Life'), which argued that humans could be distinguished by a *geist* ('spirit'), which controls thought and creates life.

The French too had their vitalists and their own terms, the most important of which was the *élan vital* of Henri-Louis Bergson (1859-1941). Bergson was a French philosopher who put particular emphasis on instinct, as seen in fine form in insects, and on the fact that man was 'the end of intelligence'. He was born in Paris, not far from the Opera House. But for a few years he lived with his family in London, obtaining a familiarity with English. By the time he was nine his parents had settled again in France. At the Lycée Fontaine he won prizes for his scientific work, and for mathematics. In fact his first publication in *Annales de mathématiques*, at the age of eighteen, was the solution to a mathematical problem. But he was soon drawn towards the humanities, and by 1881 he was set on a pathway of *philosophie*. It was not long before his brilliance was recognised world-wide. In 1908 William James (1842-1910), elder brother of the novelist Henry James and a distinguished philosopher at Harvard, said after meeting Bergson: 'So modest and unpretending a man but such a genius.' This genius was to be acknowledged by accolades such as election to the Académie Française in 1815, and the Nobel prize for Literature in 1927. But his influence can perhaps best be assessed by the impact of his most famous book, *L'Évolution créatrice* ('Creative Evolution'), published in 1907. Two leading British evolutionary experts from Scotland, Professors Geddes and Thomson, referred to Bergson's seminal text as 'one of the most profound and original contributions to the philo-sophical consideration of the theory of Evolution'.

In his treatise Bergson accepted the principle of evolution as a scientific fact, but was highly critical of the interpretation of the evolutionary process for missing the uniqueness of life. He proposed that the whole evolutionary process should be regarded as an endurance of the *élan vital* – the vital impulse or current. Bergson makes the great fact of life his starting point. Is life susceptible to definition, he asks? 'I saw to my astonishment that scientific time does not *endure*. Positive science consists essentially in the elimination of duration.' Life to Bergson was *une poussée formidable* – an original impetus. His view was that life, or the vital impulse, consists of a demand for creation. The key words of the evolutionists were 'adaptation to the environment', 'selection' and 'variation'. But Bergson argued: 'The truth is that adaptation explains the sinuosities of the movement of Evolution, but not the general directions of the movement, still less the movement itself. The road that leads to the town is obliged to follow the ups and downs of the hills; it adapts to the accidents of the ground, but it is not the cause of the road nor have they given it its direction.' Bergson would not accept that the evolution of life was merely a series of adapta-tions to accidental circumstances. Bergson had an engaging, poetic style. As Monod tells us, although he is now almost wholly discredited no one in Monod's youth could be expected to pass certain key exams without at least having read *Creative Evolution*.

Over the centuries vitalism has thus changed its image and shape, as well as the size of its following. So is it in sympathy or in conflict with Rubicon?

WHAT IT IS AND WHAT IT IS NOT

We all recognise that there is something different between a live shellfish and a lump of marble, between a sugar cube and a sugar cane, between a cadaver and a live person, and that there is something special about humans that distinguishes us from other animals. As we have seen, vitalism is concerned with what is special about life that distinguishes it from non-life, whether this be an inanimate object such as a stone, a dead cell or a corpse. Was this vital force then susceptible to scientific investi-gation or not? Does it, for example, obey the established laws of physics and chemistry?

The essence of 'scientific' vitalism was that the ultimate life-force in living processes, including all animals, plants and micro-organisms, could not be explained by the established laws of physics and chemistry. Rubicon will have none of this, but might find some sympathy with a vitalist disciple of Newton who, believing in the principle that all things in the Universe are governed by natural laws amenable to scientific discovery, argues that there are laws special to life. These would be the 'biotonic laws' of the modern vitalist Elsasser (b. 1904). The trouble was that throughout the course of this two-thousand-year-old debate the vitalists themselves have not been able to agree. Many believed that in death the 'vital force' was lost from the body. The French physiologist Xavier Bichat (1771-1802) saw life as a conflict between the vital forces and those of physics and chemistry. Only in death did the physical and chemical forces win out and destroy the body. To others the idea that a vital force could be identified by studying the chemistry of the body was ridiculous.

Quarrels among vitalists were frequent in the nineteenth century. As with so many controversies in science, vitalism has provoked mixed emotions throughout the ages: anger, confusion, desperation, succour, and polemic fervour. Charles Caldwell (1772-1835), Professor of Natural History at the University of Pennsylvania, put his views forward aggressively. Never underestimate the passion of the scientist! Writing in *A Chemical Theory of Life* (1823), he stated: 'If life be chemical, man is degraded to the level of a laboratory.' In a criticism of Liebig's *Animal Chemistry* (1842), he wrote: 'Do I understand the gentleman who has just concluded his discourse, to contend that every function, and every functional product of living organised matter, are the results of chemical agency?' He then continued with an imaginary conversation between what he considered to be a true *vitalist* and a *chemicalist*, a word he invented. The vitalist, lifting a small covered dish, removed the lid, presented it to his opponent and said: 'Here, Sir, is a small quantity of well-prepared beef, potatoes and gravy. Will you oblige me by taking it into your laboratory, and changing it into genuine chyme?' With an air of embarrassment, the chemicalist replied: 'Really, Sir, I cannot, otherwise than by eating it.' 'That I can do myself,' returned the challenger, 'and a *pig* can do the same as well as either of us.'

True or false, vitalism should also be distinguished from teleology – the concept of purpose. Nor does it matter whether one is a holist or reductionist, or both. As Monod puts it in *Chance and Necessity*: 'The analysis of living organisms makes us admit that in their structure and performance, they decide, and pursue, a purpose.' This is not a religious purpose, given us by the Divine Maker, but as highlighted in Dawkins's *The Blind Watchmaker*, every part of the body and each part of an individual cell has developed and evolved to fulfil a function – to enable us to see, to move, to digest our food and to think. The blind watchmaker doesn't know what the end result will be, for he has no blueprint to follow.

Aristotle, in *De Anima*, provided one of the first and most celebrated accounts of teleology (from *telos*, 'end' or 'final aim'). To him a full description of anything must contain both the materials from which it is made and the purpose for which it was produced. Teleology asserts that the pathway a natural process follows is determined by the fact that it is being directed towards a particular end result. In other words it knows where it is going, and when it should cross the Rubicon. It was designed for this purpose. A car moves as you let your foot off the clutch, just as the designer intended.

Clearly the molecules, the internal structures of cells, the cells themselves, and the structures they generate do have a purpose. The question
is, how did they obtain the means to achieve this rubicon and under what
conditions do they cross?

THE VITALISTS PITCH THEIR TENTS

Vitalists can be classified as either endogenous or exogenous, depending
on where they believe the ultimate source of the vital force to be. They can
then be considered as either metaphysical or scientific, depending on
whether their force was a universal philosophical concept or was proposed
by active scientists hoping to find it susceptible to hypothesis and experiment. But perhaps the most illuminating classification of nineteenth- and
twentieth-century vitalists is that of Marcel Florkin in his masterly *History of Biochemistry: The Chemo- and Organo-vitalist Schools* (1972).

To Florkin the chemo-vitalists were personified in the nineteenth century by Liebig, and in the modern era by Polyani and Elsasser, whereas
the organo-vitalists were epitomised by three French physiologists of the
nineteenth century, Xavier Bichat, Paul Barthez and François Magendie.

By the end of the eighteenth century there was a trend, particularly in
France, to subject life to a framework of laws, as Newton had in the
seventeenth century for inanimate phenomena. Some kept a mechanistic
view. But two distinct vitalist schools had emerged by the mid-nineteenth
century. The organo-vitalist school was particularly predominant in
L'École de Santé at Montpelier, its main exponents being Th. Bordeau
(1722-1776) and Paul Joseph Barthez (1734-1806). Barthez was careful to
make a distinction between the soul, which returns to God on death, and
the *vital principle*. The vital principle was thus distinguished clearly from
the anima. Barthez's vital principle was a general one, comparable to
gravitation, and common to all organisms. Analogous to physical forces,
the vital principle also had a number of forces associated with it which put
it into action: impulsion, attraction, affinity, motor, sensitivity. Another
dominant French organo-vitalist was Xavier Bichat (1771-1802), though
he did not agree entirely with Barthez's conception of the vital force. Marie
François Xavier Bichat, a brilliant young surgeon of the Hôtel Dieu in
Paris, proposed that life must have structure. He declared in 1802 that the
tissues, of which he classified twenty-one types, were the true conservators
of life in the body. Bichat was a pioneer of modern histology, but because
he could readily see tissues without a microscope he actually objected to
using one. Xavier disagreed with Barthez's unique principle. He thought
rather that the vital properties of living tissues were dependent on two
non-chemical factors, sensibility and irritability. The vital forces were in
conflict with those of physics and chemistry, the latter taking over after
death. To Bichat the life of the body was the outcome of the combined lives
of the constituent tissues.

Bichat's ideas, which were modified by another French experimental physiologist François Magendie (1783-1855), prevailed to the latter part of the nineteenth century. To the organo-vitalists, chemistry could only deal with the matter of organisms after they had died. They would have rejected the proposal of Chapter Seven that one can 'View the Rubicon'. Thus their experiments on living systems were of a physiological nature, rejecting the other dominant vitalist school of the nineteenth century, chemo-vitalism, of which Justus von Liebig was the greatest exponent.

Justus von Liebig (1803-1873), renowned for his condenser, was one of the pioneers of the chemical investigation of living systems. He extracted many substances and chemical reactions from animal and plant tissues, thereby laying the foundations of modern biochemistry. His work established how much could be discovered about the chemistry of living systems by extracting substances from them. Yet he was a convinced vitalist and unfortunately this led him astray. His explanation of fermentation was based on the idea of a cycle of 'slow combustion' progressively transforming the organic molecules into simpler substances. When the vital activity was unable to repress the chemical forces, the constituents of the organism returned to the domain of these chemical forces. This was a far cry from the truth revealed by the elegant experiments of Pasteur, who recognised the crucial role of micro-organsms in the fermentation process.

Liebig constructed a complex series of metabolic calculations to show that all tissues were derived from albumin and fibrin, and that the end-points of animal metabolism were not CO_2 and water but rather the nitrogenous components of urine and the carbon components of bile. His *vital force* was a physical force acting either with or against the chemical forces which he could observe in tissue extracts. Thus he needed a positive vital force to account for the control of muscles at will, but a repressing force to account for the oxidation of molecules in the muscles and the source of body heat. Thereby he avoided the need to explain heat production by the vital force itself.

THE ANTIS

Not surprisingly several distinguished biologists and physicists of the nineteenth century became ardent opponents of both vitalist camps, particularly Helmholtz, Bernard, Schwann and Pflüger, followed by the emerging school of biochemists, such as Hopkins.

We saw in Chapter One that Matthias Schleiden (1804-1881) and Theodor Schwann (1810-1882) were key figures in establishing the universal cellular basis of all living tissues. Schwann was a pupil of a confirmed and active vitalist, Johannes Peter Müller (1801-1858), a physiologist and comparative anatomist working in Berlin. One of the leading natural philosophers of the nineteenth century, he was well known to Darwin, for Müller had sent him a case of barnacles in 1849 as part of Darwin's epic study on this group of animals. Darwin's four volumes remain a seminal work on the subject. Darwin certainly respected Müller's work, for he offered the young T.H. Huxley a copy of Müller's book on echinoderms (sea-urchins and starfish), as a 'bribe' to develop the growing relationship between them.

Müller believed that experimentation was a way of studying the properties of the vital force peculiar to each organ in the body. Re-enter Richard Owen, the distinguished Victorian anatomist and dinosaur expert – introducing the word at the British Association meeting in Plymouth in 1841. Owen was a follower of Müller, agreeing that there was not an outside force putting life into inanimate matter. Rather living matter had an 'organising energy', which directed growth and tissue development according to a plan. The force was most concentrated in the germ, and waned as it diffused into the tissues and with age. Darwin knew Owen well, and also appears to have accepted the idea of his 'organising energy', before concentrating on the question of the origin of species. It was as well that Müller concentrated on comparative morphology. For this he became well known, though not as famous as his pupil Schwann. Schwann contributed to Müller's influential book, *Handbuch der Physiologie des Menschen für Vorlesungen* ('Elements of Physiology'), but was careful to distance himself from the vitalist views of his master. As J. Canguilhem wrote in *La Connaissance de la Vie* (1952): 'There cannot be an Empire within an Empire'!

The mistake of the vitalists was to propose that living organisms were inserted into a medium controlled by the laws of physics and chemistry but of which life is an exception. It was this philosophical argument which influenced Schwann to reject the vitalism of his time and to argue that the vital force was an unacceptable exception to the laws of God's Empire. As Descartes had done with his *animal machine*, Schwann focussed on the reductionist principle: all the properties of Nature depend ultimately on the properties of the atoms from which she is made, and imbibed in them when God created the Universe. Molecules are constructed from atoms, and Schwann realised that cells were made of special molecules which had not previously been studied. To Schwann, the vital force was simply an inevitable consequence of the special properties of these molecules and their organisation into cells.

But the vitalist debate was not restricted to the chemists and biologists. The physicists joined in too.

Herman von Helmholtz (1821-1894) made fundamental contributions to optics, electrodynamics, meteorology and physiology but is best known for placing one of the fundamental laws of physics on a proper mathematical basis, the Law of Conservation of Energy – the First Law of Thermodynamics. This was the centrepiece of his book *Über die Erhaltung der Kraft* (1847) ('Conservation of Energy'). He argued, and then showed, that the energy released when substances are burnt outside the body is the same as that when 'burnt' within it. Thus the calories produced when glucose is oxidised to carbon dioxide (CO_2) are independent of the path. In a fire all the glucose turns into gas and disappears. However, in the body not all the glucose is burnt straight away. Some is converted into other body components, such as fat, thereby maintaining a potential energy source for use at a later date. Thus the body does obey the laws of thermodynamics.

The lungs exemplify Rubicon in action. Their prime function, in each breath, is to absorb oxygen when inhaling, and to get rid of carbon dioxide when exhaling. A key question therefore was: where in the body was the carbon dioxide generated? The German physiologist Carl Ludwig (1816-1895) claimed that the blood was the main site. Wrong! The cells of the blood consume very little oxygen, and thus generate very little carbon dioxide. In fact it is the brain, muscles, heart and liver that are the main oxygen-consumers and carbon-dioxide-generators in the body. It was the work of F. Hoppe (later called Hoppe-Seyler) (1825-1895) and E.F.W. Pflüger (1829-1910) that first showed this, and thus refuted the claims of Ludwig's laboratory that the blood was the main site of CO_2 formation and oxidation. As Pflüger wrote in 1875, 'It is the living cell which regulates the magnitude of the oxygen consumption.' After Pflüger had demonstrated the intracellular nature of this respiration, and after Helmholtz had shown the production of heat by isolated muscle, it was accepted that the views of Schwann first expressed in 1839 were correct. Cells were not only units of structure, but also the site of respiration and heat production. Blood only acted as a carrier of oxygen to, and of carbon dioxide from, the cells in the tissues. The popularisation of this principle was helped by a book by Claude Bernard on animal heat.

Well, that's that then! Vitalism must surely now have crossed its ultimate rubicon and become extinct. The establishment of the chemical basis of metabolism in the unit of life, the cell, placed the last nail in the vitalist's coffin. Organo-vitalism died out, and chemo-vitalism crossed the rubicon into biochemistry. But hold on a minute! What's this funny gelatinous stuff inside cells? Now that the vitalists were inside the cell they found a much more potent substance to mystify them, the *protoplasm*.

From the mid-nineteenth century onwards scientists studying living things, who were yet to call themselves biologists, were concerned about the viscous substance that seemed to be found in plant and animal cells. Terms such as *cambium* from C.F. Brisseau-Mirbel (1776-1854) and *sarcode* from Félix Dujardin (1801-1860) began to be used to describe it. But 'protoplasm' did not appear until 1835; it was apparently first used to describe the ground substance inside cells. The Czech pioneer of experimental physiology, Jan Evangelista Purkinje (1787-1869), who gives his name to the pace-maker fibres in the heart and to large nerve cells in the brain, introduced protoplasm to describe the material substance found in eggs and early embryos. Hugo von Mohl (1805-1872), Professor of Botany at Tubingen, was the first to propose that new cells were formed by the process of cell division, something he had observed in an alga called *Conferva glomerata*. And in 1846 Mohl used the word 'protoplasm' to describe the *plastic* substance within the cell wall. To him the nucleus of the cell was surrounded by a granular, colloidal material, the *protoplasm*.

There was no getting away from it, 'protoplasm' just had to be responsible for all living processes. The arguments about its existence and significance remain with us even today. So let's examine it a bit more closely.

The mysterious protoplasm

We have already seen that crossing the Rubicon inside cells really can mean a parting of the waters. The inside of cells consists of more than seventy per cent water. However, it is not a free-flowing liquid. To see this we dissected an individual cell – not initially one from our body, for these are far too tiny to dissect easily, but rather the giant nerve of the squid, used to trigger its jet propulsion. Needing nerves to react fast and in synchrony, squid have evolved a way to achieve this without requiring the myelin insulating sheath which our nerves have around them, as highlighted by J.Z. Young. With giant nerves up to a millimetre or so in diameter, some ten to a hundred times the diameter of our nerves, they conduct fast signals to the muscles in the mantle, so that the squid squirts. If you cut one of these giant nerves it is possible to squeeze out the entire contents of the cell. It is a jelly. Add calcium to this *gel* and it converts into a *sol*ution. All cells are made in this way. The inner particles and reactions are suspended in a wobbly jelly, the mysterious protoplasm of Purkinje.

Physiologists were quick to grasp the potential importance of this mysterious fluid that wasn't a fluid. Max Schultze (1825-1874) in 1861 and Thomas Henry Huxley (1825-1895) in a book published in 1869 entitled *Protoplasm: The Physical Basis of Life* both described the cell as a 'mass of nucleated protoplasm'. To Schultze a cell was 'a small, naked piece of protoplasm with a nucleus'. An emphasis on the importance of the protoplasm continued far into this century. Lewis Heilbrunn (1892-1959), the pioneer of calcium as a signal inside cells we met in Chapters Two and Three (Plate 5(a)), was obsessed with the effect that ions such as calcium had on the protoplasm. He published books called *The Colloid Chemistry of Protoplasm* (1928) and *The Dynamics of Living Protoplasm* (1956). He even started and edited a new scientific journal with the unwieldy name of *Protoplasmatologia*. It was the reductionists' distrust of such vitalist-sounding terms, particularly about the *mysterious* protoplasm, together with an obsession with the colloid properties of proteins and other macromolecules, that sometimes undermined the importance of Heilbrunn's ideas and observations.

The disciples of the protoplasm accepted that the fragmentation of cells might be needed to isolate and characterise the inner structures within live cells: the mitochondria, the reticulum, the ribosomes, the lysosomes, the peroxisomes and so on. Indeed when isolated it was possible for the first time to define their composition and identify some of their functions, as well as learning something about how they worked. But did it really explain how their functions were coordinated inside a live cell? No! For this they needed to be surrounded by their natural protoplasm. Only then would their chemical and physical reactions become *alive.*

Even Hopkins recognised the uniqueness of the physical and chemical state of the cell. To Hopkins the life of the cell was the expression of a particular dynamic equilibrium which occurs in a system made up of many phases. Some of these phases could be separated, but life was the property of the cell as a whole. Life depended on the equilibrium shown by all the coexisting phrases. But Hopkins, an admirer of Liebig's contribution to the eventual founding of biochemistry, was determined to destroy what he saw as the vague and vitalist concept of the protoplasm. He was perplexed that so important a figure as J.B.S. Haldane, a pupil who became Professor of Biometry at University College London, and an important figure in the development of modern genetics, was aggressively against the whole philosophy of extracting chemicals from living tissues in the hope that it would explain life. In the 1920s Haldane wrote: 'The new physiology is biological physiology – not biophysics or biochemistry. The attempt to analyse living organisms into physical and chemical mechanisms is probably the most colossal failure in the whole history of modern science.' Strong words, but I know what he means!

Although the term 'protoplasm' is seldom used in biochemical discussions today, another 'plasm' is in common parlance. This is the term *cytoplasm* invented by R.A. von Kölliker (1817-1905) to describe the material inside the cell but outside the nucleus. There is some confusion about the use of this term today. I prefer to keep to the original concept. The cytoplasm contains everything outside the nucleus held within the outer membrane of the cell. It therefore includes all the sub-cellular structures: the mitochondria, reticulum, lysosomes, chloroplasts and so on. The 'jelly', the non-particulate gel in which all these organelles are suspended, is the *cytosol.*

From protoplasm to biochemistry

In 1828 a German chemist, Friedrich Wöhler (1800-1882), succeeded in converting ammonium cyanate into urea.

Urea is the substance in which nitrogen waste is excreted in our urine. Until 1828 there was only one way to make it. Use a live animal. But Wöhler's seemingly crucial transformation of an inorganic substance into an organic one turned out not to be as influential on biological thinking as is often claimed; nor did it cause a major problem to the vitalists. It may have been a *brilliant discovery,* as Dumas wrote to Berzelius in February of 1828. It may have heralded the real beginnings of organic chemistry. But to Schwann, a committed anti-vitalist, urea contained the same elements as ammonium cyanate, and he didn't believe that this molecular transformation could be used as a major weapon against the vitalist camp.

Jean-Baptiste de Lamarck, pioneer of evolution, also believed in the protoplasm. He defined life as a physical phenomenon, perfectly open to scientific investigation. To him it was inappropriate and unnecessary to speak of a soul or vital spirit. Once a phenomenon was properly defined, it was open to scientific study within the new science of biology. Like others, Lamarck was trying to explain the fundamental difference between inanimate and animate objects. We now use the word orgasm for a particular type of 'immoderate excitement' (as the dictionary defines it), but Lamarck had a much more general use for the word. Vital orgasm was the specific tension which held the molecules of all the soft parts of living things a certain distance apart. This was his vital principle, which enabled living tissues and organisms to carry out their unique functions. But he believed the barrier, the rubicon, between life and non-life could be crossed and was still being crossed somewhere in the world. In other words life was being created all the time, if only one could find out where. Thus, unfortunately for the credibility of some of his observations and ideas, spontaneous generation was crucial to his argument. In the right conditions and with the appropriate gelatinous matter, very simple organisms could be formed. Thus the transition from a mass of jelly to a simple organism was only a narrow rubicon to cross. It was still going on somewhere in the world, if only he could find the spot. By the mid-nineteenth century, before the proper identification of micro-organisms, the mysteriousness of life was supported by this great mystery – *spontaneous generation*.

The appearance of moulds, fungi and luminous meat, once they were shown to contain living microbes, led to claims that these life forms must have arisen spontaneously. But this was too fantastic a rubicon for Pasteur. He put a stop to all that. Investigating meticulously many cases of apparent spontaneous generation, and preventing contamination of broths by airborne micro-organisms and spores, he showed them all to be false. Life begets life, as always. But are the conditions on Earth now incompatible with the conversion of non-life to life, in the way it occurred some three and half to four thousand million years ago? Probably, except under special conditions created by man in the laboratory!

In fertilisation and development too the pioneers of cell biology were providing the scientific evidence to destroy vitalism. Claude Bernard never managed to extend his analysis of body regulation to cover embryology and development. Between 1900 and 1920 a contretemps occurred over this essential characteristic of all multicellular organisms. Followers of Hans Driesch still believed in the need for a 'soul-like' reality in development. But the work of a German-born American experimental physiologist, Jacques Loeb (1859-1924), showed that the initiation of cell division was controlled chemically. Loeb made the remarkable observation that a *virgin* sea-urchin egg could be provoked into cell division and then development simply by injecting certain chemicals – for example, alcohol – into the egg. Sperm was not required for this rubicon to be crossed.

The ability of virgin aphids to reproduce was discovered as long ago as the eighteenth century, and Richard Owen (1804-1892) had coined the word *parthenogenesis* (from the Greek *parthenos*, 'virgin'), to describe the reproduction of organisms without the need of sex. But it was Theodor von Siebold (1804-1885) who, in his *Whare Parthenogenesis* of 1856, used the word in its modern sense. Unfertilised eggs of certain invertebrate and lower plants, if treated appropriately, can develop. This distinguishes parthenogenesis from asexual reproduction. It has been widely used as a model for developmental biologists ever since Loeb showed its value experimentally.

As the death knell tolled for vitalism in development, as the result of the experiments of Loeb and his followers, a new school of biochemists was destroying the chemical remnants of the nineteenth-century vitalist theories. Frederick Gowland Hopkins (1861-1947) was able to establish at the University of Cambridge a school of biochemistry of immense influence in the United Kingdom and throughout the international scientific community. A list of his students and research groups spanning some forty years reads like a roll of honour. Most of the leading figures responsible for established the molecular approach to biology in the first half of this century seem to have worked with him at some time or other: Bailey, Baldwin, Chain, Danielli, Dixon, Haldane, Hill, Keilin, Krebs, Martin, Mitchell, the Needhams, Peters, Quastel, Sanger and Wigglesworth to name but a few.

Hopkins started his biochemical career as a schoolboy trying to extract the colour from butterfly wings. His individual contributions include the discovery of the catalytic nature of vitamins and the identification of glutathione. The latter led to a famous cartoon in which Hopkins is seen holding a flag with the words 'GLUTA thy OWNE'. He received the Nobel prize for the discovery of 'tryptophane' in 1929, the key paper being published with Cole in 1901 in the Proceedings of the Royal Society. But his contributions to the Natural Philosophy in which he believed go far beyond these individual discoveries. He argued fervently the anti-vitalist case. The chemical composition and properties of living systems could be defined by extracting, purifying and characterising the molecules of which living systems were made.

Early work on the analysis of biological molecules – proteins, lipoids and nucleic acids – had been dominated by German chemists such as Liebig, Kossel, Solkowski, Hoppe-Seyler and Emil Fischer. Otto Warburg, working at the turn of the century, had highlighted the importance of respiration – that is, oxygen uptake – by animal tissues. In the UK, as early as 1802, Humphry Davy at the Royal Institution had lectured on 'Agricultural Chemistry', and in 1809 the Royal Society had the vision to form a Society for the Promotion of Animal Chemistry. This died out, and it was not until W.D. Halliburton from 1884 to 1890 at University College, London and then Starling, that the new chemical physiology began to take off. But it was with Hopkins that we really associate the break from the rather sterile or vitalist chemical analysis of the German chemists. For

Hopkins it was not just the components, but how they reacted and how they were formed that mattered if one was to understand the chemistry of life.

Before Hopkins, many thought of the chemistry of living things as different from laboratory chemicals because of their protoplasm. Having entered this complex, food molecules and oxygen lost their identity and were incorporated into living molecules, known as *biogen*, thus losing their normal chemical characteristics. Sir Michael Foster wrote: 'The mystery of life lies in the protoplasm ... We must be content with knowing the beginning and the end.' Hopkins was far from content with this. The mysterious protoplasm was to Hopkins what spontaneous generation had been to Pasteur. When, in 1927, a new journal called *Protoplasma* appeared in the Department of Biochemistry, Tennis Court Road, Cambridge, members seriously wondered whether it would be allowed in the library. Hopkins was firmly against the ill-defined chemical concept of protoplasm. 'It is for chemistry and physics to replace the vague concept – protoplasm – a pure abstraction,' Hopkins wrote in an article entitled 'The clinician and the laboratory worker' (1931). His report to the British Association in 1913 restated the plea that Liebig had put in 1837: 'The new science of organic chemistry would aid the progress of biology.' But Hopkins also realised the ultimate objective of the biochemist: 'The biochemist's data gain their full significance only when he can relate them with the activities of the organism as a whole.' To Hopkins the whole was not simply the sum of the isolated parts. 'The part in the whole is no longer the same as the part in isolation,' he wrote. Against Haldane he said: 'The aim of modern biochemistry is not merely to analyse the former organisms into smaller organisms which compose them. This is a superficial though necessary task. The real analysis is the study of factors or mechanisms within organisms, the nature of surfaces and catalysts, to produce an intellectual synthesis of the whole.' Haldane thought he was doomed to failure in this latter objective.

Hopkins's holistic-reductionism turned out to be a great success, apparently, resulting in many discoveries and genuine revelations about the chemistry of life. Thus the molecular structure of vitamins and hormones were identified, and the catalytic function of that very special group of proteins – the enzymes – the oxygen-binding proteins, the cytochromes which linked oxidation of foods to the energy supply for the synthetic and functional reactions in the cell, and so on. So long as the event that occurred in the cell also occurred in the broken cell homogenate in the biochemist's test-tube, we were learning about the chemical reactions that were responsible for survival, function and reproduction of cells, tissues and whole organisms.

But what constitutes an event – an enzyme catalysing the hydrolysis of a starch molecule, a mixture of enzymes catalysing the formation of alcohol from glucose, the formation of ATP from the energy of fatty acid oxidation in an isolated mitochondrion, the contraction of a muscle fibre in a cell stripped of its outer membrane? Yes. But these events are not rubicons. All of them can be induced by the experimentalist in preparations from broken cells. We have learnt a great deal about how cells work and how their reactions are regulated. But there are events which don't occur in broken cells, and which can only be observed in the intact cell. These are rubicons. This is not vitalism, just a realistic analysis made from observations comparing agents which activate or injure live cells, with the effects of these agents on broken cells.

Is there then anything special about the physics and chemistry of life? We have found many special characteristics – chemicals, structures, reactions, gradients and rubicons. And then there is molecular handedness (chirality), the origin of which has been a source of considerable debate ever since 1858 when Pasteur showed that *Penicillium* moulds grow preferentially on (+) tartaric acid, leaving the mirror image (-) in solution untouched. Even this has been used to support vitalist arguments. In 1898, at a meeting of the British Association for the Advancement of Science held in Bristol, a chemist from Aberdeen, Francis Japp (1848-1925), invoked the vital force to explain why D-glucose and L-amino-acids had been selected for life. Well, as you may imagine, the pages of *Nature* were burning with heated argument for months afterwards. Yet still no one can provide a rational explanation for this most distinctive property of the chemistry of life.

As late as 1951 the Austro-Hungarian philosopher of science Ernest Nagel (1901-1985), an American citizen since 1919, felt that vitalism was still sufficiently popular to write in his *Philosophy and Phenomenonological Research* that vitalism was a dead issue. Yet its importance in the history of biology is unquestionable. And the problems remain, as they did centuries ago when vitalism, in its modern clothes, first emerged. This book is not intended to take us back across this rubicon, one well and truly crossed by most of us. Let us therefore finish the discussion by emphasising why Rubicon is not a return to vitalism.

The King is dead. Long live the King.

VITALISM REVITALISED?

So where does all this lead us? Interesting history but not relevant to the reductionists of today. Or is it?

Obviously there is something different about living systems. Otherwise why do we continue to study biology as a separate science? But I believe we can learn something important from the story of vitalism as it has developed over the past 2,000 years. Having separated the religious soul and spirit from the material reality of the flesh, we can see four dichotomies between the variety of vitalisms:

1. Metaphysical and pseudo-religious versus scientific.
2. An exogenous versus an endogenous force.

3. Organo- versus chemo-.
4. In conflict or in harmony with the laws of physics and chemistry.

Such debate is inevitable in science until a genuine universality has been identified. But the crucial factor for the contemporary scientist is to separate some of the vague vitalist notions of the past from truly perceptive analyses of the uniqueness of living systems, to see whether, using the power of modern molecular and physical techniques, we can learn something new.

Seven out of ten for trying for: *entelechy*, the *archêus*, the *anima* and the *élan vital*. They got the people who mattered in science thinking. But these concepts really fell between the realms of religion and science. They lacked the clarity and definition of a true scientific principle. They became an excuse for ignorance – a way of convincing oneself that by inventing a hypothetical force whose effects we could study and categorise but whose nature would always be out of reach, the ultimate basis of life would always remain elusive. This is of no use to a scientist.

The question whether the vital force was imposed from outside (exogenous) or born from within (endogenous) was important to the development of modern vitalism. Believers in spontaneous generation would be attracted by the idea that even today, if the conditions are right, some external force, but not a religious one, could transform an inanimate soup into one containing life; whereas those who can see that life begets life, and that the chemist has never been able to recreate life in the test-tube, would be happy to accept that the force was inherent within the living system. By the time the organo- and chemo-vitalist schools of the nineteenth century were established we were at least seeing some real science – a serious scientific attempt to describe what had begun centuries before as a somewhat mystical concept to describe the vital force in action. This led to the real crunch, the relationship of vitalism to the laws of physics and chemistry defined by studying non-living systems.

As more and more physiological properties and chemical components of living organisms were described, it became increasingly difficult to accept the fundamental philosophy of either the chemo- or organo-vitalist schools. By the turn of the century the key vitalist question was: 'How far would the natural laws of physics and chemistry take us?' The laws of thermodynamics, conservation of energy and entropy helped us to understand what ATP synthesis in the mitochondrion was for. The laws of electricity – Ohm's law and the Nernst equation – provided the mathematical basis for describing and predicting the voltage across biological membranes. The Law of Mass Action enabled us to predict the rate of biological reactions and to describe enzymatic catalysis in quantitative terms. The application of Quantum Theory helped us explain the nature of the electronically-excited state in living systems – in photosynthesis, in vision and in bioluminescence. Electronic orbital theory helped to explain the chemistry of bond-formation and cleavage in biological molecules and, as so elegantly shown by Linus Pauling, can be used to predict key three-dimensional structures such as the alpha helix in macromolecules, confirmed by X-ray crystallography. Diffusion and osmotic theory enabled us to describe the movement of molecules within living cells and to describe the forces which cause them to cross from one side of a biological membrane to another. Yet there remain some who still believe that the physico-chemical environment of the cell and the environment with which it surrounds itself are so special, unique in fact, that we will need new vitalist laws to describe them properly – *biotonic laws*.

The present laws of physics and chemistry have been successful in leading us along paths of genuine discovery. However, over the past century they have still not been able to provide either a qualitative or a quantitative analysis of the difference between an homogenate and a live tissue, or between a live cell and one which has just died without immediately fragmenting.

Rubicon is a marriage between the holistic and reductionist view of Nature. It uses the essential molecular and physical details uncovered by the reductionist to rationalise biological phenomena, from events occurring over a millisecond time-scale within an individual cell to events requiring millions of years of graded change for a new process or living unit to appear. This is no unholy alliance between factions which have often been portrayed as antagonists. But the most sensitive judgment is required to know when to listen to a single bar from one instrument in a hundred-piece orchestra, and when to allow one's consciousness to comprehend the complete statement from the whole ensemble. It is not necessary to reject one's religious convictions to cross the Rubicon, any more than it was to reject the figurative and historical truth in the Bible to believe in evolution and Darwinism. Nor is it necessary for Rubicon to return to a mysterious vitalist force, not subject to the laws of physics and chemistry. I will pin my colours to the mast. Just as chemistry has the Law of Mass Action, Le Châtelier's principle, Faraday's Laws of electrolysis and the rationalisation of the elements through the periodic table, so we might hope that laws, both qualitative and mathematical, truly universal to the whole of biology will emerge. If we don't find some soon we are in danger of being drowned in a rice pudding of detail.

Rubicon is a scientific principle obeying the laws of physics and chemistry. It is not a return to a mysterious, uninvestigatable vital force. The question now is whether we can exploit this principle to transform a mystical *vital* force into a genuine scientific one. To see if this is possible we must first grasp the nature of *force* itself.

9

The Missing Law?

Rubicon claims to be a universality, applicable to all living systems. So is it an hypothesis, a law, a principle, or what? Is it essential to propose a mechanism for how a biological system crosses the Rubicon or is it sufficient simply to define the banks? If a mechanism proposed for the crossing turns out to be wrong does this negate the universality principle embedded in Rubicon? The previous chapter dealt with what Rubicon is not. This chapter focuses on what Rubicon hopes to be.

THE CONCEPT OF FORCE

Let's carry out a simple experiment. Take a piece of paper, tear it into small pieces and scatter them in a cluster on the table in front of you. Now find a plastic comb, touch the pieces of paper with the comb and ... nothing happens! But now comb your hair a couple of times and then touch the pieces of paper with the comb. Magic – some of them will stick. Now repeat the experiment, but this time don't allow the comb to touch the pieces of paper. Amazing, some of them leave the table and bind steadfast to the comb. This sort of observation has been familiar to us all since childhood. It is of course the result of electrostatic attraction. The attraction of a positive charge induced in the comb from stroking your hair with an induced opposite negative charge in the pieces of paper, or vice versa. But the point I want to make is that the induction of an opposite and attractive charge in the paper did not require you to touch them. Some sort of force, wending itself through the atmosphere, caused it.

Isaac Newton's studies on the motion of bodies led to his Laws of Motion. The second of these laws defines the force necessary to produce an acceleration in any body, be it an atom, a car, or a terrestrial body. The simple equation is the mass of that body multiplied by its acceleration. The concept of this type of force is useful, but nowadays physicists prefer to think of a force as a fundamental property of Nature. There are four. One fundamental force is caused by electricity and magnetism, and another by gravity. The other two are the forces responsible for holding matter together at the sub-atomic level, and are known as the weak and strong nuclear forces. As with the electrostatic force between our comb and the pieces of paper, a universal feature of each of these fundamental forces is the ability to act at a distance. To explain this the physicist introduces the concept of *field*. It is the earth's magnetic field which causes the little magnet on a compass needle to point to magnetic north, while it is the gravitational fields of the Sun and the Earth that cause our planet to circle the Sun once each year. But what are these fields? We can't see them, we can't touch them and we can't isolate them in a bottle.

As scientists, we have long accepted that the human senses alone cannot experience directly all the facets which cause a natural phenomenon. The hypothesis for the existence of these fields is proved by the fact that every prediction based on them turns out to be true. It was Einstein's dream to discover a unified field theory to bring into one scheme the four fundamental forces of Nature – gravitational, electro-magnetic, weak and strong nuclear. Some success has been achieved, but gravity has defied attempts to rationalise it with the other three. So if the physicists accept that a fundamental property of Nature is the existence of forces which apparently have no material substance, and which enable us to explain how matter and bodies hold themselves together, why not biology? The morphogenetic fields of Rupert Sheldrake can perhaps be regarded as such an attempt. His thought-provoking book *A New Science of Life* (1981) had the distinction of being described in an editorial in *Nature* 293:245-6 (1981) as 'a book for burning'. The essential ingredients of a morphogenetic field are the ability to transmit through space the influence for shape and form, and to transfer, through morphic resonance, the success or failure of an event learnt by one life form to another without direct contact. Sheldrake gives as an analogy of the lining up of iron filings along the magnetic lines of force from a magnet. His morphogenetic field enables the shape, form, development and behaviour of organisms, which never have any contact with each other, to occur.

The idea may seem far-fetched and unscientific. It has been rejected or ignored by most professional scientists. Yet surely we must have some sympathy with the motive behind the hypothesis and Sheldrake's analysis. Clever molecular biology has identified the importance of the *homeobox* genes in development. By mutating these genes in the geneticist's favourite creature, the fruit fly *Drosophila*, the whole side of a fly can be made to disappear as it develops. Gradients of their products, the hox proteins, have been found between cells in the developing embryo. Yet this does not explain *how* these genes cause a particular organ to have the shape it has. The mutation experiment only shows that they are essential for normal development.

Rubicon does not suggest or predict the existence of hitherto undiscovered and uninvestigated fields and forces. The chemical and physical properties of life depend on the four fundamental forces of Nature. But what Rubicon says, and firmly, is that this is not enough.

Quantum theory explains the nuclear and electronic energy levels in individual atoms. An excited electron can lose its energy in many ways: by a chemical reaction, for example. But it can also lose it by emitting a light photon. This is how luminescence occurs. The glow of a glow-worm or the flash of a firefly are caused by a chemical reaction raising electrons to higher energy levels in molecules, which then lose this energy as green or yellow light. Yet for decades the physicists virtually ignored how the electron actually jumps from energy level to energy level. Since this is a quantum leap the electron has no existence in between. It is not like a satellite changing orbit, gradually moving closer or further from the earth, pushed by the energy of its retro-rockets. So with Rubicon. Our first job is to find and then describe the banks on either side of a biological rubicon, be it a molecular cluster or a whole ecosystem. Then, and only then, can we decide whether the existing forces of Nature are sufficient to explain how the crossing occurs.

HYPOTHESIS OR FRAMEWORK?

What is science?

Natural science is the study of natural phenomena and the discovery of the natural laws which govern them. But what do I mean by a natural phenomenon or a law, and where does Rubicon fit in? Central to all this is the language of experiment. This is what communicates science through the centuries. At school we learnt Le Châtelier's *principle*. This states that, if any change of conditions is imposed on a system at equilibrium, the system will act to counter the imposed change. Now where have I heard that logic before? We learnt about Newton's *laws* of motion and the three *laws* of thermodynamics, of Einstein's *equation* $E = mc^2$, of quantum *theory* and the *theory* of relativity, and of universalities in the physical world, the universal constants of Planck, Avogadro and Boltzmann – numbers which appear in certain key equations in physics.

But why do we use the word *principle* for Le Châtelier and *theory* for Einstein? What is the difference between a theory and an hypothesis, or a principle and a law? Where are the universalities and laws which apply to biology? The scientific world is full of principles, hypotheses, theories and laws. But what is the difference between them? Why Heisenberg's uncertainty *principle*, Darwin's *theory* of evolution and Newton's *laws* of motion and gravitation but the Rubicon *hypothesis*. Is Rubicon an hypothesis at all, or just a framework for rationalising natural phenomena, as I argued for the Gaia hypothesis? And where do the two languages of science, experiment and mathematics, fit in?

In a legal sense a 'law' is something we must obey. But it can be broken. By contrast, a scientific 'law' cannot be broken. The way scientists carry out their endeavours was first laid down by Francis Bacon (1561-1626). But it was Isaac Newton in his *Principia* (1687), and his other scientific works such as *Opticks*, who laid down the experimental and mathematical basis of modern science. In the days of Newton one of the prime aims of science was to uncover the Laws of Nature. This has worked well for three

centuries in physics and chemistry. Unfortunately it has been less successful in biology.

'A fact is fact is a fact,' one of my medical colleagues stated vehemently
to me once during a heated debate at a party. True. 'All grass is green' is
a statement of fact. But it is not a scientific theory. The point is that unless
we can put facts, which are a collection of descriptions or observations, into
some sort of rational framework we cannot see the wood for the trees.

An *hypothesis* is usually the first reasonable explanation for an observation, or collection of observations. Once we have tested the hypothesis
to our satisfaction it becomes a *theory*, something we believe to be a
fundamental truth. If there is some unifying mechanism which explains
how the theory actually works then we have a *principle*. *Laws* arising from
these theories and principles can then be formulated either in the form of
statements or in mathematical form, such as Ohm's law of electricity,
showing what a statement designates.

But what of biology?

In a medical or biological dictionary you will find several 'laws'. For
example, Behring's law states that 'the blood and serum of an immunised
person, when transferred to another subject, will render the latter immune'. But is this the same type of universality as in Avogadro's law? This
states that 'equal volumes of all perfect gases at the same temperature and
pressure contain the same number of molecules, or atoms if we are
considering monatomic gases'. It was this law which enabled us to calculate
the number of molecules in different compartments of a cell. And what of
the dogmas in biology – DNA makes RNA makes protein, for example? HIV
has an enzyme which converts its RNA back to DNA. Chirality, the
handedness of biological molecules, and the principle of catalysis are also
universalities in biology. But, like Behring's so-called law, these come into
the 'all grass is green' category. They are facts.

Biology has continued as it began at the end of nineteenth century,
essentially a descriptive science with few if any fundamental principles
and laws. Animals and plants have been classified into different groups by
the taxonomists. The fine structure of organisms has been dissected by the
anatomists and the cellular basis of life described by the microscopists.
The various functions of organisms, tissues and individual cell types have
been described by the physiologists, and abnormal features identified by
the pathologists. The chemicals in and outside our cells which make them
tick have been elucidated by the biochemists and molecular biologists.
Descriptive hypotheses abound to explain the pathways defining the birth,
development, evolution and death of individual organisms, species or
whole groups. But there are precious few principles and laws which can be
formulated either qualitatively or mathematically that can be applied
universally to the whole of biology. This is one reason why Darwin's and
Wallace's Natural Selection principle has had such a dominant influence
on the course of biology in the past hundred and fifty years. For the

principle of evolution, through step-by-step changes in the inheritable DNA, is perhaps the only concept which unifies all living species.

'Evolution' is *the* unifying principle in biology, and between the scientists themselves – the development of life through transmutation and development of one species into another, and the extinction of others. The principle of natural selection provides one mechanism by which this can occur. But what about the universality of DNA? DNA is the material by which characteristics are inherited. The trouble is that as soon as we seem to have a universality in biology we find an exception. Are RNA viruses then an exception to the DNA principle? We could change the principle to: 'Nucleic acid is the molecular basis of inheritance.' But this would be a distortion, for DNA is the inheritable material in all animals, plants and micro-organisms. Only in certain viruses is RNA used. Other biological universalities include the handedness of certain key molecules, the principle of enzymatic catalysis, and the three fundamental cell types: prokaryote, archaebacteria and eukaryote. So where does Rubicon fit in?

Rubicon claims to be a universal *principle*. All biological events are determined by a pathway of thresholds interspersed by graded physical and chemical change. At present this principle is an hypothesis. But how can we find out whether it is correct? How many experiments will we have to do? How many observations must we make? If we find an exception will this prove that the whole idea of Rubicon is false? The real power of any new scientific principle is its ability to predict new discoveries which wouldn't have been found without it. The excitement of science is in discovery and invention, embodied in the language of experiment. Before we step through this looking-glass, I must now refute a philosophy which has corrupted science – the scientific 'logic' of Sir Karl Popper.

POP ... GOES THE WEASEL

Natural philosophy

Let there be no doubt, practising scientists do think about the philosophy of their discipline!

'Lovers of wisdom', or 'philosophers', first appeared in the West in the civilisation of ancient Greece. Science is knowledge of the world of Nature. Its foundations can also be traced back to China in the second millennium BC, but how much these early beginnings influenced Western science is unclear. There were no scientific journals then, no libraries, no computer searches. According to Greek tradition, Thales of Miletus in the sixth century BC was the first natural philosopher. He is credited with the prediction of a solar eclipse in 585 BC, and the origin of the word *kosmos*, 'order'. Until the mid-nineteenth century 'natural philosopher' was the most popular word to describe someone studying Nature and the natural world. Copernicus, Galileo, Aristotle, Plato, Ptolemy, Archimedes, Pliny and Newton were natural philosophers as well as being experimentalists.

Even Hopkins liked to be called one. Yet during this century there has emerged an *unnatural* philosophy, led by Karl Popper.

Popper and his disciples

Popper was born in 1902 in Vienna. As a teenager he was a Marxist, but he later became a keen Social Democrat. Foreseeing the demise of his native Austria, and brought up a Protestant of Jewish stock, he moved to New Zealand in 1937. In 1946 he came to England, where he became Professor of Logic and Scientific Method at the London School of Economics, and was knighted in 1965. His first book, published in 1934, *Logik der Forschung* or *The Logic of Scientific Discovery*, laid the foundations of his thought, appearing in English in 1959.

You will probably have anticipated from the title of this section that I am about to blast off a tirade against his ideas which, in my view, have done so much damage to science in the second half of this century. They have indoctrinated two or more generations of leading scientists with wholly negative approaches to scientific endeavour. If anyone doubts the influence Popper has had, how about a few quotations?

Arthur Koestler wrote of Popper's *The Poverty of Historicism* when it appeared in 1957 that he considered it 'probably the only book published this year which would outlive this century'. Far more serious, however, was the enthusiasm for Popper seen in distinguished scientists such as Sir Peter Medawar, Jacques Monod, Sir John Eccles and Sir Hermann Bondi, three of whom were Nobel Laureates. Medawar (1915-1987), Nobel Laureate for Physiology or Medicine in 1960 for showing that immune tolerance could be acquired and so making transplantation surgery possible, said in a radio programme in 1972: 'I think Popper is incomparably the greatest philosopher of science that there has ever been.' Sir John Eccles (b. 1903), Nobel Laureate of 1963, also for Physiology or Medicine with Hodgkin and Huxley for pioneering studies into how nerves transmit signals and thus how the brain and muscles work, wrote in *Facing Reality*: '... my scientific life owes so much to my conversion in 1945 ... to Popper's teachings on the conduct of scientific investigations ... I have endeavoured to follow Popper in the formulation and in the investigation of fundamental problems of neurobiology.' And Sir Hermann Bondi (b. 1919), who with Hoyle and Gold formulated the influential 'steady-state' theory of the Universe, the rival of the 'Big Bang' theory, remarked: 'There is no more to science than its method, and there is no more to its method than Popper has said.' Quite a daunting array of alumni! Yet I must take them on – without, I hope, losing the admiration I have for their own individual scientific contributions, made in spite of their respect for Popper. Unless we can loose ourselves from the shackles of Popperism the next generations will not be able to make the discoveries that biological and medical science so desperately needs. So what exactly did he say and what is the objection?

Popper argued that knowledge evolves from experience of the mind. He rejected the inductive method of the empirical sciences – the traditional method, initiated by Bacon and Newton, of testing and verifying a scientific hypothesis by the repeated outcome of experiments which substantiate an hypothesis. David Hume (1711-1776) claimed in his *Treatise of Human Nature* (1739) that such inductive arguments are invalid. You would need an infinite number of experiments to prove that any hypothesis was correct! Oh, ye of little faith. This really is a pathetic argument. The result is that Popper comes up with the 'brilliant' notion that hypotheses are validated by '*falsifiability* criteria'. In other words, the best way of testing Rubicon is to try to destroy it. Many in the scientific community have been hoodwinked into following this negative philosophy. The damaging result has been negative and over-competitive thinking.

Popper and his three disciples – Kuhn, Lakatos and Feyerabend – have had a field-day negating the inspiration of discovery and the ingenuity of invention. The past four centuries have been a story of incredible success for scientific discovery and invention. Yet the Popperians would have us deny this, or at least be reluctant to accept it. They see it more as a series of 'problems', 'conjectures', 'Socratic and Presocratic dialogues' and critical discussion. Success words are rejected from their argument, and the misuse of language abounds. All-embracing questions, stimulating excitement from the very awe of them, are condemned. 'What is light, Dad?' my eldest son once asked me. Two hours of stimulating conversation later ... Popper would deny us this. 'What is ...' questions are forbidden. We are apparently not allowed to ask 'What is light, gravity, magnetism, electricity', and so on. 'We must regard all laws as ... guesses,' Popper tells us. Popperian poppycock!

In any case, when a 'law' appears to break down, the hypothesis may simply need modification. The discovery of quantum and relativity theory did not mean that we threw Newtonian mechanics out of the window. We simply restricted their application to macro-phenomena, and replaced them by quantum mechanics when inside the atom. Lamarck's 'mistake' over evolution did not negate the importance of his contribution to the development of the principle of evolution.

It is often said that Popper's seminal achievement was his solution of the problem of induction. What an achievement! Induction is the intellectual process of basing generalisations on the interpretation of accumulated observations and data from selected examples of a phenomenon. All glow-worms emit light. True or false? True, but only some of the time. And the females are much more obvious than the males. The renowned Popperian example of this type of inductive reasoning is: 'All swans are white. True or false?' One sighting of a black swan proves the statement false. Thus, Popper argues, the way to test the validity of a scientific hypothesis such as Rubicon is to try to falsify it, rather than try to verify it. But what does the word *test* mean?

In fact what real scientists do, or should do, is to make positive predictions which will lead to new discoveries. By all means think of what *might* be wrong with the hypothesis. Have you really identifed the banks of the main Rubicon or is it simply a tributary? But follow the falsifiability route and you are unlikely to discover anything. Stick to the negative Popperian approach and you will be in danger of missing the significance of an observation which apparently falsifies your hypothesis. This doesn't mean you must falsify your results or twist and turn to save unsustainable hypotheses. When I first saw a black swan I was amazed, and couldn't keep my eyes off the beautiful creature. I certainly wasn't disappointed, nor did I feel dejected to find that all swans were not white. The hypothesis wasn't worth testing in the first place!

Poor Popperians. They are condemned to sterile talk away from where the action really is, the laboratory. Popper rejects the 'pseudo-sciences' of astrology, Marxist history and Freudian psychoanalysis because they cannot live up to the falsifiability criterion. Well, at least we can agree on something. But once again the point has been missed. A crucial component of any biological experiment is what we call the 'controls'. Experiments in physics and chemistry rarely need such controls. But they are essential in any study of a biological system. This is because of the natural variability in living cells, organs, organisms and ecosystems. Pure water always boils at exactly 100°C. But take a solution of plasma from various people and animals and measure the precise temperature at which it boils. Because it has salt in it you will not boil it exactly at 100°C. The variation between samples may not be great – perhaps less than 1°C, but it will be there.

You have discovered a drug which you think cures rheumatoid arthritis. It passes all the preliminary tests, and you set out a proper clinical trial on patients. For it to pass both the scientific and ethical test you must design the trial properly. A bad trial, which will not give a clear answer, is unethical, *a priori*. A crucial part of the design is the control group. It is no good just giving it randomly to patients you think have the disease. Rheumatoid arthritis often goes into remission. And there is the so-called placebo effect – people can get better just because they believe that the medicine they are taking must do them good: the doctor gave it to them after all! So to take account of these possible false trails there will be four groups, two sets of patients and two sets of healthy people, some on the drug and some on a placebo tablet. Everything is coded so that neither the doctors nor the subjects know during the trial which group any subject belongs to. When all the data is in the analyst decodes and sees whether there is any statistical evidence that those with rheumatoid arthritis are better or in less pain. Furthermore, the healthy group will help check that there aren't any funny effects of the drug that we need to know about. Every biological and medical study has a set of controls to compare the experimental group against. Mind you, whether a real discovery needs a great deal of statistical analysis is another story altogether. Take ten children who have just crossed the diabetic rubicon. They are all seriously ill and may even die, unless given insulin. Insulin will enable every sick child to return across the rubicon to health. No statistics are required if you really have found the right substance. But in a biological experiment we do need controls, just in case the molecules, cells or organisms cross the rubicon spontaneously, without needing the trigger we are testing.

This is why Marxist history, astrology and Freudian psychoanalysis are pseudo-sciences! They can never have the right controls. In fact they have no control group at all. The same problem arises in politics and management. A politician predicts that by altering the interest rate the economy will return across an economic rubicon – recession will turn into growth. Instead things get worse. The opposition parties then produce a scientific-sounding argument that the government got it all wrong. But no one can *prove* that it was the change in interest rate that caused the trouble, because there was no control group. Economics is thus also a pseudo-science. You can never have a true control population, in which the status quo is maintained while the environment of the rest is altered. Rubicons in economics can be speculated on but not tested.

Without a mechanism

It is often difficult to persuade people to accept a new principle without providing a mechanism to explain how it operates. Heilbrunn's principle about calcium inside cells was not accepted until mechanisms were discovered explaining how it was controlled in cells and how it worked. Darwin himself had this problem. How could small changes in one species lead to the evolution of another? How could small changes even occur? Though DNA was isolated in 1868, its role wasn't established until the 1940s, and there was no science of genetics for Darwin to use. Aware of the problem of lack of mechanism to explain natural selection Darwin therefore developed an idea of his own. In *The Variations of Animals and Plants under Domestication* (1875) he called it 'pangenesis' (vol. II, ch. 27, pp. 349-69: Provisional; hypothesis of pangenesis). On p. 350 he quotes Whewell: 'Hypotheses may often be of service to science, when they involve a certain portion of incompleteness, and even of error.' Then he says: 'under this point of view I venture to advance the hypothesis of Pangenesis, which implies that every separate part of the whole organisation reproduces itself. So that ovules, spermatozoa, and pollen grains – the fertilised egg or seed, as buds – include and consist of a multitude of germs thrown off each separate part or unit.' He was getting perilously close to Lamarckianism here. For something to be inherited, and thus be susceptible to the forces of natural selection, it had to be in the germ line. Darwin proposed the movement of bits from tissues to the germ line by globules. But far from increasing the credibility of natural selection it actually undermined it.

Mitchell had a similar problem when introducing the principle of chemiosmosis in the 1960s to explain how food energy is converted into the cell's fuel of ATP by the powerhouses in all our cells, the mitochondria.

Instead of focussing on the experiments to support or refute the principle of electrochemical gradients not chemical intermediates, many of the early opponents of Mitchell's idea attacked the lack of a mechanism linking the two together. Mitchell provided one, but it still remains unproved, and probably wrong. Yet the principle is valid. Rubicon to the rescue. In a cell which has a thousand mitochondria Rubicon predicts that the ATP is synthesised in a quantal, synchronised fashion, i.e. all at once. Rubicon may not have all the mechanisms, and some I have suggested may be wrong. The key issue is whether new discoveries will be made.

I am not interested in turning somersaults to find ways of destroying Rubicon, but that does not mean I am complacent about the rubicons highlighted throughout this book. I am not sure I have always got it right, or that Rubicon is fully in bloom. Popper and his philosophical disciples may give the impression that they are experts in science, yet few of them have ever been in a laboratory when an experiment is in progress, or a discovery, however small, is made. Their philosophy is sterile. So let's see if we can find a more positive approach than Popper's to take us forward, one based on discovery and experiment.

Discovery

We saw earlier that in the blood there is a navy firing chemical bullets and mortar bombs at invading cells. Some fifteen years ago my good friend Paul Luzio and I predicted that the first thing that should happen to the cell in this battle was not leakage of things out of the cell, but rather movement of our old friend calcium into the cell. We showed that this was true, but the movement was so fast that we immediately and excitedly began talking about the idea that the bombs might not always be lethal. This led to the discovery of my first Rubicon sequence (p. 80, Figure 6).

Experiments and hypotheses are vital in science, but they are not the beginning! A scientist begins by observing something strange, fascinating, puzzling, beautiful, and then asks penetrating questions about it. Imagine we are in the garden looking at the grass. All plants are green. Popperians would be pleased with this as a start. But now, instead of trying to find a plant which is not green, ask a question. How about 'Why is grass green?' To answer this we need to do some experiments. Let's dig up some grass, plant it in some pots and put it into a jar in which you can control and measure the composition of the gas phase. We could blow nitrogen into one, air into one and pure oxygen into another. Only the one with air will survive. Plants need oxygen – a discovery. Oxygen is toxic to plants – a discovery. Now let's leave one of the plants in air in the dark for a few days. The one in the dark will go white, the one in the light will remain green. Another discovery and another rubicon crossed. Now let's carefully measure the oxygen and carbon dioxide above the plant under these conditions. In the light the plant generates oxygen, but in the dark it uses it and generates carbon dioxide, as we do. Well, how about this for an hypothesis:

the green stuff somehow generates oxygen when light is absorbed. Now let's get the biochemists in to grind up the plant and look for the green stuff. They tell us its structure and call it chlorophyll. It is found inside a tiny sub-cellular compartment which we will call a chloroplast, but only some cells have them. Shine light on these and they will make ATP and oxygen. In the dark this chemical energy is stored in a long-term depot, as sugar in the form of starch. But aren't seaweeds plants? How come they are often brown or red and only a few are green? Does this falsify our hypothesis? No. If we grind up the seaweed we shall also find chloroplasts, but there are also other coloured compounds helping the seaweed to trap more of the sun's energy than can grass. We can now develop a unifying theory for photosynthesis. All plants, including algae and seaweeds, contain light-absorbing pigments. Chlorophyll is the primary one, which causes them to be coloured and produce oxygen. Chemical, biochemical, cellular, physiological, morphological and pathological discoveries abound in this series of experiments. Followers of Popper would have you look for plants which aren't green. Once the seaweeds have been discovered the hypothesis is rejected. It will take you on a negative path, and not a path of discovery.

From the renaissance of science in the fifteenth century right through to the present day the real contributors *discovered* by being positive. The Polish-born astronomer Copernicus (1473-1543) set the world alight by showing that the earth had a daily motion on its axis and a yearly one around the sun. This contradicted the long-held belief of Ptolemy of Alexandria (*c*. AD 100 – *c*. 178), the ancient astronomer, geographer and mathematician, who convinced everyone that the earth was the centre of the Universe. Galileo (1564-1642) was put under house arrest for the last eight years of his life for supporting Copernican theory. He developed astronomical telescopes, discovered craters on the moon, and showed that the Milky Way was made up of stars. He also suggested the use of pendulums as clocks and proposed the law of uniform acceleration. In other words, drop a ton of bricks and a ton of feathers from the top of a cliff, and discover which will reach the bottom first. Thanks to Galileo we can predict the right answer, in a vacuum both will reach the rocks at the same time! These scientists may have had a lot of flak from the Church and elsewhere, but their predictions led to new discoveries about the Earth and the Universe. Doubts they may have had, but their experiments were not burdened by attempts to disprove hypotheses and theories as Popper would have us believe. Incorrect hypotheses and theories were rejected by the natural course of positive experiments which didn't work as they should, or by lateral thinking at a crisis point.

Humphry Davy had an hypothesis that salts were composed of negative and positive parts. How to test? Pass an electric current through them and the two parts should separate. Brilliant! He constructed a battery at the Royal Institution, and *discovered* sodium, potassium, calcium, barium and several other elements. If you use a solution of common salt all you get is hydrogen and chlorine. But initial failure did not make him give up. He decided to use moist molten potash and caustic soda instead, and to capture the potassium or sodium as an amalgam of mercury at the negative electrode. You can feel the excitement emanating from the page as he describes distilling off the mercury, to reveal for the first time to human eyes potassium and sodium metal. They are soft, grey, burn brightly in air, and luminesce at the surface. This is what science is really about. No wonder Davy rushed around the room when he saw it all!

Gowland Hopkins's unifying principle for the chemistry of life was the concept of 'catalysis'. Very small amounts of some substances, far too small to be a source of fuel for the body, were catalytic to the bulk substance responsible for energy supply and the building materials of the body. One molecule of an enzyme catalyst could generate a thousand molecules of glucose in a few minutes from starch ingested in plant food. Without a catalyst nothing happens at all, not one rubicon can be crossed. As a result large numbers of enzymes were discovered, as well as hormones and vitamins. OK, there are some non-catalysed reactions in living systems, but they are few and far between and do not negate the overriding importance of catalysis in the chemistry of life. Alexander Fleming had the idea that there were protection mechanisms against invading bacteria. He began looking at an enzyme in tears, called lysozyme, which breaks down the walls surrounding each bacterium. He ended up *discovering* antibiotics. Without a positive approach to the principle of heredity, geneticists and biochemists would not have gone searching for the substance which conveys this in all *sex*. DNA may have been isolated in 1868 by Miescher, but it was Avery and others in the 1940s who found that certain bacterial characteristics could be transferred from one bacterium to another by DNA. They went re-*searching* and *discovered*.

Yet the hallmark of a really good scientist is that he worries more than anyone else about whether he is right or not. As the Nobel Laureate Richard Feynman once remarked: 'When I attend scientific conferences I can't believe how certain some scientists are. I have been working in particle physics all my life and I am still not sure I have got it right.' This makes one think hard about why the theory may not be right, but not necessarily to try to disprove it.

The influence of Popper's negative philosophy is not always obvious. Few practising scientists refer to the principle of falsifiability; yet many have been indoctrinated by it all the same. We must put negativism aside, reject complacency, and rely on the excitement of discovery to guide us.

CHAOS OR ORDER?

The nineteenth century saw a revolution in both physics and chemistry. One of the most important developments was the establishment of the laws governing energy – thermodynamics. In the early 1800s incredible ingenuity went into trying to construct perpetual motion machines. To no avail – the first law of thermodynamics tells us that when a physical or chemical process occurs we can neither gain nor lose energy. It is conserved. William Thompson (1824-1907) – later Lord Kelvin – was one of the great protagonists of the laws of thermodynamics. He gave his name to the temperature scale which goes down to absolute zero below which nothing can go. This is the third law. But it is the second law to which I want to draw your particular attention. A French physicist, Sadi Carnot (1796-1832), following the engineering tradition of his father Lazarre Carnot (1753-1823), carried out a fascinating analysis of the energetics of steam. This highlighted the importance not only of the energy one must supply for a given process to proceed but also of the energy of the heat exchanged at a particular temperature. In 1859 Rudolf Clausius (1822-1888) called this entropy. It is a measure of the disorder in a system. The appreciation of this concept lead to the prediction that one could design a heat exchanger which was cold at one end and warm at the other. The refrigerator was invented because of the discovery of the second law of thermodynamics! But Clausius's combination of the first two laws produces a crucial conclusion. The total energy in an isolated system remains constant, but the entropy is always increasing. Order goes towards disorder.

In the early 1960s a French mathematician, René Thom, realised as we have in Rubicon that while mathematical principles are excellent for analysing smooth, continuous processes, they are hopeless at analysing many real phenomena. Newton's laws of motion help us to estimate the force required to give a car a particular acceleration, and with his law of gravity we can calculate the dynamics of the planets spinning round the Sun. However, these cannot explain or describe the bursting of a bubble, the fracturing or buckling of a piece of metal, the collapse of a bridge, the transition of water into ice, a flash of lightning, or a thunder clap, the breaking of a wave on the beach, and so on. Thom also realised that there were many similar discontinuities in biological processes. He therefore developed a mathematical treatment of discontinuous phenomena. The principle is elegant. Each phenomenon, whether physical, chemical or biological, is represented by an array of surfaces. These surfaces are not flat, nor simply curved, but moulded with gentle slopes leading to steep slopes which lead to wells or precipices. When dealing with simple phenomena there may be only one, two or three surfaces, and thus these can be drawn pictorially. One can even mark on them the positions of the various rubicons. The visual perception gets into trouble with complex phenomena which need more than five dimensions. These can only be imagined, of course. He called it *catastrophe theory*. More recently *chaos theory* has developed as a slightly different treatment of systems not at equilibrium.

The geneticist C.H. Waddington was particularly keen to apply Thom's new mathematical ideas to the development of an embryo and other examples of shape and form. It has many other applications, even in psychology: for example, manic depression or schizophrenia. More recently it has been applied to rhythms, oscillations and waves which play such an important role in the daily, monthly and seasonal behaviour of animals and plants, and within cells themselves.

So is Rubicon saying anything new?

Catastrophe or synthesis?

It is a pity in some ways that the name 'catastrophe' was given to the theory, for although the breaking up of a ray of sunlight or a jet of water into droplets or the splash of a stone after falling into a pond could be regarded as a catastrophe, in biology rubicons do not create catastrophe or chaos, rather order or synthesis. Things happen. Rubicons are creative not destructive.

The question is: has anything new been learnt from applying Thom's analysis? I fear not, though Thom is hardly to blame. One can take the horse to water ... So with Rubicon. Rubicon is not yet ready for such a detailed mathematical treatment, because we have yet to define properly many of the rubicon sequences in Nature.

Some time in the 1960s Thom crossed the Rubicon and realised that many physical phenomena are not graded but depend on discontinuities, and he provided a mathematical and graphical representation of such phenomena. Rubicon has different intentions, however. Eventually we may be able to provide such mathematical representations – Rubicon diagrams – but the first objective is to identify the banks and the principle of crossing. Rubicon is a more positive idea than catastrophe or chaos, since biological rubicons lead to order and organisation rather than catastrophe and chaotic disorder. Some might argue that this is an argument for *anti*-chaos. But equally what new discoveries have arisen for this? Anti-chaos examines the building up of organised structures from randomly moving objects – a snowflake from water crystals, a cell from DNA, an ecosystem from individual organisms. But Rubicon is not saying the same as catastrophe or chaos, even though superficially there are similarities. Rubicon is not in favour of randomness and descriptions in terms of probabilities or reductionist principles. The problem with mathematical models is that they tend to be either digital or analogue. Rubicon shows that real phenomena are a marriage of both. The passage to the banks is analogue, while the crossing results in a digitisable event.

Circular sheep

The danger with mathematical models is highlighted in the following scientific joke. If I may, let me plagiarise a Welsh legend, normally sung, and embellish it with a scientific anecdote.

Once upon a time there was a Welsh sheep farmer. The sheep had given him the wool to make a tweed coat. He went everywhere in this coat. Up the mountain Tryfan, overlooking his farm, shopping, to church. He even got married in it. But he had a problem, and I don't mean with the EC. He wanted to improve his wool yield, which was rather poor. But being scientifically-minded he called in three experts – a zoologist, a geneticist and a physicist – and off they went to try to solve the problem.

A few weeks later the zoologist hastily drove into the farm and in great excitement rushed in to find the farmer.

'I've solved it,' he shouted. 'All you have to do is follow this feeding regime, increase the vitamins by 20 cent and you have a 75 per cent chance of improving your wool yield by 60 per cent. It's no good just letting them graze on the Snowdonia grass.'

'Diolch am fawr (thanks very much),' said the farmer. 'But I've already tried this and many other different feeding regimes. None of them worked.'

Disappointed, they both went back to their respective tasks.

A few months later the geneticist drove into the farm – a little more subdued and serious than the zoologist.

'I think I've cracked it,' he announced. 'What you have to do is get hold of two rams, one from France and the other from the USA. If you then follow the breeding programme I have outlined you will have an 80 per cent chance of producing the type of wool flock you want.' Triumphantly he placed a complicated genetic tree on a large role of paper on the table.

'Well, that percentage is better than the one offered by the zoologist,' said the farmer. 'But how long will it take?'

'Not too long in evolutionary terms,' replied the geneticist in a scientifically confident tone. 'About twenty-five years, I reckon.'

'What!' exclaimed the farmer. 'I'll be dead and gone long before that. But thanks anyway.'

A year went by and the farmer wondered what had happened to the physicist. So he drove off to the University to find him. He knocked on the door.

'Come,' a voice called after he had knocked three times. The office was a shambles – papers, books and electronic bits and pieces everywhere. There in the middle of the debris was the physicist immersed in a computer screen. He looked up.

'Oh, hello,' said the physicist. 'Now I remember why I started on this problem.'

'Well,' said the farmer, 'have you solved it?'

'Yes,' replied the physicist. 'But the trouble is, it's only for a perfectly circular sheep.'

When the farmer died he was buried in – what else? – his tweed coat. But the sheep are still grazing high up on the mountain.

The challenge

The dichotomy of biology is diversity versus universality. Each species, each tissue, even each cell is unique. Yet there are principles common to all life. The challenge for biology now is to cross the Rubicon from being an essentially descriptive science to one based on principles and laws, ultimately definable in mathematical terms. Rubicon is a principle applicable to all biological phenomena. Its success will be judged by the inspiration it gives to the new generation of explorers as they wrestle with the task of trying to understand the molecular basis of life and its evolution rather than on negative experiments designed by Popperians to rubbish it.

Throughout the book I have described many examples where a single substance or pathogen is reponsible for triggering a cell, a species or even a complete ecosystem to cross the Rubicon. However, there are other physiological and pathological rubicons where searching for a single cause is a mistake. The challenge Rubicon presents is to construct a rubicon-matrix from the jungle of the substances, cells and other living units modern molecular and cell biology has identified for us. It is the four dimensions of this matrix which will enable us to see why the fifth dimension happens when and where it does. We will then be able to use the matrix to predict how to prevent or modify it. My dream is to construct a computer graphics program to do this. But that is for the next book to tackle!

Rubicon gives us an opportunity to transform from laws *for* biology to laws *of* biology! Scientific laws are the end of the beginning not the beginning of the end of our discoveries into Nature's processes. Four centuries of scientific discovery are surely beacons to this view.

Return across the Rubicon

THE MUSIC OF SCIENCE

We are the music makers,
And we are the dreamers or dreams,
Wandering by lone sea-breakers,
And sitting by desolate streams:
World-losers and world forsakers,
On whom the pale moon gleams:
Yet we are the movers and shakers
Of the world for ever, it seems.
                Arthur William Edgar O'Shaughnessy (1844-1881)

This book is a musician's celebration of science.

As a teenager the first LP I ever bought was *The Enigma Variations* of Edward Elgar (1848-1918). As with many scientists, music and science have gone hand in hand all my life, but I have not found the ability to compose music. For me, as a scientist, the composer's creative outlet has been the design of experiments and the writing of books. Over the past four centuries the UK has had its fair share of writers and scientists. It is, therefore, something of an enigma that British composers do not have the same high profile internationally. Everyone has heard of Bach, Handel, Mozart, Beethoven and Brahms. But Dowland and Elgar – who are they? Yet John Dowland was perhaps the greatest lutenist of the Elizabethan and Jacobean periods, and in our century Elgar's music has inspired generations of Englishmen, and Welshmen for that matter. June 19th 1899 at St James's Hall in London was a landmark in the history of English music. Not since Henry Purcell (1659-1695) had there been a British composer of true international stature. It was the *Enigma Variations* that achieved this for Elgar, giving him the encouragement to blossom forth and inspire others through his music. The top of the manuscript reads:

'Dedicated to my friends pictured within.'

All but the last of the fourteen variations have the initials or pseudonyms of the person to whom it is dedicated. The first has the initials of his wife, and the last is presumed to be a self-portrait. Within the variations can be found the mischievous twinkle of the eye, a laugh, a warm-hearted gesture, grace, aggression, excitement, inspiration and many a serious moment. Any more than with the other analogies in this book, I would not wish to take this one too far. But I ask you to consider it, as it gives an insight into my motivation for writing this book. Many of the chapters contain conversations with my special friends. I leave you to guess to whom I was talking at the start of Chapters One and Two!

Scientists experience great joy from their experiments, from the excitement of their own discoveries, however small, and from reading about past successes in science. As we approach the end of a century which has been dominated by the technical successes arising from these discoveries, it is perhaps timely to look to science as a dominating creative force in the next century of opportunity, just as music, poetry and the fine arts have been in previous eras. As practising scientists we are composers and artists, as communicators we are performing musicians and actors. But from where does the inspiration come for a new avenue of approach, a new invention, or a new theory – the resolution of a 'crisis'? These require a thought-rubicon to be crossed!

We still know virtually nothing of what triggers lateral thinking or how the neurons in our brain link up to make it happen. Nor do we know how to teach students to unlock the potential they have for this 'originality'. Lateral thinking has a central role to play in the creativity of the scientist or artist – a nice example of Rubicon in our brain. This is the music of science. As Beethoven once said, the task of the composer is to express beauty through the language of music. As with music, art and literature science can be appreciated at different levels, i.e. there are rubicons in our understanding of culture. A symphony has an attractive tune or an exciting rhythm. It may be background music, or, at full concentration, we may listen for an hour or more, and it gives us inspiration and greater depth to our lives. We may appreciate a novel simply because it's a good story, sexy or not. So with science.

Now to the point of quoting O'Shaughnessy's poem at the start of this chapter. Arthur O'Shaughnessy (1844-1881) was a friend of William Rossetti (1829-1919), co-founder of the pre-Raphaelite Brotherhood. O'Shaughnessy was a zoologist at the British Museum in London and also a poet. Of his four volumes of poetry, representing a Victorian attitude of concentrating on musicality and emotions more than the intellectual content, it is 'The Music-Makers' for which he remains famous. In 1908 Edward Elgar had permission to set it to music. The first performance was on October 1st at the Birmingham festival. 'The Music-Makers' reflects on the general theme of 'inspiration'. It contains reminders of many of Elgar's finest works: *The Dream of Gerontius*, *Sea Pictures*, the violin concerto and his symphonies. And there are even brief references to the Empire's glory, the Marseillaise and Rule Britannia. Elgar was a musical polymath. He was brought up in an atmosphere of music. He played piano, violin, cello, double-bass, bassoon and trombone, conducted and, of course, composed. He was 42 before he reached the front rank of composers. His music has always been regarded as distinctly English. The Introduction and Allegro for strings has pictorial reflections of the Malvern hills near where he grew up and died.

Likewise with Rubicon. Science and music are my inspiration. My 'Malvern hills' are the salt-marshes and sandy beaches of Anglesey, and in the distance across the white horses the peaks of Snowdonia, the Rivals, the Nantll-Garn ridge, the Elephant, the Carneddau, and Snowdon itself. All are in view from the window by which I write this book. Many of the ideas have had their beginnings here or while I was looking out across Plymouth Sound. Others have developed while I was talking to my friends and family. Some are snippets and recapitulations of ideas from my other books. I therefore offer them to you. The Rubicon variations: 'Dedicated to *my* family and friends pictured within.'

The joy of Nature is the music of science.

PUTTING THE BIO- BACK INTO BIOLOGY

Computers can be digital or analogue. So with life. One can live it through events or one can exist from day to day in a graded continuum of ups and downs. There has been much debate as to whether the brain works like a computer. The more one learns about how the networks of neurones interconnect the more one sees that the brain behaves both as a digital and an analogue system. If living systems are to cross the Rubicon – the fifth dimension – they must be both digital and analogue, but not at the same time. For an idea to be generated, to sense pain or sexual desire, for cells to reproduce or die, the four dimensions of the analogue and digital pathways are critical. Just as we select from a computer menu, the switch from analogue to digital triggers the crossing itself. By analysing natural phenomena in a Rubicon framework we have seen that, from ecosystems down to the sub-cellular structures which control the events in each cell, biological events are controlled by a sequence of rubicons interposed by smooth change. *Rather than struggling with the problems of defining life, illness, death, extinction and pollution as single events, consider them instead as a sequence of rubicons.*

Rubicon provides a unifying framework to bring all biological disciplines together. If we are to solve the problems facing medicine and the environment in the next century, the boundaries between physiology and pathology, between natural balance and pollution, between life and death, must be redefined. A man dropping down with a heart attack is not just a specific medical problem which is of importance to millions of people. It highlights a much wider issue: what research in biology and medicine should be trying to explain: how do living systems in life, in death and evolution get to, and then cross, the Rubicon.

I have sometimes been negative, but not, I trust, before putting a positive position forward. Rubicon has some iconoclastic views. It forces us to re-examine theories about cell signalling, homeostasis, evolution and ecology. Sometimes an entrenched theory is rejected all together; at other times it simply needs to be restated within a Rubicon framework. Even if the ideas of Darwin, Cannon, Margulis and Lovelock had to replaced by something completely new, their importance in the development of science remains.

Rubicon is not happy with the probabilistic approach, which dominates the analysis and design of experiments and interpretation of data in biology and medicine. This is an excuse for ignorance, and of little help to the man who unsuspectingly drops down with a heart attack. 'God did not play dice with the Universe.' Qualitative and quantitative approaches are both required in science, but mathematics is not necessarily the ultimate objective for the law seekers. Maths is itself limited. If science comes up with an equation, we must be sure that it makes predictions for the future and is not simply a retrospective analysis.

By over-specialising science has created fields which trigger artificial rubicons. Scientists create observations in the laboratory, even phenomena, which are man-made – true artifacts. Rubicon argues that when we carry out laboratory experiments we must use real systems, and use live cells. If we want to study disease we must find an imaginative, ethical way of studying humans. Animals and cell systems are not models. They can only be so constructed in retrospect. Enzymologists in the 1950s and 1960s described all sorts of properties of enzymes which told us nothing about their function inside a live cell – the boiling nitric acid phenomenon. If we are to study cells or cell fragments *in vitro* we must relate the conditions of our experiments to physiological or pathological rubicons *in situ*. In the lab we use so-called model systems and do experiments *in vitro* – in glass. As someone aptly remarked at a recent symposium, *in vitro, in transfecto, in comprehendo!* Reductionism ad absurdum.

Homeostasis still plays a major part in thinking in physiology and ecology. But, as I have tried to argue, we must not be misled by small changes. That they are small doesn't mean they aren't significant. The deviation of the strings in a highly-strung tennis racquet is tiny when the ball hits it. Yet this provides the force to allow the ball to fly back across the net. Likewise with living systems. Small changes often provide the initiation signal for an event, so that the cell, tissue, organism or ecosystem can cross the Rubicon.

What is drug addiction? Most of us drink coffee and tea. Yet we don't consider ourselves drug addicts. Similarly, hardly a day goes by for many adults when they don't imbibe some alcoholic drink. Are we all alcoholics then? Rubicon can thus also have applications in defining the pathway of behaviour.

But putting the bio- back into biology means more than making researchers think about real biological problems under natural conditions. It also means putting life back into how we teach biology, so that schoolchildren and their parents, as well as University students, can experience at first hand the inspiration and joy of science. Rubicon uses the language of experiment with discoveries and inventions from the past, so that new pathways can be identified enabling biology and medicine to cross the Rubicon in the future. The rubicon we are aiming for is the solution to problems of fundamental and practical importance.

It is well-known to mathematicians that the countries on any map can be distinguished with only four colours without any two coloured countries touching each other. Yet there is still no complete mathematical proof of this. Common sense still has a place in a rigorous discipline like science and maths. Every process in the Universe behaves in a quantal manner. It may appear sometimes to be a continuum, but in reality either at the macro- or micro-level the reactions, the behaviour, the shapes, the evolution of every object, however big or small, progress in leaps and jumps. Rubicon – the fifth dimension– puts the bio- back into biology.

NATURE KNOWS BEST

Learning from Nature

This century has seen remarkable success in medicine and agriculture. Vaccination, antibiotics, blood transfusion, infertility treatment, baby nutrition, hormone replacement in diabetes, thyroid and Addison's diseases, HRT and the menopause, *in vitro* fertilisation, tissue-typing and transplantation have all been a consequence of medical science learning from Nature. But therapeutic disasters abound: thalidomide causing foetal abnormalities; excessive use of steroids in rheumatoid arthritis, other inflammatory disease and asthma, causing TB, growth retardation in children and leg ulcers; pain killers inducing death by kidney failure; overuse of antibiotics allowing resistant strains to develop. Many of the problems after an operation, or worries during one, are caused by synthetic anaesthetics for which we have no mechanistic basis. The basis of anti-depressants, which are sold in billion-dollar markets, is unknown. Many modern drugs are chemical poisons, nearly all of which have some unwanted, unpleasant or even lethal side-effects, at least in some unsuspecting people. The probabilistic analysis of a drug trial may have shown that there is a benefit overall in the population, but that is little comfort if you happen to be an individual who reacts unfavourably to the drug. But this doesn't mean that we should reject all the efforts of the pharmaceutical industry.

What Rubicon seeks to do is to get medicine to escape from using scientific analyses obtained from the statistical analysis of populations. It is individuals who need treatment. If our research was aimed at understanding how Nature has solved the problems of physical, chemical and biological attack, how it repairs damaged tissue, cells and molecules, and how it removes unwanted cells and chemicals, we will be able to exploit mechanisms which are common to us all. Vaccination and antibiotics work in every man, woman and child on Earth. I do not argue that we should seek refuge in unscientific, so-called alternative, medicine. But can you blame people in severe pain doing so?

And what of natural remedies – alternative medicine, herbal remedies, copper bracelets, fish oil and other anecdotal 'cures'. Do these tell us anything about the natural history of arthritis, multiple sclerosis or heart disease? How old are these diseases? Did dinosaurs get arthritis? Yes, they did. Anecdotal evidence from those desperately seeking a cure is often rejected as unscientific. Yet if a dialogue is developed perhaps the professional researchers might be able to identify a rubicon which could be susceptible to rigorous scientific investigation.

When we get a fever we are told to take aspirins to get our temperature down – an analogue mechanism. Certainly we don't want our body temperature to rise to more than 42°C; otherwise we will precipitate a disastrous digital event, we will be dead. I am the first to rush to the aspirin bottle when I have a bout of flu. But am I right to do so? The army of cells which gobble up invading bacteria work better at 42°C than they do at 37°C. Once again, I have a horrible suspicion that Nature knows best. Does alleviation of a fever by drugs slow down the body's natural defences and thus increase the time taken for the body to return across the Rubicon to full health? We have a way of getting rid of mutant cells and cancer cells. Perhaps the problem of cancer would be solved quicker if we devoted the bulk of our research resources to discovering how this works and then exploiting it, as Jenner and Pasteur did with vaccination, rather than being obsessed with the idea of finding a single cause.

Bucking the market

The underlying philosophy of this book is that we should learn from Nature, and then find ways of exploiting the natural mechanisms responsible for the evolution of life, and its defence against attack. But you can't buck the market. If we try to beat Nature she will eventually turn her wrath on us. The most successful health-care developments of the past two centuries – clean water and sewage systems, hygiene in preparing and storing food, vaccination, antibiotics from moulds and bacteria, control of tissue-rejection in transplantation – are a direct result of applying this philosophy.

There is a warning here about the use of protein engineering. Exciting as the potential of this is in therapy, we must be aware of the hazards. Those of us who work with it take great care, and by law have to calculate risk factors – access, expression and damage. This enables us to decide what containment facility we need to do our experiments. But the numbers upon which the calculations of containment are based have little scientific basis. They were 'guessed at' by a committee.

Inject a piece of DNA into the muscle of an animal and it can get expressed. This has been achieved with several genes, including the gene which is abnormal in muscular dystrophy. Our gut contains millions of bacteria. One – *Escherichia coli* – occasionally crosses the Rubicon and causes severe diarrhoea. It is routinely used in thousands of genetic engineering labs throughout the world. Although the strain of *E. coli* we use in the lab is not supposed to grow in the human gut, can we be sure? Experimental evidence is needed to justify our faith. We multiply genes in the lab using the natural bacterial sex process. Bacteria can fuse together and then transfer small bits of DNA via a plasmid – a circular piece of DNA some thousand times smaller than the *E. coli* chromosome itself. We can engineer our gene of interest into these plasmids. In order to transform *E. coli* in the lab with our engineered plasmid we have to shock the bacteria really hard. It is supposed that, if we swallowed a small amount from contamination on our hands, they would not infect our own gut bacteria. If they did it could be serious. We select by antibiotic resistance. So even if the inserted gene was quite safe, if these plasmids were to infect our own *E. coli*, our gut bacteria would start to produce enzymes which destroy penicillin. We have strict procedures to prevent this. The reason for raising the question here is that this is another situation where Rubicon ought to be of practical help.

The two key questions are: first, can workers handling the bacteria cross a rubicon where the bacteria grow in their own gut, and secondly, can our own bacteria cross the transformation rubicon and grow up containing plasmid ingested by the handler? There are some quite simple measurements, on faeces for example, which would a give sound experimental basis to our safety procedures. To my knowledge these have not been done.

Only when we are able to identify the rubicons of Nature can we gain the full inspiration from the beauty of her mechanisms, and then exploit them in a way which works effectively without disaster to mankind or the environment.

NEVER THE SAME AGAIN!

Many of the events we have discussed in this book appear to be reversible. But are they really?

Once a molecule, a cell, or an entire organism has crossed certain rubicons it cannot be the same again. Cell division, transformation and death are three examples. The same is true of events which remain in the memory – love, hate or an idea. Yet after some events the biological unit appears identical with what it was before the crossing. It has returned across the Rubicon. But is this really so? How many heartbeats is one allowed in a lifetime? During a lifetime your heart may cross the Rubicon a billion times. The same will be true of nerves, and many other cells in your body. Most cells are replaced regularly, but nerves don't divide. Instead they are continually being repaired and chemically maintained.

Could the dinosaurs return? Is the pathway of evolution unidirectional? Can evolution go backwards? There are a few examples of this occurring – in a particular marine fish, for example. But in general there is no evidence for it. We do not expect any of the millions of organisms which have become extinct over the 4,000 million years of evolution to reappear. But why not? And what of the molecular level? The revolution of protein engineering now gives us the opportunity of experimenting with evolution, to jump 100 million years – back or forward – in a day or so. A particularly intriguing problem is the evolution of the traffic-lights system in cells, and the question of what the consequences would be if this went in evolutionary reverse. We have seen that chemical signals generated within cells by this system are responsible for determining when and where a cell moves, secretes, divides, transforms, defends itself, or dies. How did this signalling system become so intimately linked to the body's defence? Without intra-cellular signalling we would be unable to defend ourselves against physical, chemical or biological attack. The uncovering of this cornerstone in the evolution of mammalian cells could revolutionise our understanding of the biology of modern cells, and will be essential if we are to use genetic manipulation as a successful means of treating disease, without consequent disaster.

What if the laws of the universe were not constant? What if the universal constants of physics are different now from what they were when the first atoms formed, or when the solar system came into being – the Boltzmann and Avogadro constants, the speed of light and absolute zero. Mathematical constants such as *pi* and *e* must be timeless, but is it possible that the laws of physics and the constants that we scientists take for granted as universal have changed at certain times during the 15,000 million years since the Universe as we know it began to evolve? And what about time? Could this go backwards?

NEW LAMPS FOR OLD

When I began to write my first book – on calcium as an intracellular messenger – I soon realised that the book needed a theme which would flow from the first chapter through to the end. I chose to emphasise thresholds – I didn't call them rubicons in those days. It was soon pointed out to me that, good as the idea was, it was not new. So is Rubicon saying anything new?

The key point about Rubicon is that it argues that every biological process is a pathway of discontinuities. This point is well-illustrated by the chicken-and-egg problem. It seems an intractable problem. But I believe it can be answered in full, eventually. To do this the pathway of evolutionary molecular and cellular rubicons must be identified. Then these can be imposed on the organism and species rubicons upon which natural selection acts. Rubicon determines what you choose to do. Do you choose to study live cells or cell extracts? Do you analyse in terms of individual cells and sub-cellular structures or multi-cell populations? How do you define the phenomenon in the first place, and what are the initial questions? Rubicon argues that at every stage in the scientific sequence it is essential to ask about the rubicons responsible for a real natural event, to identify them and to test the truth of their existence – in physiology, pathology, evolution and ecology.

Illuminating science

In 1871 Darwin took the plunge and published in two volumes his ideas on how man had evolved as an animal, *The Descent of Man*. The full title, however, was *The Descent of Man, Selection in Relation to Sex* (1877). Part I dealt with the 'Descent or origin of man', including 'The evidence of the descent of man from some lower form'. Part II focussed on sexual selection. Darwin addressed the development of civilisation from barbarians in an evolutionary way, arguing how natural selection had worked to select successful changes in man's intelligence and physical attributes. A hundred or so years later the BBC screened what might at first glance appear to be a TV sequel – 'The Ascent of Man'. Composed by Jacob Bronowski (1908-1974), it was an inspiration to an eager public, and was published as a book in 1973. The aim was to match a previous series by Lord Clark entitled 'Civilisation'. 'The Ascent of Man' remains a landmark in the history of television, illuminating the history of science in its full glory. It exposed millions of people to the excitement of discovery, the elegance of mathematical solutions, and how the evolution of man at every step has involved the development of a culture to satisfy his insatiable thirst for knowledge and his unquenchable curiosity. But do we still appreciate the importance of fundamental questions about natural phenomena to the making of discoveries and inventions, which many see as the reason for funding science through the public purse?

In the UK the Open University programmes and some nature programmes are models of how beautiful and exciting science on TV can be. However, many prime-time TV science programmes miss the point altogether or even distort the scientists' view – failing to distinguish between science and technology. The curriculum of science in schools and universities often lacks inspiration, is weak in scholarship, fails to explain how the scientific method works in practice, and is presented in a boring, sterile manner to talented pupils and students. No wonder so many become disillusioned with science. The Royal Institution provides us with a model upon which to build a new vision for researching and communicating science. Here many have received inspiration both as school pupils and adults, and through the writings of key figures in the development of science such as Davy, Faraday and Dewar. Lighting up the rubicons of biology through the language of experiment and discovery is the key. Darwin may be best known for his concept of natural selection and the scholarship in his books. But he was also a great experimenter. How better to test whether seeds could be transferred from one part of the world to the other than to try to see if the germination rubicon could still be crossed in seeds that had been incubated in sea water or isolated from the crops of pigeons? Some did germinate, others had crossed the death rubicon and were sterile for ever.

THE PROBLEMS OF MODERN BIOLOGY AND MEDICINE

Science is the description and understanding of natural phenomena. Technology provides us with inventions and techniques arising from the discoveries of science, enabling us to make new ones. There is much misunderstanding about the relevance of medical problems to the advancement of science as a whole. The vocational side of medicine deals with the practical skills associated with helping sick people, but research in medicine must not be separate from basic biology. The rubicons crossed by a malfunctioning cell or tissue often highlight fundamental biological questions hitherto hidden or ignored. Furthermore, the system found in every organism and individual cell that defends it against physical, chemical and biological attack has been of central importance to the evolution of life on this planet. It is this which malfunctions in many diseases. It is the exploitation of this natural system which gives us the vision to enable sick people to return across the Rubicon.

And what of industry? Is it on the right track? Society needs to provide a clear route by which original ideas can be applied penetratively to an identifiable problem. Otherwise the discoverers and inventors will remain isolated, frustrated and often misunderstood by those who should know better. Biotechnology has yet to have the impact which it surely must have if we are to survive and flourish in the competitive world of the next century, without long-term damage to the human race and the environment. Does the pharmaceutical industry need to return across the Rubicon and discard the 'chemical poisons' which still dominate their approach to therapy, even now using genetic engineering? Is industry really backing and investing in the real inventors? Where are the creative thinkers, best suited for 'blue-sky' research, and in what environment does their work flourish so that it crosses the Rubicon of success? To date, in spite of millions invested in such research, industry, predictably, has failed to come up with a really effective cure for, or prevention of, the major ailments of Western society, nor has it touched the infection problems of the Third World. The major causes of disease and death both in the West and in the Third World – namely atheroma, heart disease, cancer, various forms of arthritis, diabetes, neurological and mental disorders, and infection by viruses and protozoa remain unconquered. The horror of a major viral calamity looms large.

What is needed is a five-dimensional geography – a new philosophy. Rubicon defines the medical problem in a way that natural processes can be exploited therapeutically without disasters ensuing. Rubicon, as a marriage between the reductionist and holistic philosophies, could also provide the catalyst to break down the divisions created by academic institutions between pathology and physiology, between basic and applied research, between teachers and researchers, between academia and industry which limit the scope for identifying and solving the real problems of biology and medicine. We must recognise the fifth dimension – Rubicon.

CODA – THE SIXTH DIMENSION

In 1846 Darwin rented an acre-and-a-half strip at the back of the garden. Here he planted trees and shrubs, and marked out a path of about a quarter of a mile – his think-path (Plate 9(a)). At the start of the 'sandwalk' Darwin would, it is said, often place a pile of the requisite number of stones. Each time he passed he would kick away one stone. This left the mind focussed on the conversation, or matters in the mind, rather than the trivia of how many circuits had been travelled.

I myself have several such 'rounds' close to my cottage in Anglesey (Plate 9(a)). Walk in the mountains or along the beaches at night and the blackness excites every sense. Any sound – a crack of a twig, the rustle of foliage – or a strange whiff make one jump. A glow-worm shines like a beacon. In the absence of street lights she is visible from fifty metres or more. The darkness of the forest enables me to see the faint glowing fungus infecting some of the rotting wood. On the beach I lift a rock, and squirt on to it some potassium chloride from the 'gun' I have taken with me. It excites extraordinary shapes, lighting up flashing hydroids, scale-worms and starfish.

Wales has a sensitive culture, a musical language and an inspiring natural environment which have inspired generations of visiting scholars and naturalists, and layfolk, for centuries. Here the mind can cross and return across many rubicons. Anglesey in particular is an area of outstanding natural beauty and scientific interest. Many rare animals and plants flourish here. The summer sea-birds and orchids are a delight to behold, freeing city-dwellers from the shackles of their hectic urban existence and enabling the mind to discover new paths of thought, new ideas and fresh inspiration. The cliffs and natural bridge at Ynys y Fydlyn have been contructed by Nature, but the stone circles of Bryn Celli Ddu and the burial chamber at Cable Bay, the Dovecot and Priory at Penmon all bear witness to the ancient history of the people of the island.

The mountains and beaches of Wales have been a source of enjoyment for thousands of families and holiday-makers, including the young Darwin. Darwin learnt much of his geology here from Adam Sedgwick before his voyage on the *Beagle*. The history of Wales is embedded in the science of geology, thanks to Sedgwick and Sir Roderick Impey Murchison (1792-1871): the Cambrian after Cambria, the Roman name for Wales; the Ordivician after the Ordivices, an ancient Celtic tribe who inhabited the area of Snowdonia in Roman times, and the Silurian after the Silures tribe, who once inhabited central Wales. It was here that Sedgwick took the 22-year-old Darwin in August 1831. In a week or so the tour included limestone caves along the river Elwy above St Asaph where they found mammalian bones embedded in mud. Then the Cambrian rocks of Bangor, and on to Capel Curig, and then the Old Red Sandstone in the Vale of Clwyd. If there was this wealth of geology to be found less than a hundred miles from his home in Shrewsbury, what might there be in far off lands on the other side of the world. Little was Darwin to know, but the inspiration and knowledge gained from Sedgwick's crash course in practical geology was to be of immediate benefit, for on Monday 29 August 1831 he opened a large envelope from London which he found on his return to Shrewsbury. Inside was the chance of a lifetime, an offer of a trip around the world! Darwin was to cross many rubicons over the following five years; yet without crossing the rubicon into Wales few, if any, might have been crossed at all. On 23 April 1835 he wrote from Valparaíso to his sister Susan while on land in South America: 'As for the view behind the house I have seen nothing like it. It is the same with North Wales. Snowden (*sic*) to my mind looks much higher & much more beautiful than any peak in the Cordilleras.'

By contrast, some of Alfred Wallace's earliest memories were of *South Wales*. In 1841 he and his brother returned to Glamorganshire to survey the parish of Cadoxton-juxta-Neathors. He wrote later of the time he had on his hands: 'What occupied me chiefly and became more and more the solace and delight of my lonely rambles among moors and mountains, was my first introduction to the variety, the beauty, and the mystery of nature as manifested in the vegetable kingdom.'

Such exploits have been written up as 'Tours of Wales' by generations of visitors inspired by what they have found and seen. Edward Lhuyd was one of the first in 1695. The archaeology, the geology, the natural history, the sea and the mountains, the salt spray and icy waters of the clear mountain cwms, living relics of the ice age some 10,000 years ago, the Stone Age remains, the burial chambers, still wetted by salt spray, the thirteenth-century castles all await the eager explorer.

I grew up just a few miles from the village where Darwin lived and worked, Downe in Kent. Now I find myself in this quite different environment of inspiration, Ynys Môn, a few miles from where I was born. I look out of the window and see the peaks of Snowdon, soon to live up to its English name. It will be nine months before it is worth searching the slopes for the greenish gleam of the glow-worm's amorous fire – they have returned across their rubicon for now. Being close to Nature gives one a breadth of perspective rarely achievable with mere 'artifacts', however creative and clever these may appear. The wind whistles across the dunes of Aberffraw, the bee and pyramidal orchids have gone and the sandy beach is now empty of people. The holidays are over. Instead the beach is littered with *Vellela vellela*, Jack-sail-by-the-wind, a type of jelly-fish with a blue sail float. The cob at Malltraeth overlooks the expansive Cefni estuary on one side and the pools on the other, always a delight for the bird watcher. There are migrating waders at Foel, and there is comradeship at the Mermaid Inn and Nant-yr-Odyn. On the tip of Llanddwyn island is the old lighthouse. A seal pops his inquisitive head above the water. The Three Rivals lead the eye to the end of the Lleyn Peninsula and Bardsey Island, another favourite haunt of the bird-watcher. The puffins and peregrines have left South Stack for this year but the striking 'ping' of that very Welsh bird the chough remains – jet black and uninteresting viewed from afar, yet what a surprise when one discovers its bright red beak and legs. Not a boring old jackdaw after all. Biological rubicons are everywhere to excite the mind.

Anglesey certainly is the place for me. My DNA comes from here; the tiny church at Llanfairynghornwy where several of my ancestors are buried, the cross of the altar is in memory of Grahame Pryce – my great-uncle who lived too soon for vaccination to prevent the rubicon of TB while still a medical student. By the age of twenty-five he was dead.

For me science is a means of developing an intimacy with natural things, enhancing and not diminishing their inherent natural beauty and elegance. The more one learns of the molecular basis of life the more awesome Nature becomes. As if this weren't enough, how rewarding it is to see an idea or discovery evolve into something practical from which large numbers of people could benefit or find similar inspiration and enjoyment!

This then is the sixth dimension.

I leave you with this historical backcloth, in the hope that it will provide a legacy of inspiration, scholarship and fellowship for those who have enjoyed this book.

Within a stone's throw of my house in South Wales live two animals which do something quite remarkable: they glow in the dark. The glow-worm *Lampyris noctiluca* and the common piddock *Pholas dactylus*, and luminous animals like them, have given medical science a family of chemicals capable of lighting up the chemistry of the living cell, in health and disease. The study of bioluminescence takes one on a voyage of discovery from the ecology of the deep ocean, through the biology, biochemistry and chemistry responsible for controlling the emission of the light to the nature of light itself – a true natural science. It is the inspiration and infectious enthusiasm engendered by such natural phenomena that has provided me with the stimulus and enthusiasm to write this book. Most children at school have heard of Robert Boyle and his law about gases. A co-founder of the Royal Society, Boyle (1627-1691) was one of the first to investigate light scientifically and the rubicon we now call luminescence. His wisdom from the past gives us our vision and hope for the future:

> Light is so noble a thing. I cannot but hope that something would be produced, not only of light but divers other bodies, and perhaps also of good use to human life.

And so to the cadence – a chord from Elgar. Is the theme in this book an enigma? I hope so!

Bibliography

Most scholars expect to find statements in the text supported by references. I hope I shall be forgiven for not cluttering up the text of this book thus. But I list here a selection of sources from which I gleaned much of the detailed information for the book. Rather than divide them chapter by chapter I have grouped them into main topics. I hope that the titles will indicate their relevance and suggest a likely source of further material for a specific area in which the reader may be interested. I also provide a selection of key books and papers of my own.

Scholars write, read and wax enthusiastic over books. A major hope of mine is that this book will encourage my readers to a similar enthusiasm. Here are some books that have inspired me.

Historical

Bynum, W.F., Browne, E.J. and Porter, R., eds (1981). *Dictionary of the History of Science*. Macmillan, London.

Cannon, W.B. (1933). *The Wisdom of the Body*. Kegan Paul, Trench and Trubner, London.

Chambers, R. and Reznikoff, P. (1926). Micrurgical studies in cell physiology. I. The action of the chlorides of Na, K, Ca, and Mg on the protoplasm of *Amoeba proteus*. *J. Gen. Physiol.* 8, pp. 369-405.

Chambers, R. and Chambers, E.L. (1961). *Explorations into the Nature of the Living Cell*. Harvard University Press, Cambridge Mass.

Coleman, W. (1977). *Biology in the Nineteenth Century*. Cambridge University Press, Cambridge.

Cormack, R. (1972). First use of the word apoptosis. *Brit. J. Cancer* 26, pp. 239-57.

Dampier, W.C. (1942). *A History of Science and its Relations with Philosophy and Religion*. Cambridge University Press, Cambridge.

Dubois, R. (1884-5). Note sur la physiologie des Pyrophores. *Comptes Rend. Séanc. Soc. Biol.* 12, pp. 559-664.

Dubois, R. (1887). Fonction photogénique chez le Pholas dactylus. *Comptes Rend. Séanc. Soc. Biol.* 4, pp. 564-5.

Florkin, M. (1972). A history of biochemistry; Part I. Proto-biochemistry; Part II. From proto-biochemistry to biochemistry. *Comprehensive Biochemistry* 30, pp. 1-343. Elsevier, Amsterdam.

Goodwin, T.W. (1987). *History of the Biochemical Society 1911-1986*. The Biochemical Society, London.

Heilbrunn, L.V. (1943). *An Outline of General Physiology*. Saunders, Philadelphia and London.

Krebs, H.A. (1981). *Hans Krebs: Reminiscences and Reflections*. Clarendon Press, Oxford.

Macullum, A.B. (1925). Correspondence. *Science* 62, p. 511.

Mitchell, P. (1966). Chemiosmotic coupling in oxidative and photosynthetic phosphorylation. *Biol. Rev.* 41, 445-502.

Needham, J. and Baldwin, E., eds (1949). *Hopkins and Biochemistry*. Heffer and Sons, Cambridge.

Olmsted, J.M.D. and Olmsted, E.H. (1952). *Claude Bernard & the Experimental Method in Medicine*. Abelard-Schuman, New York and London.

Pirie, N.W. (1938). The meaninglessness of the terms life and living. *Perspectives in Biochemistry*, pp. 10-22, ed. Needham, J. and Green, D.E. Cambridge University Press.

Sampson, M.M. (1925). Conditions of validity of Macallum's microchemical test for calcium. *Science* 62, pp. 400-1.

Steinbach, H.B. (1960). L.V. Heilbrunn: General Physiologist. *Science* 131, pp. 397-9.

White, G. (1788). *The Natural History of Selborne; with observations on various parts of Nature, and the naturalist's calendar*. Chidley, London.

Wiedemann, E. (1888). Ueber fluorescenz und phosphorescenz. *Ann. d. Physik u. Chemie* 34, pp. 446-63.

Signalling Rubicon

Arends, M.J. and Wyllie, A.H. (1992). Apoptosis: mechanisms and roles in pathology. *Int. Rev. Exp. Pathol.* 32, pp. 223-54.

Berridge, M.J. and Irvine, R. (1989). Inositol phosphate and cell signalling. *Nature* 341, pp. 197-205.

Bowen, I.D. and Lockshin, R.A. (1981). *Cell Death in Biology and Pathology*. Chapman and Hall, London and New York.

Carson, R. (1962). *Silent Spring*. Penguin, Harmondsworth.

Cohen, P. (1988). Protein phosphorylation and hormone action. *Proc. Roy. Soc. Lond. B* 234, pp. 115-44.

Franks, F. (1983). *Water*, pp. 1-96. The Royal Society of Chemistry, London.

Gilkey, J.C., Jaffe, L., Ridgway, E.B. and Reynolds, G.T. (1978). A free calcium wave traverses the activating egg of the medaka, *Oryzias latipes*. *J. Cell Biol.* 76, pp. 448-66.

Harvey, E.N. (1952). *Bioluminescence*. Academic Press, New York.

Heilbrunn, L.V. (1940). The action of calcium on muscle protoplasm. *Physiol. Zool.* 13, pp. 88-94.

Heilbrunn, L.V. (1956). *Dynamic Aspects of Living Protoplasm*. Academic Press, New York.

Heilbrunn, L.V. and Wiercinski, F.J. (1947). The action of various cations on muscle protoplasm. *J. Cell. Comp. Physiol.* 29, pp. 15-32.

Heilbrunn, L.V. and Wilbur, K.M. (1937). Stimulation and nuclear breakdown in the *Nereis* egg. *Biol. Bull. Woods Hole* 73, pp. 557-64.

Hershko, A.P., Mamont, R., Shields, R. and Tomkins, G.M. (1971). Pleitypic response. *Nature* 232, pp. 206-11.

Kamada, T. (1940). Ciliary reversal of *Paramecium*. *Proc. Imp. Acad. (Tokyo)* pp. 241-7.

Lovelock, J.E. (1979). *Gaia: A New Look at Life on Earth*. Oxford University Press, Oxford and New York.

McLaughlin, S.K., McKinnon, P.J. and Margolskee, R.F. (1992). Gustducin is a taste-cell-specific G protein closely related to transducins. *Nature* 358, pp. 563-9.

Mendes, P., Kell, D.B. and Welch, G.R. (1993). Metabolic channeling in organized enzyme systems: experiments and models. *Adv. Mol. Cell. Biol.* 12, pp. 1-40.

Poinie, M. and Tsien, R.Y. (1986). Fluorescence ratio imaging: a new window into intracellular ionic signalling. *TIBS* 11, pp. 340-55.

Pollack, H. (1928). Micrurgical studies in cell physiology. VI. Calcium ions in living protoplasm. *J. Gen. Physiol.* 11, pp. 539-45.

Raff, M.C. (1992). Social controls on survival and cell death. *Nature* 358, pp. 397-400.

Rasmussen, H. (1989). The cycling of calcium as an intracellular messenger. *Sci. Amer.*, pp. 44-51.

Ridgway, E.B. and Ashley, C.C. (1967). Calcium transients in single muscle fibres. *Biochem. Biophys. Res. Commun.* 29, pp. 229-34.

Shimomura, O. (1985). Bioluminescence in the sea: photoprotein systems. *Soc. Exp. Biol. Symp.* 38, pp. 351-72.

Smith, D.C. and Douglas, A.E. (1987). *The Biology of Symbiosis*. Edward Arnold, London.

Stephen, J. and Pietrowski, R.A. (1986). *Bacterial Toxins*. Van Nostrand Reinhold, Wokingham.

Tsien, R.Y., Pozzan, T. and Rink, T.J. (1982). Calcium homeostatis in intact lymphocytes: cytoplasmic Ca^{2+} monitored with a new, intracellularly trapped fluorescent indicator. *J. Cell Biol.* 94, pp. 325-34.

Woodcock, A. and Davies, M. (1978). *Catastrophe Theory*, Penguin Books, London.

Woods, N.M., Cuthbertson, K.S.R. and Cobbold, P.H. (1986). Repetitive transient rises in cytoplasmic free Ca in hormone-stimulated hepatocytes. *Nature* 319, pp. 600-2.

Evolution

Bowler, P.J. (1983). *The Eclipse of Darwinism*. Johns Hopkins University Press, Baltimore.

Danson, M.J., Hough, D.W. and Lunt, G. eds (1992). *The Archaebacteria: Biochemistry and Biotechnology*. Biochem. Soc. Symp. 58, pp. 1-212. Portland Press, London.

Darwin, C. (1985). *The Correspondence of Charles Darwin*, vols I-VII. ed. Burkhardt, F. and Smith, S. Cambridge University Press, Cambridge.

Darwin, C. (1859). *On the Origin of Species by Means of Natural Selection or the Preservation of Favoured Races in the Struggle for Life.* John Murray, London. 1st edition.

Darwin, C. (1876). *The Origin of Species by Means of Natural Selection or the Preservation of Favoured Races in the Struggle for Life.* John Murray, London. 6th edition.

Darwin, C. (1881). *The Formation of Animal Moulds through the Action of Worms with Observations on their Habits.* John Murray, London.

Dawkins, R. (1986). *The Blind Watchmaker*. Longman Scientific and Technical, Harlow.

Denton, M. (1985). *Evolution: A Theory in Crisis*. Burnett Books, London.

Desmond, A. and Moore, J. (1991). *Darwin*. Michael Joseph, London.

Hardy, A. (1965). *The Living Stream: Evolution and Man*. Collins, London.

Hardy, A. (1966). *The Divine Flame*. Collins, London.

Jordanova, L.J. (1984). *Lamarck*. Oxford University Press, Oxford and New York.

Kimura, M. (1983). *The Neutral Theory of Molecular Evolution*. Cambridge University Press, Cambridge.

Lovelock, J.E. (1988). *The Ages of Gaia*. Oxford University Press, Oxford.

Margulis, L. (1970). *Origin of Eucaryotic Cells*. Yale University Press, New Haven.

Margulis, L. and Sagan, D. (1987). *Microcosmos: Four Billion Years of Evolution from our Microbial Ancestors.* Allen and Unwin, London.

Mason, S.F. (1991). *Chemical Evolution: Origin of the Elements, Molecules, and Living Systems*. Oxford University Press, Oxford.

Midgley, M. (1985). *Evolution as a Religion: Strange Hopes and Stranger Fears*. Methuen, London and New York.

Milton, R. (1992). *The Facts of Life: Shattering the Myth of Darwinism*. Fourth Estate, London.

Persechini, A., Moncrief, N.D. and Kretsinger, R.H. (1989). The EF-hand family of calcium-modulated proteins. *TINS* 12, pp. 462-7.

Raup, D.M. (1991). *Extinction: Bad Genes or Bad Luck*. W.W. Norton, New York and London.

Watkins, N.J. and Campbell, A.K. (1993). An evolutionary pathway for aequorin and coelenterazine bioluminescence. *Bioluminescence and Chemiluminescence, status report*, in press, ed. Stanley, P.E. and Szalay, A. Wiley, Chichester.

Philosophy

Baerlocher, F. (1990). The Gaia hypothesis: a fruitful fallacy. *Experientia* 46, pp. 232-8.

Burke, T.E. (1983). *The Philosophy of Popper*. Manchester University Press, Manchester.

Gunn, J.A. (1920). *Bergson and his Philosophy*. Methuen, London.

Magee, B. (1976). *Popper*. Fontana, Glasgow.

Monod, J. (1972). *Chance and Necessity*. Collins, London.

Schrödinger, E. (1951). *What is Life? The Physical Aspect of the Living Cell*, pp. 1-92. Cambridge University Press, Cambridge.

A selection of my own publications

Ashley, C.C. and Campbell, A.K., eds (1979). *The Detection and Measurement of Free Ca2+ in cells*. Elsevier/North Holland, Amsterdam.

Campbell, A.K. (1991). The Rubicon Hypothesis: a quantal framework for understanding the molecular pathway of cell activation and injury, *Calcium, Oxygen Radicals and Cellular Damage*, pp. 189-217. SEB seminar series 46, ed. Duncan, C.J. Cambridge University Press, Cambridge.

Campbell, A.K. and Morgan, B.P. (1985). Monoclonal antibodies demonstrate protection of polymorphonuclear leucocytes against complement attack. *Nature* 317, pp. 164-6.

Campbell, A.K. (1983). *Intracellular Calcium: Its Universal Role as Regulator*. John Wiley and Sons, Chichester.

Campbell, A.K. (1986). Lewis Victor Heilbrunn: pioneer of calcium as an intracellular regulator. *Cell Calcium* 7, pp. 287-96.

Campbell, A.K. (1989). *British Patent Application* 8916806.6. Modified proteins. *International Patent Application* PCT/GB90/01131. Bioluminescent proteins: Rainbow protein.

Campbell, A.K. and Herring, P.J. (1990). Imidazolopyrazine bioluminescence in copepods and other marine animals. *Marine Biology* 104, pp. 219-25.

Campbell, A.K. (1988). *Chemiluminescence: Principles and Applications in Biology and Medicine*. Horwood and VCH, Chichester and Weinheim.

Davies, E.V., Campbell, A.K., Williams, B.D. and Hallett, M.B. (1991). Single cell imaging reveals abnormal intracellular calcium signals within rheumatoid synovial neutrophils. *Brit. J. Rheum.* 30, pp. 443-8.

Hallett, M.B. and Campbell, A.K. (1982). Measurement of changes in cytoplasmic free Ca in fused cell hybrids. *Nature* 295, pp. 155-8.

Kendall, J.M., Dormer, R.L. and Campbell, A.K. (1992). Targeting aequorin to the endoplasmic reticulum of living cells. *Biochem. Biophys. Res. Commun.* 189, pp. 1008-16.

Knight, M.R., Campbell, A.K., Smith, S.M. and Trewavas, A.J. (1991). Transgenic tobacco aequorin reports touch, cold-shock and elicitor effects on cytoplasmic calcium. *Nature* 352, pp. 524-6.

Knight, M.R., Campbell, A.K., Smith, S.M. and Trewevas, A.J. (1991). Recombinant aequorin as a probe for cytosolic free Ca^{2+} in *Escherichia coli. FEBS Lett.* 282, pp. 405-8.

Matthews, S.B. and Campbell, A.K. (1984). Neutrophil activation after myocardial infarction. *Lancet* ii, pp. 759-7.

Patel, A. and Campbell, A.K. (1987). The membrane attack complex of complement induces permeability changes via thresholds in individual cells. *Immunology* 60, pp. 135-46.

Patel, A.K., Hallett, M.B. and Campbell, A.K. (1987). Threshold response in production of reactive oxygen metabolites in individual neutrophils detected by flow cytometry and microfluorimetry. *Biochem. J.*, pp. 173-80.

Sala-Newby, G. and Campbell, A.K. (1992). Engineering firefly luciferase as an indicator of cyclic AMP-dependent protein kinase in living cells. *FEBS Lett.* 307, pp. 241-4.

Watkins, N.J. and Campbell, A.K. (1993). Requirement of the C-terminal proline residue for stability of the Ca^{2+}-activated photoprotein aequorin. *Biochem. J.* 293, pp. 181-5.

Index